Technology, Change and Society

Technology, Change and Society

Edward C. Pytlik
Iowa State University

Donald P. Lauda
Eastern Illinois University

David L. Johnson
Indiana State University

Davis Publications, Inc.,
Worcester, Massachusetts

LIBRARY

JUN 1 9 1981

UNIVERSITY OF THE PACIFIC

382086

Copyright 1978
Davis Publications, Inc.
Worcester, Massachusetts U.S.A.

All rights reserved. No part of this publication
may be reproduced or transmitted in any form or
by any means, electronic or mechanical, including
photocopying, recording, or any storage and
retrieval system now known or to be invented,
except by a reviewer who wishes to quote brief
passages in connection with a review written for
inclusion in a magazine, newspaper or broadcast.

Printed in the United States of America
Library of Congress
Catalog Card Number: 78–54617
ISBN 0-87192-100-6

2   3   4   5   6   7   8   9   10

Contents

List of Tables

Preface

The study of technology has become a necessity. Inhabitants of the planet Earth have only recently come to realize that the nature and characteristics of the technological systems employed by people have been and continue to be significant factors in shaping the world in which we live. These systems impact directly and indirectly on the nature of society and the quality of life and living. In earlier times humankind had to know about and understand the natural environment in order to survive. Now, it is necessary to know about and understand the technological environment and the reciprocal relationships among the human, social, technical, and natural environment as well. Decisions made by individuals and groups about their tools, machines, techniques, or technical systems during previous centuries of civilization had little impact beyond their immediate social and geographical environment. Today, decisions made by individuals or groups about technological systems can impact on people throughout the world, often in adverse and unplanned ways.

Two factors, the rate of technical change and the potential of new technical systems to significantly alter critical elements in the organic world, have caused concern among people about the potential disruptive and destructive factors associated with continued technological change. This concern has generated an awareness that the immediate and long-term future of civilization, now more than ever before, will depend on how well the present is managed. How well the present is managed will depend on how well *all* citizens understand the behavior of technological, sociological, and ecological systems and their relation to human existence and purpose.

Creating a society in which technological systems serve human purposes will require a new discipline of technology, a discipline which focuses on a human centered technology which serves social purposes rather than technical purposes. It is for this reason that Davis Publications initiated, with considerable insight and foresight, a series of publications designed to serve a critical educational need of society existing at all learning levels.

The adult level, of which this text is one of five, includes publications ranging from an introduction to the study of technology to others which explore technological and sociological factors associated with communication, production, and transportation systems as essential elements in all societies regardless of their level of development. The present text, by Pytlik, Lauda and Johnson, explores the relationships of *technology, change and society* and provides a necessary foundation for any critical study of technology by focusing on the human meaning of social and technical change.

Individuals concerned about participating in the creation of a more humane and ecologically sound future will find the exploration of the basic issues by the authors of this text a rewarding beginning.

Paul W. DeVore
Consulting Editor
Morgantown, West Virginia
April 1978

Acknowledgments

The authors would like to thank their colleagues for the time, expertise, and effort they gave us in preparing this text. Special thanks go to Betty P. Pytlik, Iowa State University, for reconciling the disparate writing styles of the three authors, and to Ray Loyd, also of Iowa State University, for providing us with the technical information in Chapter 10, The Ecological Question, and for his creative graphics.

For the photographs, we thank the Consulate General of Japan (Chicago); Fisher Body Division, General Motors Corporation; The Ford Motor Company; Information Service of India (New York); and Unimation, Inc.

David L. Johnson wishes to acknowledge financial assistance provided by the Indiana State University Research Council and by the Yamamoto Shoten of Tokyo, Japan, which contributed to preparation of part of the manuscript.

Our typist, Karen Maak, also contributed greatly to the project by her patience, efficiency, and careful eye for detail.

Introduction

This is a book about technology and its impact on human society. In planning and writing this book, we worked with the conclusion that technology is altering human lifestyle to its existential roots. Technology is, therefore, considered a primary determinant of social change. As a result, we could not deal solely with materials and technical processes, as many readers might expect in a book about technology. Since technology precipitates social change, the material had to include *an analysis of the impact* technology has on people and their institutions.

Virtually all segments of human life are touched by technological growth. It is paramount therefore that a text treating such a vast topic be written by individuals with diverse backgrounds. This text has been written by three individuals representing the technologies and the humanities; to disregard either segment of knowledge would make this volume incomplete. We believe that our society cannot cope with a mentality restricted by single-discipline, decision-making endeavors.

Although over one hundred years ago, writers such as Karl Marx acquainted scholars with material power as a measure of advancement, it has been only in recent times that a concerted effort has been made to understand the concept of technology. Henry Adams was the first American historian to note the significance of the accelerating velocity of history. He noted that the world did not double or triple its movement between 1800 and 1900 but, measured by any standard known to science—by horsepower, calories, volts, mass in any shape—the tension and vibration and so-called progression of society were fully a thousand times greater in 1900 than in 1800. Today, Henry Adams would be astounded to see the growth that has taken place since 1900. The innovations and inventions since World War II alone have surpassed any other era in speed of accumulation and in pervasiveness. John Platt put it into perspective when he estimated that the current transformation is as enormous as ten Industrial Revolutions and Protestant revolutions combined and occurring within a single generation.

The phenomenal rate of technological growth in evidence today has prompted the study of how technology affects (or fails to affect) the existing and future social order. In spite of the avalanche of books and other written materials about this topic, the subject remains highly debatable and confused. These debates began in earnest in the nineteenth century when varied reactions to mechanization took place. Since that time, reactions have continued to follow three different views. One view holds that the growth of technology is beneficial to the human race and promises a golden age for the future. Another holds that it is an unmitigated curse that will ultimately destroy the human race. The third view holds that technology is desirable to cure many problems of the world, but should be subjected to some type of control to insure constructive progress. Although writers are in fundamental disagreement about the cause-and-effect relationship of technological development, they all agree on one fundamental issue: The accumulation of technical innovations will continue to have a profound impact on our social system. History books will most certainly devote countless pages to the agent of social change we call technology.

We have attempted to define the elusive term "technology" in Part I, while presenting the viewpoint of prominent writers in the field. Chapters 3 and 4 are specifically devoted to the impact of technology on the individual and on our basic institutions. This discussion reveals that virtually every segment of our culture has been intrinsically affected by technological innovation. We realize that it is evident in all cultures throughout the world, and in the remaining chapters of Part I, we deal with levels of technological development and the transfer of technology. As the concept of finite resources and infinite demands becomes internationalized by all societies, the need for global interdependence will mandate a global view for the use and management of the technological order.

Since World War II, the human has surpassed the achievement of all previous ages. Today, satellite communications, computers, synthetics, organ transplants, and space exploration are almost taken for granted. Eighty-two new nations have appeared since 1945, and the world population has increased to staggering proportions; all of which makes excessive demands on dwindling natural resources. At the same time, the gross world product (GWP) has increased even more rapidly while the demand for affluency continues to expand worldwide. This transformation has not come without its consequences. The growth of technology progressed after World War II in a seemingly "unchecked" fashion. Innovation bred innovation while also breeding the by-products we know as pollution, inflation, dehumanization, alienation, and many other negative elements. Compounding many of these problems is the fact that they demand attention simultaneously, making many unmanageable. The accumulation of microproblems creates macroproblems that haunt not only nations and institutions but individuals as well. It becomes difficult for many persons to cope with stress prompted by rapid change, as well as with changing cultural universals. This difficulty is also compounded because individuals and institutions are handicapped by the fact that they are trying to cope with cross-purposes and beliefs. Therefore they are in conflict with one another.

Whether living in a highly developed country or in one that is considered primitive, every human has the right to utilize natural resources, to live in a clean environment, to enjoy good health, to have full employment.

Naturally these demands vary from culture to culture, but in no case is deprivation justified. Any discussion of these inalienable rights raises many questions. Who should control technology so that humans and their environment are not exploited? How can we cope with exponential growth? How do we conserve finite resources? Can the United States continue to use one-third of the world's resources when it has only one-sixth of the world's population? These issues are explored in Part II.

Global society has witnessed many transformations in its millions of years of existence, with each transformation being unprecedented. The last major shift, known as the Industrial Age, created totally new industrial models and economic systems. Like all stages of development, this age was accompanied by conflicting views of technology. Today we are on the threshold of a new transformation where physical and social changes will be consummated in very short periods of time. The technologies will be more potent than ever before, allowing the human to alter the human condition radically. We cannot rely on history to show us the way through this era since no element of the past can approximate the potential provided by our current technological prowess. The way to cope with these potentialities is through viable strategies for the future. Technology assessment and technological forecasting, discussed in the final chapter, are two innovations that will assist in finding potential solutions to problems and in assessing alternative policies and actions. Although the peoples of the world do not share a common past, it is possible, through the rational use of technology, to share a common future.

Technology is a product of human effort, and the answer to the questions raised by the use of technology affect each of us. Yet, many of the answers may not be available at this time. These solutions must come from diligent efforts of individuals and groups throughout the world. As authors of this text, we hope this book will help the readers synthesize the vast storehouse of knowledge that awaits them as decision makers in the technological order. Making sense of today's technology with a view toward a humane future is the human's greatest challenge.

PART I

Chapter 1
Technological Culture

Survival of the human is dependent upon the human's capacity to apply rationality in solving problems within the environment. To accomplish this, every society, even the most primitive, relies on scientific and technological pursuits in its daily existence. The search for new mental constructs and tangible expressions is a human phenomena determined by complex social and environmental conditions. When we look to the past, therefore, we soon realize that each stage of development differs from the one preceding it. These changes are consciously initiated by humans, making science and technology a social phenomenon.

The distinction between science and technology in our culture is obscured by popular thinking, which results in many misconceptions of both terms. With the exception of those who study technology, the field of technology is considered subordinate to other forms of human activity and it is rarely afforded an independent role of its own. Perhaps this is due to the fact that technology is consistently defined in a limited sense, utilizing such terms as "technique" and "things." Repeatedly, the distinction between the two is phrased as "science is the understanding of natural phenomena" and "technology is the application of knowledge." By maintaining that distinction, we deny the discipline of technology its rightful role in the past, the present, and the future. This book is about the use of technology as a social phenomenon to perpetuate the human race. Therefore, a clear distinction must be made between these two elusive terms.

A Definition of Science

Eugene Rabinowitch, who is labeled as the "conscience of America's scientists," defined science as ". . . a system of data and relationships covering vast areas of information derived from observation, analysis, and manipulation of natural phenomena." It is therefore the foundation knowledge by which the human reconstructs the world. Of course science cannot claim exclusive rights to the search for truth since religion, philosophy, art, and other disciplines seek truth as well.

Considering the totality of human existence, science is a rather new discipline. Primitive societies did not have science as we know it today although they understood elements of nature. Even though botany, zoology, climatology, and other areas of science were vaguely understood, a formulation of scientific principles was not evident. Newtonian laws were unknown when the lever and the wheel were introduced. In fact, a large number of inventions precipitated the discovery of scientific principles. An example of this was the invention of the high-pressure steam engine, which led to the development of the laws of thermodynamics. Even today, a decision to generate a particular technology may precede the development of science. The decision to land on the moon is an example of such an effort.

Science was long sheltered in clerical institutions—the university and the church. To those who were uninformed, scientists seemingly possessed an element of magic and threatened to prove false many accepted ideas. New findings necessitated social adjustment just as it does today. Galileo avowed Copernican theory openly and was tried by Pope Urban VIII as a heretic. Many of his contemporaries suffered similar persecution, and the defiant Giodano Bruno was burned at the stake in 1592. Science continued to make its impact and became well entrenched through the effort of such persons as Newton, who changed mathematics from a static state to the invention of fluxions (differential calculus). He helped to make the scientific method rigorous and precise in interpretation.

Eventually the process of science led to utility—a concept that had great public appeal. Astronomy advanced navigation, while chemistry had practical applications for medicine and industry. Hall concluded that scientific theory was of slight use to technology prior to the nineteenth century. Engineering could not develop in the seventeenth century because of the limits on existing materials. This limitation was subsequently overcome through the use of concrete and metals as a result of chemical knowledge. But advances were delayed until the middle of the nineteenth century when the first useful body of chemical theory was formulated.

The linkage of science with practical application was at last consummated in the seventeenth century. Comparable claims were being made in the social sciences as well. Human behavior and economic systems were found to have pathologies of their own. Economics made its appearance in the eighteenth century and was followed in the nineteenth century by psychology and sociology. Common to these assertions was the belief that every flaw affecting the human was definable and could be solved through science–technology. To many, science seemed infallible, making people tolerant of its by-products but unable to assimilate its true meaning. However, being very visible, technology soon made it very difficult to isolate the consequences of the sciences. The reality for science indeed became technology. But before we discuss this relationship further, we need to define the other term in question—"technology."

A Definition of Technology

The term "technology" has been defined in many ways, ranging from the very specific to the broad and general. Some examples are listed below:

1. Technology embraces the means by which man controls or modifies his natural environment. (Spier, 1968, p. 131)

2. The information, techniques, and tools with which people utilize the material resources of their environment to satisfy their various needs and desires. (Lenski, 1974, p. 498)

3. The technology of a people is their major means of adjusting to the environment. (Arensberg and Niehoff, 1971, p. 40)

4. A special kind of knowledge which is directed toward practical applications in the physical and social world. (Popenoe, 1971, p. 64)

5. . . . that great, growling engine of change—technology. (Toffler, 1970, p. 25)

These definitions, as well as many others that are presented in the literature, tend to cloud the true meaning of technology. Even in the monumental work, *History of Technology* by Charles Singer, E. P. Holmyard, and A. R. Hall, technology is defined as "how things are commonly done or made" and "what things are done or made." Since technology did not acquire scientific content until the seventeenth century, these definitions imply that technology does not have a knowledge base and that it did not exist prior to that time. Pacey circumvents this problem by utilizing terms such as "practical arts" or "mechanical arts" to refer to technical skills before the seventeenth century. He argues that once practical applications had a scientific basis, the term "technology" took on its modern interpretation. As a result of this interpretation, many persons still refer to technology as applied science. As a new discipline, it emphasized analytical thinking and used quantitative concepts of limited application but, in the opinion of many, failed to acquire a socially oriented mentality.

Bronowski, in his monumental work *The Ascent of Man,* reminds us that the human has what no other animal possesses—creativity. As a result, every animal leaves traces of what it was, but the human leaves traces of what it created. The evolutionary process developed genetic specializations among many animals, providing them with the ability to adapt to diverse environmental conditions. Species that did not have the necessary speed, protective size or coloration, instinctual skills, and fast reproductive ability became extinct. Those that survived this evolutionary process demonstrated their ability to survive in severely restricted environments.

One animal did survive this process and achieved the ability to adapt to a myriad of environments. This animal is *Homo sapiens.* Emerging approximately one million years ago, after moving through many evolutionary changes, *Homo sapiens* was left with distinct characteristics. Among these are the ability to stand (*Homo erectus*), the ability to grasp (the opposable thumb), an increased brain size, the ability to generate history and language, and the ability to give symbolic meaning to elements of culture. As a result of these traits, there is virtually no environment on earth that the human has not challenged.

Like all other living creatures the human was vulnerable to the realities of the environment, requiring the extension of human capacities to ensure survival. In spite of the human's ability to process food for strength, to eliminate wastes, to repair itself, its limitations are a reality. The human eye can see within specific limits, the body can exist only within a specific temperature range and can manipulate its natural environment only to the extent the muscles will allow. These and a vast number of other limitations led to the development of "extensions" of the human body. This we call *technology*.

Identification of the extensions of human capacities is the role of the archeologist who investigates cultures of the past. When judgments of advancement or retardation of a culture are made, developments in these survival mechanisms are cited as evidence. Such research has revealed that the evolution of tool development was a slow process. For several million years, *Australopithecus* made rudimentary stone tools on which a simple blow put an edge on a stone. Eventually the human developed the fundamental invention which radically expedited the development tools. That invention was the purposeful act we call *accumulation*. The human learned to store materials for future use and began to utilize the knowledge learned from one invention to perfect another, a process called *synthesis*. It was at this point that the human became future-oriented and moved beyond the capacity of other creatures.

Today, the processes of accumulation and synthesis continue to advance the human's potential. Of course our present inventory of knowledge and skills is so vast that it is beyond comprehension. Just as with the advance of science, technology has become specialized, professionalized, and institutionalized. This pace of change magnified the difference between the scientist–technologist and the layperson. In the early 1900s a university graduate could expect to utilize most of the knowledge learned with an element of currency for an entire career. Today, the vast holdings of information, processes, and materials continue to grow exponentially, making obsolescence a universal problem that business and industry must face.

For our purposes we define technology as: *A process undertaken in all cultures (a universal), which involves the systematic application of organized knowledge (synthesis) and tangibles (tools and materiel) for the extension of human faculties that are restricted as a result of the evolutionary process.*

This definition is used because it identifies the following characteristics of technology:

1. It is evident in all cultures regardless of their stage of development.

2. It is knowledge based and involves the application of knowledge to solve problems.

3. It is accumulative.

4. It is fundamental to humanity.

5. It is fundamental to survival.

6. It alters culture and society.

7. It is future-oriented.

8. It is observable.

9. It seeks a harmonious relationship between human life and nature.

10. It is an extension of the human faculties.

Technology and Cultural Change

Initial definitions of culture emphasized that culture includes all that humans receive from their social heritage. This emphasis had its origin in the nineteenth century when social scientists attempted to distinguish between the human's cultural world and biological inheritance. Historically it was an attempt to avoid the biological explanations provided by Charles Darwin's discoveries. There was a strong tendency to extend biological theories into social theories during Darwin's lifetime. Defining culture as anything that was not biological helped to establish the limits of the newly established social sciences.

Over the past century the concept of culture has been defined and redefined as the realities of technological developments altered its meaning. Perhaps the most definitive review of concepts and definitions of culture was made by A. L. Kroeber and Clyde Kluckhohn. From the many definitions offered by anthropologists and sociologists in that work, we can identify certain basic ideas that have remained constant.

Culture Is Symbolic

The human has the creative potential to assign meaning to human behavior, to events, and to other phenomena. At the same time, the human can give meaning that is not found in an object itself but that is created out of those experiences in which objects become meaningful. Therefore, the meaning we give to elements of our environment are expressed through symbols that evoke ideas and emotional responses.

Social scientists refer to material objects constantly in their research. As a result, it was common procedure for many decades to refer to material culture. One of the primary proponents of this categorization was William F. Ogburn. He argued that in most cases it is the sequence of technology that causes social change. His thesis had a great deal of support from many of his colleagues. Anthropologist Leslie White, for example, stated explicitly that social systems are secondary and subsidiary to technological systems. He concluded that technology is the independent variable and the social system is the dependent variable.

The most commonly accepted position today is that objects of technology are not in themselves included in the concept of culture. The definition of these objects, including the process for making and using them, as well as the value placed on them, is included. The current theory holds that "culture" lies in the symbolic meaning of an object, not in the object itself. This does not imply that the study of culture does not include a study of technological advancement. It is doubtful that any anthropologist or sociologist would refute the significance of technology in the advancement of our culture.

Culture Is Transmitted

This concept implies a heritage that is passed on from one generation to another. Since humans create culture and constantly attempt to improve their lifestyle, each generation alters its heritage before passing it on to the next generation. Prior to this century, this was not a difficult task since the inventory of technology was quite small. Since that time, however, and especially since World War II, the inheritance from generation to generation is almost beyond comprehension. Making sense of culture in the midst of radical change is a difficult task and accounts, in part, for the alleged confusion that exists in today's youth. This turmoil is evidenced in our society by the actions of persons who are committed to technology with conscience, technology with foresight, and technology with rational thought.

Many analyses of culture also refer to limitations imposed by geography. Naturally climate would influence the everyday life of people, as would the type of available terrain, the availability of natural resources, and so on. Such an analysis is adequate when discussing a specific culture. However, when discussing "world culture" as influenced by technology, the concept of culture transmission needs redefinition. Before the last half of this century, a time when we did not have the elaborate communications and transportation systems we now enjoy, many cultures could not utilize many of the technologies available in the highly developed countries. Since so many countries did not have the production resources to utilize, they were unable to advance to the extent that American industry did. As a result of this inequitable distribution of potential, parallel inventions rarely occurred among different cultures.

Today, technology is transferred from industry to industry, from state to state, and from nation to nation. With the communications and transportation systems in evidence today, this is a simple task. New developments can be transmitted via satellite systems, and materials can be delivered with little difficulty. Equally important to this process is the transfer of human talent around the globe. Enhancing this concept we call "technology transfer" is the realization that the world is made up of *interdependent* systems. Our current use of technology requires vast amounts of finite resources. Since these resources are not evenly distributed on planet earth, survival is dependent upon the rational use of shared resources. These two concepts, *technology transfer* and *interdependent systems*,[1] will undoubtedly have more impact on global culture than any event in history.

Culture Is Learned

It has been recognized for many decades that the human does not inherit culture through genetic transformation. Utilizing native intelligence, the human learns from institutions which assign meaning to the elements of the environment. We might refer to the newborn as a "cultural void" since the child has not accrued the capacity to attach values, ideas, and other symbolic forms to the environment. In a sense, the acquisition of culture emancipates the infant from its biological inheritance. Therefore, the attitude one develops about technology and its concomitant social consequences depends on the exposure received in the home, the educational system, the church, the mass media, as well as through the political and economic system. Therefore, to understand the processes that take place in culture, one must understand the significance of human behavior against the background of motives and emotions institutionalized in that culture.

Summary

Humans have always struggled for survival in their particular environment. In this process they acquired the ability to develop sophisticated contrivances to help ensure their survival. There is a significant difference between the struggle our ancestors faced and that which we face today. Initially, reality was the continual struggle with nature. Today, humans struggle with environments of their own making. This awesome capability raises crucial questions that must be answered in concert with the finite limitations inherent in nature and human life.

We cannot ignore the challenge of the future, which intrudes on us in dramatic and unexpected ways. With the problems of overpopulation, the imminent exhaustion of many finite resources, the continued demand for affluence, among many other problems, our rational concern for society must be universal. We must realize with conviction that our cushion for trial and error has been exhausted. Our problem is not with reducing the "bigness" of culture, but of organizing and controlling it. We need to reorient our value system in a malleable and dynamic social system.

We have learned, and hopefully not too late, that the disjunction between nature and technology manifests itself in social instability. This is not caused by the products of technology by themselves, because they take on a value-neutral position. It is the meaning we assign to these products and the use to which we put them that creates this disjunctive force.

---

[1] These two concepts are discussed at length in Chapters 7, 8, and 9.

It is the human who creates technology, and it is the human who must take responsibility for it. In a culture that is constantly in a state of flux, the doctrine that values are relative to and based upon a set culture and cannot be challenged therefore, is utterly ridiculous. Science and technology are now in a position to influence social decisions. These decisions, if made humanely, might possibly make both science and technology part of the universal human discourse.

Today our technology gives us the power to determine our own evolution. As this and other potentialities unfold before us, we must realize that the scheme of identifying elements in one-way causality is insufficient. We must think in terms of systems of elements in mutual interaction. Unlike natural systems, which are self-regulatory, technological systems demand human intervention. As technology advances, new processes of integration must take place with the interdependent variables. Therefore, a technological culture is always in a state of flux, and arbitrary decisions without considering the total social system will be self-defeating. Although transforming the world into a humanistic and self-regulating community poses problems, it is the highest priority facing humankind. Human cultures can survive only to the extent that their actions remain meaningful to the experience of the human.

DISCUSSION QUESTIONS

1. Can any generalizations be made about the impact of technology on the quality of life?

2. Is rapid technological growth desirable in a society?

3. What can our educational system do to help transmit the concept of technology as a reality of our culture?

4. How will the roles of planning, control, and leadership have to change for society to incorporate rapid technological change?

5. Are your value systems significantly different from those of your parents or your grandparents? Why? How will they change by the year 2000? Why?

6. Cite examples of how science and technology have caused social change.

7. Jacob Bronowski has stated that the ascent of man covered tens of thousands of years. The reshaping of human life now under way can occur within a few decades. What impact will this have on your life?

BIBLIOGRAPHY

Allen, F. R. et al. *Technology and Social Change*. New York: Appleton-Century-Crofts, 1957.

Arensberg, C. M., and Kimball, Solon T. *Culture and Community*. New York: Harcourt, Brace & World, 1965.

Arensberg, C. M., and Niehoff, A. H. *Introducing Social Change*. New York: Aldine-Atherton, 1971.

Barnett, H. G. *Innovation: The Basis of Cultural Change*. New York: McGraw-Hill Book Co., 1953.

Benedict, R. *Patterns of Culture*. Boston: Houghton Mifflin Co., 1934.

Bertalanffy, L. *General System Theory*. New York: George Braziller, 1968.

Bierstedt, R. *The Social Order*. New York: McGraw-Hill Book Co., 1974.

Bronowsky, J. *The Ascent of Man*. Boston: Little, Brown and Co., 1973.

Capra, F. *The Tao of Physics*. Berkeley: Shambhala, 1975.

Cassirer, E. *The Philosophy of Symbolic Forms*. New Haven: Yale University Press, 1953.

———. *The Problem of Knowledge*. New Haven: Yale University Press, 1950.

———. *Scientific Knowledge and the Concept of Man*. Notre Dame: University of Notre Dame Press, 1971.

Clifton, J. A. *Introduction to Cultural Anthropology*. Boston: Houghton Mifflin Co., 1968.

Cottrell, W. F. *Technology, Man and Progress*. Columbus, Ohio: Charles E. Merrill Publishing Co., 1972.

Coult, A., and Habenstein, R. *Crosstabulations of Murdock's World Ethnographic Sample*. Columbia, Missouri: University of Missouri Press, 1965.

Dewey, J. *The Public and Its Problems*. New York: Henry Holt and Co., 1927.

Ferkiss, V. C. *Technological Man: The Myth and Reality*. New York: George Braziller, 1969.

Hammond, P. B., ed. *Cultural and Social Anthropology*. New York: The Macmillan Co., 1974.

Herskovits, M. J. *Cultural Anthropology*. New York: Alfred A. Knopf, 1966.

Kluckhohn, C. *Mirror for Man*. New York: Whittlesey House, 1949.

Kroeber, A. L., and Kluckhohn, C. *Culture*. New York: Alfred A. Knopf, 1952.

Laszlo, E. *The Relevance of General Systems Theory*. New York: George Braziller, 1968.

———. *A Strategy for the Future*. New York: George Braziller, 1974.

———. *The Systems View of the World*. New York: George Braziller, 1972.

Lenski, G., and Lenski, J. *Human Societies*. New York: McGraw-Hill Book Co., 1974.

Matson, F. W. *The Broken Image*. New York: George Braziller, 1964.

Mead, M. *Culture and Commitment*. Garden City, N.Y.: Doubleday and Co., 1970.

Mott, P. E. et al. *Sociological Perspectives*. Columbus, Ohio: Charles E. Merrill Publishing Co., 1973.

Mumford, L. *The Myth of the Machine*. New York: Harcourt, Brace & World, 1966.

Ogburn, W. F. *Social Change*. New York: Dell Publishing Co., 1966.

Pacey, A. *The Maze of Ingenuity*. New York: Holmes & Meier Publishers, 1975.

Popenoe, D., *Sociology,* New York: Appleton-Century-Crofts, 1971.

Rabinowich, E. "The Mounting Tide of Unreason." *Bulletin of the Atomic Scientist,* May 1971, p. 4.

Rogers, E. M., and Shoemaker, F. F. *Communications of Innovation*. New York: The Free Press, 1971.

Schneider, L. *The Sociological Way of Looking at the World*. New York: McGraw-Hill Book Co., 1975.

Spier, R. F. "Technology and Material Culture." In *Introduction to Cultural Anthropology,* edited by James A. Clifton. Boston: Houghton Mifflin Co., 1968.

Toffler, A. *Future Shock*. New York: Random House, 1970.

Turner, C. H. *Radical Man*. Garden City, N.Y.: Anchor Books, 1971.

U.S. Department of Commerce. *Index of Patents, 1974*. Washington, D.C.: U.S. Government Printing Office, 1975.

Wirth, A. G. *Education in the Technological Society*. New York: Intext Educational Publishers, 1972.

Chapter 2
Technology and Human Life

Technology and human life are connected through complicated interdependencies and interactions: New tools create new opportunities for humans to achieve new goals and do things in new ways. But, in order to take advantage of the new opportunities, people often must learn to live differently, which entails reorganizing society. So technological change is almost always accompanied by social change.

When social change occurs, strain among people is felt at two levels: First, between the old way of living and the new techniques since some techniques contradict old ways; and second, between different groups of people, some of whom prefer the old values, goals, and techniques. Such strains usually result in conflict of some sort among people.

The Steam Engine, the Factory and Work

This complicated relationship between technology and life is apparent from a look at the way the meaning of work has been changed by technology in America. During Jefferson's presidency at the beginning of the nineteenth century, American society was one in which work centered mostly on the family farm or in the craftsman's shop. Work life was highly influenced by the view that productive effort has its own rewards and that individuals prove their worth to society through their skill and commitment to work. On the farm or in the shop, work corresponded neatly with social requirements for respectability and a sense of individual worth. People found significance and meaning through individual productive effort. And a blueprint for behavior was clear to any person—a blueprint that coincided with the dominant forms of work available.

When the steam engine was invented, however, changes occurred that brought about a radical revision in thought concerning the meaning and value of work. Technologists succeeded in applying steam machine power for use in the factory system of production. The factory system put machines and workers together to produce goods on a mass scale. Steam power and factory workers on assembly lines built an industrial empire many times more economically productive than the older, simpler system of production.

Yet in many respects, the new system of production brought by new technology destroyed the values concerning work that had been central to the Jeffersonian era. The older meanings of work did not easily correspond to the factory workers' employment situation. The factory worker was not a craftsman or a free producer of goods; he was in a sense almost owned by the factory owner, upon whom he had to depend. And the worker could not easily identify his own interests with the foreman, the factory owner, or even the products passing on the assembly line. This new work system caused individual and social strain. The older ideas and values about work did not correspond to the new conditions for work.

The social strain produced by the factory system of production soon developed into collective behavior and group action that violently challenged the older values of work, respectability, and social order. The conflict ended with the creation of labor unions, which represented the interests of the workers to the factory management and owners.

In short, a new and more complicated social pattern emerged, which not only forced a redefinition of work, but which created new problems in defining and determining productivity, wages, and benefits. The new system of production based on machine technology destroyed some old values associated with work. It created a new, often morally unstructured and morally undefined, social situation. Over a period of time, however, labor unions helped to evolve new norms of behavior so that the individual worker could once again know what the social expectations were and how to act appropriately.

The introduction of the steam engine into the work life of Americans dramatically altered human values and social organization. The new tools produced problems and tensions that eventually called for a new definition of work. In the process, social institutions such as family, economics, politics, education, and religion were also modified.

The Issue of Technological Determinism

Because technology has a close relationship to the way people live, many thinkers of our time believe that technology actually dominates human life so much that it determines human values, character, and destiny. Thinkers such as Jacques Ellul, Lewis Mumford, Marshall McLuhan, Hannah Arendt, Herbert Marcuse, and Pierre Teilhard de Chardin are among those who hold the view that the technology of the modern era shapes and reshapes human life according to its own dictates.

To those thinkers who are convinced of its determinative powers over human life, technology is not to be identified simply with tools that help people do new things in new ways. For them, technology is a way of thinking, which creates a whole new "world view"—that is, modern technology is itself a new organization of meanings and assumptions about the world and about human life. The sort of thinking that has come to dominate modern cultures forces a new way of life, a new morality, and a new purpose upon human beings.

The Erosion of the Human Self

The most significant change that the new world view of technology forces, it is alleged, is a progressive erosion of the self. Modern technology is a way of thinking that destroys human individuality, autonomy, spontaneity, irrationality, and freedom. Whereas many people think that technology has to do only with tools that can be used to manipulate the object world (things apart from the self), technology is actually a way of thinking that forces the human self to become subordinate to the object world. The sphere of the self is eroded to the point where individual freedom and responsibility are no longer characteristics of modern human beings living in societies that are given over to technological development. This means that ideas of self-consciousness, human purpose, free will, and even moral responsibility are obsolete for those people who have submitted to modern technology—as obsolete as other premodern ideas such as magic and witchcraft.

Jacques Ellul, in his book *The Technological Society,* provides one of the most vigorous and comprehensive arguments for the view that technology today determines human life. Ellul identifies a single force as the central power of technology and he traces its effects in every segment of human life—economics, politics, law, education, religion, eating habits, work, and recreation. He argues that the central motive of modern technology is technique. And technique is a way of thinking that applies to all human life "methods rationally arrived at and having absolute efficiency . . . in every field of human activity." Technique, then, is the concern, the desire, the will to integrate the machine into human life in such a way that the values associated with the machine dominate society. These values of the machine are *organization, rationality,* and *efficiency.*

A consequence of the technological way of thinking (technique) is to change human life into something that is no longer human, according to Ellul. The desire for organization (that is assigning appropriate tasks to individuals or groups so as to attain all goals in the most efficient way) does away with spontaneity, whim, and individuality among people. It forces a standardization of life: All people are made to do the same things in the same way. Rationality is the principle by which standardization takes place. Rationality rejects the unconscious, the spontaneous, and the intuitive aspects of life. Instead, it favors the reasoned, clear, ordered, organized life. The criterion that is used to evaluate society, the individual, and, indeed, all aspects of culture, is efficiency. Efficiency arrived at through rational analysis becomes the chief value of the technological way of thinking.

The progressive erosion of selfhood gains momentum when all people in a culture are forced to submit to the technological way of thinking. A symbol of this capitulation to technology is the mechanical clock. With the widespread use of the mechanical clock, the experience of time shaped by seasonal rhythms or human biology is repressed, ignored, or forgotten. The mechanical clock, worn on the wrist or hung on the wall, reshapes human life according to its own time. And everyone living in a society that uses the mechanical clock is expected to standardize life in terms of that clock. To be late for work, for school, for supper because of individual needs, preferences, or desires is to violate standards dictated by a tool.

Ellul finds further erosion of human selfhood to take place because "it is the essence of technique to compel the qualitative to become the quantitative." The technological way of thinking redefines qualities into something that is measurable—that is quantifiable. Qualities such as love, courage, and beauty are not immune. Love becomes something measured by number and time (as in the slick, sex magazines that depict the "great" lover as one who has many partners and who masters a particular sexual method). Courage is redefined in terms of technique also (the astronaut is admired not so much because he explores the unknown, but because he is master of a complicated technical system). And beauty is redefined by the technological way of thinking as the line or form most adaptable to use (contemporary architecture avoids useless, purely decorative elements in building in favor of "functionalism").

Jacques Ellul thinks that domination by technology is a curse to humanity. The lure of technology is its promise of a better life for all people. Yet, Ellul argues, a threefold contradiction exists between the promise and the actuality of human life.

The first contradiction alleged by Ellul is that the world of technique is a world of material things subject to quantitative analysis. But the essence of human life is quality, not quantity. Excellence, beauty, integrity, courage, justice, or love are, in the last analysis, not measurable. Quality cannot be made into quantity without forever destroying it as quality. Love, for example, cannot be quantified, measured, or subjected to controls. A society can legislate against divorce and thereby prevent the disintegration of marriage and family; but a society cannot make people love one another. Love is not such an element. Yet the technological way of thinking attempts to make qualities into quantities.

The second contradiction is that at the same time that technological thinking produces great human achievements, it also threatens the annihilation of humanity. This contradiction occurs because the power to achieve something is looked upon by the technological value system as a good in itself. Yet, when power becomes the reason for human activity, distinctions can no longer be made between good or evil actions. If a society has the power to do something, Ellul maintains, it will. Even if that act promises annihilation of the human race. This contradiction creates, in the modern world, the absurd situation where nations stockpile nuclear weapons as a way to guarantee world peace.

The third contradiction is that while technology appears to create freedom for humanity, it actually does not and cannot. The technological way of thinking promises to free humanity by eliminating certain age-old limitations imposed on life by time and space. Humans are, in fact, freed by technology from excessive heat and cold, from famine, from the rhythms of nature. But other, more oppressive constraints are imposed by the very technical means necessary for the elimination of the older constraints. Thus there is a built-in contradiction to technology. As humans submit to technical means, new and greater demands are put upon them, with the result that they have less opportunity for free choice or for individual action. The automobile and the airplane, with all of their promises for speed, escape, and excitement in travel, also force people to keep to rigid schedules, to keep pace physically and emotionally with the auto industry and the airlines, and to earn enough money to afford the pleasures of each. It is impossible to have the promised freedom without submitting to the constraints imposed by the new devices.

Ellul thinks that the adoption of the technological way of thinking and valuing by the Western countries of the world is a mistake. Yet remorse for the loss of a previous way of life is futile. Once the technological way of thinking has been adopted, there is nothing that an individual in a society can do. Even to "drop out" is futile since, according to Ellul

> . . . one can scarcely make the serious claim to be able to revive the past, a procedure which . . . scarcely seems to have been, globally speaking, much of an improvement over the human situation today. (Ellul, 1972, p. 90)

The Evolution of Mind

There are other thinkers, however, who though they share the determinist assumptions about technology, paint a much more positive picture of human life. Pierre Teilhard de Chardin, a Jesuit priest and paleontologist, and the Indian philosopher Aurobindo Ghose contend that technology does determine human life, but that it works for the betterment of all humanity. For them, both as a way of thinking and as a way of material improvement, technology is part of a divine plan for humanity.

Teilhard sees technology as a stage of human development that is part of a long process of evolution. The material "stuff" of the universe has been growing into increasingly more elaborate organizations. This evolutionary process he calls *complexification*. Subatomic units change into atoms, atoms into inorganic molecules, inorganic molecules into organic molecules, and so on until living cells and multicellular units appear. Complexification is the tendency of each new development to integrate with a previous level, to elaborate on it, and to build upon it. Human life and society are simply one stage of the development that began with subatomic units. Since the process began prior to human life, there is no reason to believe that the evolutionary process should stop with human life as we know it today.

According to Teilhard, a new mode of evolution occurred with the appearance of the human race. Human life brought into existence the *noosphere*—a level of development distinct from the previous stages of biosphere and geosphere. The noosphere marks the "rise of consciousness," the development of rational thought and reflection. Prior to the noosphere, evolution occurred in an almost mechanical fashion through the built-in tendency of energy to link similar elements together and to produce through such unions greater complexity and concentricity. The noosphere, with its development of consciousness, allows energy to manifest itself in psychic phenomena.

Teilhard regards human consciousness as a continuation of the evolutionary process. And because human life is limited to the earth, the energy of consciousness does not diffuse, but returns into an ever greater interlocking web of thought. This complexification of thought continues to evolve toward a state of intense unification of psychic energy and social organization, which Teilhard terms "omega point."

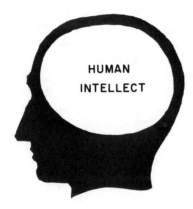

NOOSPHERE

Technological thinking and its results, therefore, are simply a part of the universal evolutionary process. There is no way to stop technological development, and there is no good reason to want to stop it. And, to Teilhard, the technological society promises to save humanity from limitations, disorganization, and irrationality. He sees the promise of technology to be the creation of a new society, distinct from previous human societies. This new social life, says Teilhard, "shows signs . . . of requiring us . . . to sacrifice our individuality." In other words, the development of the individual and the values of individualism are not the end of evolution. These are but a step along the way. Technological thinking is a higher mode of thought, and it requires a giving up of obsolete values associated with previous eras. Technology promises "totalization of political regimes," closer physical contacts among people, and "the increasing impossibility of being or acting or thinking *alone*—in short, the rise, in every form, of the *other* around us." Technology eliminates the human self; but that is not necessarily something humans should fear, according to Teilhard.

Aurobindo Ghose, a philosopher of India in recent times, created a synthesis of scientific, technological, and religious thought surprisingly similar to Teilhard's. Aurobindo drew on ancient Indian thought to show that the evolutionary development of mind and thought have important religious significance. The Divine Spirit is behind all evolutionary development, according to Aurobindo, even development taking place among material things. In his book, *The Life Divine,* Aurobindo traces the revelation of God in evolutionary development through history. He maintains that it is the Divine Spirit which pushes and pulls all of reality toward a realization of God. Technological advance is also a revelation of God—it is divinity revealing itself in human progress.

The Emergence of a New Tribalism

Other thinkers are less religious or moralistic than Ellul, Teilhard, or Aurobindo. Yet they share the same assumptions regarding the power of technology to dominate, direct, and control human life. One of the most controversial and creative of these thinkers is Marshall McLuhan, who maintains that the dominant technologies of a society produce social consequences that determine the lives of people. The dominant technology of Western culture did at one time produce people who were disposed to value rationality, organization, and almost mechanical living. But, he says, recent technological innovations force humans to adopt a new way of life with distinctly new values.

In his books, *The Gutenberg Galaxy* and *Understanding Media: The Extensions of Man,* McLuhan holds the determinist view that the tools humans create determine what people become. A tool (for McLuhan, a "medium") is not only an implement that may help people do some task. A tool is more than that: It is an extension of some part of the human body. For example, an automobile is a tool that serves as an extension of a person's legs. Whereas humans can walk or run to cover distance, the automobile covers distance at greater speed with less effort expended by humans. So the automobile extends the legs.

Yet a tool also eliminates some human functions. When a person uses the medium of an automobile, the legs of that person are in a sense eliminated. The tool user no longer needs the bodily equipment that the medium replaces. Clothes, too, function as an extension of the skins of those who wear them. But clothes also eliminate those functions which they extend: The human skin no longer is the medium of contact with the external world.

Modern technology eliminates many human capacities at the same time that it extends some new ones, according to McLuhan. And by creating new tools, humans keep remaking themselves, extending some capacities and eliminating others. The technology that surrounds people who live today in the Western world creates a complete environment that determines human life. And the dominant technologies are the technologies of communication: the television, the radio, the telephone, and the computer.

McLuhan is particularly interested in the way in which modern technology has altered the sensory organs of humans. Changes in communication technology change the balance of the sensory organs. One of the most dramatic of these changes in sensory balance occurred with the development of the printing press in the fifteenth century. Before that time, the dominant sense was hearing. People got their information, their news, their understanding of their world, by hearing things. Such a sensory orientation created a certain type of human being. McLuhan calls the hearing-oriented person *tribal man*—the human that lives spontaneously, unreflectively, emotionally. Tribal man experiences things simultaneously. For tribal man there is no sense of history, of pastness, because there are no reference books for anyone to consult. Words are not examined, preserved, or analyzed. Words are heard, experienced, and sometimes remembered. But everything important is what happens in the immediate present.

Great change takes place when humans construct an alphabet and develop the means for communication through writing. Writing separates the sound of a word from its meaning and transfers sound into sight. Separating sound from meaning also transfers speech into something that can be localized, preserved, contained, and analyzed. With writing, a reorientation of the senses takes place to de-emphasize sound and to emphasize sight.

The printing press as a tool brought the mass production of written items. The new technology imposed its own changes. People could now get their information primarily by seeing it rather than by hearing it. The widespread conversion of sound into abstract visual symbols led to the public habit of categorizing, dividing, ordering, and analyzing. For many people, language became intimately associated with writing rather than with speaking or hearing.

Print technology caused what McLuhan terms a cultural "explosion." The human eye and ear were separated by print; people became disposed to think that seeing is believing; and a dualism between heart and head, mind and matter, emotions and intellect became a part of a new way of understanding life and behavior. Habitual reading created people who were detached, critical, even skeptical. It also created people who placed high value upon the ability to quantify, to control, and to manage reality.

The environment formed by the new electronic media, however, causes a reversion toward tribal man. Electronic media bring an "implosion," according to McLuhan. Television, radio, the telephone, and the computer force people back together into a unity unknown and unappreciated by people who prefer a print environment. The electronic media emphasize once more the aural sense. People can read, but they get their information primarily from the telephone, the television, the radio. Television particularly helps to create a new sensory pattern because of its low picture definition and its two-dimensionality. Viewers of television must participate in what they watch because the medium forces them to fill in the spaces and contours of the picture with their imaginations. So television integrates sight with sound to produce a new tribal culture different from the old, preliterate tribalism, but also quite different from the literate culture of the immediate past.

McLuhan does not choose to moralize about the changes that the new sensory pattern entails. He simply notes that the sensory change is taking place today. And with the change occurs a necessary adjustment in values, wishes, styles of life, and human goals. Changes in political, educational, social, and, indeed, all human life, must follow. Moreover, there is no way to stop such changes. The new technology of communications forces change.

The Search for Human Freedom

An important question is raised by the view that technology determines human life, and it is a troubling one: Are humans free to choose and to accept responsibility for their choices? If technological determinism is the case, what control over technological development can human beings exercise?

Thinkers such as Emmanuel Mesthene, Jacob Bronowski, Victor Ferkiss, and Paul Goodman insist that while at times technology seems to threaten an absolute domination of human life, it need not and should not do so. For these people, technological thinking is only one mode of human thought and creativity. Culture, mythology, habit, and religious values all continue to influence human life considerably, and technology does not and cannot displace these. Technology, wherever it appears, is itself shaped in fundamental ways by cultural values.

Paul Goodman, a noted literary and social critic, observes that technological thinking in the present era still remains under the control of familiar human motives of desires for comfort, health, excitement, profit, power, or prestige. In spite of the premium placed on rationality, analysis, predictability, and efficiency by modern culture, the old motives control its direction. If, in fact, technology were simply a matter of "applied rationality," the world of the present era would be much more efficiently organized and a good deal more humane. Instead, there exists in the world a great waste of time and talent, complications to life that the technological way of thinking cannot tolerate, a cluttering of the environment, and education systems forever producing inept and lazy students.

According to Goodman, technology does not really dominate modern life. And the only serious threat posed by technology is that it may fall under the control of political, military, and economic interests that can subvert the objective and rational values that normally guide it.

The Occasion for Choices About Technology

Yet the crucial question raised by those who allege that technology determines human life is the question of whether individuals or societies are able to do what they want to do or whether technology forces them to do what it demands. Emmanuel Mesthene is one thinker who speaks directly to this question. He maintains that a condition of freedom does remain for people within a technological society, but it sometimes appears that technology is in control because of the complicated relationship technology has with human life.

Technology, Mesthene says, does bring about and inhibit changes in the physical world. These changes are of two sorts. The first is the ability of technology to change the physical environment; the plow, for example, alters the soil in specifiable ways. The second sort of change is the creation of new physical possibilities; the space missile is an instance of a new possibility created by technology. While the new possibilities invite change, they do not actually force change. People do not have to fly to the moon once they have a rocket. But the new possibilities suggest that some changes are likely.

Technology also removes some options previously available in a society. Technology inhibits. This consequence of technology is often misunderstood because the inhibitive consequences are derivative, indirect, and difficult to predict or to anticipate. Only after a new technology has been adopted are the older ways of doing things seen to be irrelevant, dysfunctional, or useless. For example, blacksmithing was removed as a vocational option for many people after the introduction of the automobile into society. Specialists in shoeing horses were no longer needed once the widespread use of the automobile took the place of the horse and buggy. But the removal of options is not due directly to the new tools or techniques so much as it is due to a choice concerning the new tools or techniques. Preceding the social change is a choice about the tools. The removal of options is thus indirect.

Also, because the removal of options is usually not seen until after the new technology has been chosen and adopted, the consequences of technological innovation are difficult to anticipate. It is only after the adoption of a technique that change becomes apparent. Plumbing, for example, contributed directly to convenience and hygiene in societies. Only later was it discovered that the sort of life associated with communal use of the village pump was no longer an option.

Some social change almost always follows a change in technology, according to Mesthene. He maintains, however, that the change is not determined by the technology. A circumstantial freedom exists between the new technology and the people who adopt the technology. Any innovation must be compatible with other existing human conditions before it can determine anything. The circumstances of a society must support the innovation. Those changes that do occur are always of the type that can exploit the new possibilities created by the technology.

Therefore, for Mesthene, technology does alter the mix of possibilities for social change. But *which* technologies are to be developed at a particular time depends on what social institutions and values prevail in a given society at a given time. It is a fact, for example, that Japanese workers continue to operate under the old customary rule that once employed by a firm they are obliged to continue with that firm until retirement. And the business firms of Japan take the view that to discharge a worker because of age or because of economic difficulties would be a violation of a sacred agreement. Such a customary cultural arrangement is neither rational nor efficient. Yet the deep-seated cultural commitments remain stronger than the demands of technological thinking.

Making Choices About Technology

We have seen that many social critics argue that technological thinking dominates and directs contemporary life and social policy. And the arguments deplore the subtle and persistent erosion of human selfhood, subjectivity, and traditional qualitative values. There is no doubt at all that the impact of technology on human life has been enormous. The important question is whether humans can do anything at all to control the direction and the limits of technology.

The issue of technological determinism, then, is one of great significance. If technological determinism is in fact the case and if all things that shape human life today are outside of human control, then technology itself would appear to be an autonomous and uncontrollable force at work among humanity. If, on the other hand, thinkers such as Mesthene and Goodman are correct in their assessment of the human situation, then it is extremely important that humans exercise their freedom to make choices about technology. Much of the rest of this text will spell out areas where important technological innovations are being introduced into human life. If humans can make choices about technology, then that right and freedom must be exercised. To choose not to choose is still to choose.

DISCUSSION QUESTIONS

1. What social strains are felt because of the introduction of new technology in recent years?

2. Examine some technological innovations and show what changes resulted from their introduction into human society.

3. Debate the issue of whether technology's effect on mankind is for good or for evil. Site your own evidence to support the position you take.

4. What are some practical consequences of holding the view that technology dominates and directs human life and social policy?

5. See if you can find some specific instances where a group or society exercised freedom of choice about technology.

BIBLIOGRAPHY

Brinkman, D. "Technology as Philosophic Problem." *Philosophy Today* 15, no. 2 (Summer 1971): 122–28.

Bronowski, J. *The Common Sense of Science.* New York: Vintage Books, n.d.

————. *Science and Human Values.* (rev. ed. with a new dialogue, "The Abacus and the Rose.") New York: Harper & Row, 1965.

Buchanan, R. A. "The Religious Implications of Industrialism and Social Change." *The Technologist,* 2 (1965): 245–55.

Burke, J. G., ed. *The New Technology and Human Values.* Belmont, Calif.: Wadsworth Publishing Co., 1966.

Ellul, J. "The Technological Order." In C. Mitcham and R. Mackey, eds. *Philosophy and Technology.* New York: The Free Press, 1972.

————. *The Technological Society*. New York: Vintage Books, 1964.

Ferkiss, V. C. *Technological Man: The Myth and the Reality*. New York: George Braziller, 1969.

Freeman, D. M. *Technology and Society: Issues in Assessment, Conflict, and Choice*. Chicago: Rand McNally, 1974.

Goodman, P. *People or Personnel* and *Like a Conquered Province*. New York: Vintage Books, 1968.

Greer, S. A. *Social Organization*. New York: Random House, 1955.

Johnson, D. L. "The Primitive Mind and the Study of Religion." Unpublished paper.

Kranzberg, M., and Davenport, W. H., eds. *Technology and Culture: An Anthology*. New York: Schocken Books, 1972.

Lauda, D. P., and Ryan, R. D., eds. *Advancing Technology: Its Impact on Society*. Dubuque, Iowa: Wm. C. Brown, 1971.

Lewis, C. S. *The Abolition of Man*. New York: The Macmillan Co., 1950.

Mesthene, E. G. *Technological Change*. Cambridge, Mass.: Harvard University Press, 1970.

————. *Technology and Social Change*. Indianapolis: Bobbs-Merrill, 1967.

Mitcham, C., and Mackey, R., eds. *Philosophy and Technology: Readings in the Philosophical Problems of Technology*. New York: The Free Press, 1972.

Muller, H. J. *The Children of Frankenstein*. Bloomington, Ind.: Indiana University Press, 1970.

Shriver, D. W., Jr. "Man and His Machines: Four Angles of Vision." *Technology and Culture,* 13, no. 4 (October 1972).

Stearn, G. E., ed. *McLuhan, Hot and Cool*. New York: New American Library, 1967.

Susskind, C. *Understanding Technology*. Baltimore and London: Johns Hopkins University Press, 1973.

Teilhard de Chardin, Pierre. *The Future of Man*. New York: Harper and Row, 1964.

Wallia, C. S., ed. *Toward Century 21*. New York: Basic Books, 1970.

Chapter 3
Technology and Society

Technology changes society. It provides society with new capabilities and new opportunities; it makes obsolete some ways of life and some values. The opportunities and the strains that result from technology's impact upon society are the subject of this chapter. It is wise to remember that the kinds of changes that occur in a society depend on the condition of the society in which they are occurring—that is, on its habits, traditions, and values. General trends, however, can be determined by examining the impact of technology on basic social institutions such as family, politics, economics, education, and religion.

Families and Modern Technology

Two factors associated with modern technology appear to threaten the continued existence of the family: industrialization and the technology of contraception. The first factor, industrialization, appears to threaten family structure by eliminating the family as a producing agent within society. In almost all traditional societies, the family functions as a producer of goods, as the prime socialization agent, and often as the agent of protection. The traditional family works together to produce necessary economic, moral, and religious cohesion to sustain itself.

Industrialization breaks down the family structure initially by separating work from the residence and by encouraging economic diversification within the family. Instead of all members of the family working to contribute to the maintenance of the group, the father is made into the economic provider for the family. Moreover, the work that the economic provider does is separated from the home.

Separation of work from the residence creates a number of complications for the traditional family. The family is dispersed intially by the move to the factory or city where increased contacts with strangers occur; an increasing number of possible interpersonal relations develop. Also, the acquisition of new skills for new employment often requires a readjustment of the father's identity as a worker and a provider. All these factors tend to break down the traditional family pattern.

Economic diversification in the family is encouraged by technological work-reducing devices in the home, which allow women to seek some form of employment, recreation, or community service projects outside the home. The housewife, too, is forced to redefine her role as wife and/or mother; the working woman is freed from economic dependence upon a man, a development that forces readjustment of relations within the family. The woman who is devoted to community service work or to recreation finds meaning and significance apart from the household, a situation that forces a readjustment of relations within the family.

The technology of contraceptives further complicates the family situation. Contraceptives, with their social consequences of divorcing sex from procreation, make the family system only one of a number of ways to order sex in a society. The technology of contraception, therefore, seems to abolish one of the important traditional functions of the family—namely, the ordering of sexual relations. Census statistics released in 1976 indicate that over a million divorces occurred among 214 million Americans. Precisely what role technology might have played in these divorces is not known; however, the loosening of family structures that occurs as an indirect consequence of technological innovation is surely apparent.

The Persistence of Family Relationships

Yet, despite the complications brought to the family by technological innovation, some recent studies indicate that the family, as a social institution, remains strong, even in America. Two factors account for the strength and persistence of the family. First, technology tends to redefine the family as a consumer rather than as a producer. Thus, a vital social function remains for the family. Even a cursory perusal of advertising and marketing in the United States indicates that households remain the backbone of the economy. Families purchase most of the automobiles produced in America; families purchase most of the household appliances, from television sets to washers and dryers. And shopping for goods such as groceries and clothing is still done primarily through the household.

A second factor that accounts for the persistence of the family is the significant change in the structural pattern of the family that has occurred within the last generation. The change that has occurred (and is still occurring) is from the "traditional" family pattern to a "companionship" family pattern. The traditional family, which still remains strong in some societies, is one in which members of the family are united by rules, regulations, duties, and obligations. Religion, law, and social mores make very clear to all of society the obligations of individuals to the family. A common form of the traditional family is the patriarchal family, which is often held together by powerful sanctions derived from a religious conception of God as father and as prime authority. Decisions in the patriarchal family are made autocratically by the father, the chief authority, and marriages within the family are often arranged by parents. A high value is placed upon complying with duty and following tradition.

The new family structure that is emerging today (the companionship family) derives its unity from mutual affection, intimate communication, and mutual acceptance of the division of labor and procedures of decision making within the family. Not held together by patriarchal authority or even by rigid rules of procedure, it adopts a democratic form of shared decision-making and shared housework. Advocates of the traditional family pattern regard the companionship family pattern as an indication that the family is eroding as a social institution. Others insist, however, that the companionship family is simply an adjustment to realities of life in societies that are influenced by advanced technology. At any rate, the family persists and endures, despite significant change brought by technology.

Studies of families in societies less industrialized than the United States indicate that even traditional family patterns are amazingly adept at adjusting to early technological changes. Neil Vincent Williams, in a study of the village of MaHallat Abu Ali in Egypt, concluded that the extended family pattern of traditional Egypt continues even when urbanization and industrialization occur. Williams discovered that for industrialized workers marriage to relatives and to nonrelatives did not change significantly with moves to the industrial centers. Family ties continued to be strong, and transformation from extended family patterns to nuclear patterns did not take place. Extended family ties continued to be important, with the web of kinship obligations and social relationships maintained even in an urban and industrialized environment.

Milton Singer, in his book *When a Great Tradition Modernizes,* notes that the traditional joint family pattern typical of India (featuring a network of family obligations governed by both law and custom) continues within urban, industrialized locations. The Indian joint family—patrilineal in descent, patrilocal in residence, patriarchal in authority—holds an inheritance rule that divides property equally among adult males through as many as four generations, and adapts well to industrialization in the Madras city area of South India. Although many social scientists had thought the Indian joint family incapable of adjusting to urbanization and industrialization, Singer found that the traditional family pattern actually offered some advantages for organizing industrial enterprises. The joint family unit is able to provide a nucleus of capital, a well-structured pattern of authority, and structured inheritance procedures. The joint family meets well the requirements for industrial organization of direction, management, diversification, and continuity. Singer, however, does not comment on how the family system fares for workers within the Indian factory system. But with a family model that supports industrialism from the top levels of management, the family system is not drastically threatened for Indians.

Political Order and Technological Change

Politics, in its broadest sense, is the set of means by which humans develop social organization. "Political" in this sense encompasses all the decision-making structures and procedures that deal with allocation and distribution of wealth and power in a society. This implies that the word "political" perhaps should connote economic–political since the market mechanism, decision making by business, labor unions, churches, political parties, and trade associations all relate to the allocation and distribution of wealth and power in a society. It is important to remember, however, that politics so defined bridges public and private organizations as well as formal and informal procedures. For example, whenever a labor leader endorses a presidential candidate, there are political consequences.

If technology, on the other hand, is a means by which humans organize nature for human use through discovery of the forces and laws of nature, it is both directly and indirectly related to political activity. The indirect influence of technology on politics takes place in two ways: First, technology aids in the periodic reorganization of political forces; and second, technology occasionally becomes a political asset.

Indirect Influences

There are many specific instances of political reorganization taking place by the indirect influence of technology. Peter F. Drucker has argued that the irrigation cities of Mesopotamia, Egypt, India, and China were all social and political reorganizations indirectly related to a technological change. He cites the development of new technologies as instrumental in bringing about several things: an established government as a distinct and permanent institution, the development of standing armies to protect surplus commodities, the emergence of social classes forming around new occupations, and even the creation of a sense of individuality. All these are indirect consequences of irrigation technology.

Joseph Needham, in his multivolume work entitled *Science and Civilization in China,* maintains that military technology based on gunpowder, the cannon, and rockets helped to end a whole way of life in Western Europe. In 1449, when the king of France blasted apart all the English castles in Normandy at the rate of five a month, the death knell was sounded to feudal aristocracy. Without the castle as a fortification, political power could no longer be maintained in the old ways by the old rules. Moreover, at sea the slave-manned galleys were found to be inadequate for the new methods of warfare once gun platforms became a necessity. So both feudal aristocracy and at least one form of slavery were rendered obsolete by the new technology of warfare. But technology as a definite political asset is apparent in Needham's examples. The king who had a superior military technology had the means by which to extend and consolidate his power.

Direct Influences

The direct influence of technology on political life can be examined in terms of the political organizations themselves. Such a direct influence involves management—the technical capacity to organize the state. Management generally entails office machinery for processing information, collecting data, monitoring various agencies and branches of government, and organizing relations between government and society. The actual power of the political machine increases in direct proportion to the skill, efficiency, and speed with which the bureaucracy processes its information. With the introduction of computerized data banks (automatic systems for storing, analyzing, and recalling information), the speed and efficiency of the bureaucracy might be expected to increase considerably, with an accompanying increase in power for bureaucracy. Many see this direct influence of technology on politics as an advantage to those who govern but as a threat to those who are governed. Technological management, it is feared, may lead to the capture of decision-making either by the machines or by the technicians who run the machines.

In a report for the Harvard University Program on Technology and Society, Alan F. Westin studied the effects of new technology on government operations in the United States. He concluded that no takeover by either machines or technicians is imminent. In fact, he notes that there is not the slightest sign that the traditional leadership elites of middle-management people are being displaced. Machines are available, and in some cases they are being purchased. But they are not doing the sort of work that they could do; instead, computers have been used for the consolidation of power, information, and data, rather than for the redistribution of it. Although machines are available, they are not being used for decision-making or for program evaluation.

Technology also has a direct impact on public participation in politics. The technology of television provides direct visual contact with politicians, a situation similar to the Athenian democracy of ancient Greece. Television offers the citizen a sense of participation in the broader political life of a nation. Through news programs, bulletins, and reporting, the citizen can see government officials doing at least a part of their jobs.

Yet, it must be remembered that participation in politics through television is different from participation in a pure democracy. Through the medium of television, the citizen is an observer–participant; that is, he participates only as an observer. He has little opportunity to influence directly political decisions or policies. Yet because he does observe, he is therefore informed.

The limitations of political participation built into the medium of television are worthy of note. It is possible that television might be used as a political instrument by people who have the power to control the medium. Moreover, since personalities and events transmit far better than do ideas and principles, a temptation exists for those who control the medium to emphasize political drama and action at the expense of substantive issues. Thus, while politics enters the citizen's home through the television set, politics does not amount to issues and ideas, but rather personalities, images, and publicity. This trivialization of politics by television may be a more serious threat to democracy and to public participation in government than bureaucratic governmental control of the medium itself.

The direct impact of technology on politics, therefore, can be seen from two sides. Technology provides the government with the tools that dramatically speed up the collection, processing, and dissemination of information; at the same time, it provides the potential for greater efficiency and accuracy in planning, policy formation, decision making, and program implementation. From the citizen's side, however, technology through telecommunications provides a new kind of participation in the political sector. The new participation is largely unconnected to the powers of decision making, however.

Education for a Technological Society

Education is another area of social life that is subject to technological change. The demand for increased specialization in technological fields such as electronics, communications, and computer science requires a different sort of education than has been traditionally provided. Four basic patterns of educational curriculum structuring are apparent in modern societies: the classical model of education, the religious model, the humanistic model, and the managerial model.

The classical curriculum model is based on the assumption that knowledge of the values and achievements of antiquity are paramount for life in the modern world. The curriculum developed by promoters of the classical model is structured to help students preserve a memory of the past and concentrates on history, literature, philosophy, and the languages.

The religious curriculum model is concerned with bringing a student to an awareness of and a relationship to what is conceived to be "the holy." It generally emphasizes piety over factual knowledge and practice over theory. Humanistic education, on the other hand, assumes that an education ought to free individuals to realize themselves as persons relating to other persons. Curricula developed on the humanistic principle of education focus on the arts, with enough of the sciences added to provide theoretical insight into scientific method.

The managerial model of education, the most recent one to be developed, tends to dominate educational institutions in technological societies. Its curriculum emphasizes vocational skills that can provide the human resources for other social institutions. It assumes that a good education is one that is useful to both the student and the society. The advantages that recommend the managerial model are that it is both efficient and testable since it provides practical goals. Society can evaluate how well the educational institutions are doing their job by observing how well the students (the products) fit into the job market.

Although the managerial model tends to fit well with the expectations of societies that are interested in promoting technological development, many educators are uncomfortable about structuring education to serve

social institutions rather than pupils. Current educational theory raises
questions concerning whether an education should provide a student with
intellectual tools for a career or with intellectual insight into mankind,
nature, and living. Robert M. Hutchins, a longtime advocate of the humanistic model of education, argues that students are victimized by an
education directed toward specialization in one field of knowledge or occupation. Hutchins maintains that the managerial model of education produces
students stuffed with facts but without any theoretical insights into what to
do with them. Since, in a technological society, facts tend to increase exponentially as research and development continue, the range of facts any
one student is able to master narrows increasingly to the point that a student learns more and more about less and less. Hutchins argues that a
liberal education that provides insight into the theoretical underpinnings of
modern culture is more important than a specialized knowledge. Specialization in one area of technical education, such as medicine, electronics, communications, or law, can be added later to the theoretical ground provided
by a humanistic curriculum.

Educational Technologies

But what of the impact of technology on the learning process itself?
How has technology altered learning and teaching procedures? Technological devices have been a part of education for a long time, so long in fact
that it is difficult to separate learning from the use of such devices as
books, printing, blackboard, pencils, paper, the compass, and the slide rule.
More advanced and more recent technologies include the slide and movie
projector, tape recorders and phonographs, and the television set.

More complicated and sophisticated technologies presently available
are audiotapes for language instruction, television systems for prerecorded
lecture–demonstrations of an otherwise limited access event, and the computer. The computer opens fantastic quantities of data to the student, including books, videotapes, and holograms, which can be made available at
millions of terminals.

The introduction of advanced technology into the educational institutions may render obsolete the traditional lecture method of presenting information and explanations. Some even suggest that education as a class-
room phenomenon might easily be replaced by home terminals, through
which students can work through their own individually programmed
learning modules. The school building, then, might become simply a place
for students and teachers to meet occasionally for testing, counselling, and
guidance. The advance of technology in education might eliminate both
the traditional classrom and the traditional teacher. The teacher, re-
emerging as a counsellor, a guide, and helper, would lose his old role as a
resource person who holds information otherwise unavailable.

The major difficulty preventing radical reorganization because of technology in education is the general conservatism of educational establish-

ments everywhere. Even in America, which is considered the country most flexible in its curricula and teaching techniques, institutional rigidity over a yet infant technology precludes significant developments in educational technology for some time to come. The easiest changes could occur at advanced levels of education where learning is already on an individualized system. Graduate students in nearly all areas of study do their major work alone and consult only occasionally with a teacher. Thus, individualized study using technological devices easily fits the requirements for most graduate work.

But at an even deeper level than the general conservatism of educational establishments is the problem of discovering a philosophy of education to guide the advance of technology in education. Any significant change requires a philosophy that can guide that change. Technological development is not simply a matter of engineering applied to learning. Questions regarding the quality of education as opposed to the quantity of information or quantity of those educated must be asked and answered. Three major issues remain for education theorists: (1) In the face of a glut of information, what information is necessary for an education? (2) What kind of education is best in a technological society? (3) How can the most important techniques of education be selected from among the many new possibilities?

New technological systems suggest almost limitless possibilities in education. What needs to be done and what ought to be done, however, are issues requiring a general theory of education that would emerge from a philosophy of education.

Modern Technology and Economic Systems

Technology and economics is a subject of increasing concern in the modern world; it is also a subject that remains controversial, sometimes speculative, and always complicated. Worldwide expansion of energy demands; the use of energy resources as an instrument of foreign relations; multinational corporations; conflicts of race, religion, and nationality; together with general monetary inflation have convinced many economic theorists that the impact of technology on economics is so great that new systems of economics must be developed to handle the new problems. Well-known thinkers such as John Kenneth Galbraith, Alvin Toffler, and Daniel Bell maintain that technology has helped to create a worldwide situation that must eventually force some new economic order to emerge.

Galbraith, Toffler, and Bell believe that a new economic situation exists today in industrial societies. Three general changes in the economic situation result from technological innovations.

Economic Changes Fostered by Technology

A first factor of change is a rapid increase in the productive power of any society with some technological sophistication as more and more goods are machine produced. But machine production often significantly reduces the need for workers. The effect of the replacement of men by machines on the economy is significant. But once machine production begins, an increased demand for liaison is also required. In business, liaison is generally an information exchange that helps to maintain the smooth function of the production system. Liaison personnel also alter the economy because, not only do they possess different skills than do production workers, but they also differ in personality. Successful office workers are those who are able to get along with others, who present a respectable image for their company, and who develop skills that relate to the office rather than to the plant.

A second factor of change brought about by increased technology is in the nature of what a society consumes. Not only is the rate of consumption altered with increased technology, but what is consumed changes too. Consumer items become redefined to include education and health, along with staple items such as food, clothing, and shelter. The shift to increased demand for services, ranging from delivery service to medical care, forces the service occupations to organize themselves along the impersonal lines of industry. But since performance of services cannot be easily fit into the market scheme of supply and demand as a basis for wages, profits, or losses, the classical economic laws become increasingly irrelevant to any society preoccupied with services.

A third factor produced by technological change is the introduction of high-speed computers, improved telecommunications systems, and increased activity in the multinational banks and corporations. One result of this development is that money moves around the world at high speed, changing hands rapidly, often by means of computers, and going through national devaluations and international revaluations. Economists generally agree that the rate at which money changes hands in a society is a key variable affecting prices. The faster money moves, the greater the expenditures. Thus, an increase in speed acts like an increase in money supply, making inflation an international problem. Currency increases, prices rise, more money is available for everyone; but the money is not worth as much in the marketplace.

John Kenneth Galbraith, in his controversial book *The New Industrial State,* describes the new economic situation characterized by increased technology. The economic child of technology is the large corporation, which, Galbraith says, is no longer concerned simply with the classical capitalist goal of maximizing returns. Rather, a modern corporation is concerned with very conservative and prudential matters: a secure earnings level, gradual growth, technical virtuosity, and rising dividends. All these can be accomplished easily by collaboration with government. Taxation, government spending and planning, together with selective intervention in the economy of a nation, can protect the corporation from undue risks in the public sector. Careful advertising campaigns by the corporation can control demand for products and keep it equal to supply, so government intervention in the economy is welcomed by the new large corporation.

According to Galbraith, business and government need one another in the new situation. Employment needs, shortages, excesses, and pricing can all be controlled through careful management operations. The state can provide domestic stability, education, technical advance, and even tax breaks to stimulate production.

The polarization of the world into superpowers competing for goods and services can only enhance the prestige of the new, large corporation. Since competition among nations often occurs as economic competition, the union of industry with the military, space exploration, communications, and climate management solidifies arrangements previously established between corporations and governments at the national level. Galbraith concludes that old economic theories based on notions of free production, free enterprise, and supply and demand must be revised to meet the new situation produced mainly by worldwide technological sophistication.

Religious Life and Technological Thinking

Some aspects of technology clearly influence religion: Urbanization, specialization, new social classes, transportation, communications, social security, and new political forms all indirectly influence traditional ways of being religious. Changes in transportation, for example, have made religious pilgrimage possible to many more people, as in the flights of Islamic faithful in and out of the city of Mecca. Modern publishing technology provides many millions of people with religious scriptures and books. The technology of radio and television increases the scope of those religions that wish to propagate their faith.

Yet, a far deeper impact of technology upon religion has been the introduction and general acceptance of a new way of thinking. Traditional ways of thinking (and here religion shares an important role) generally assume the authority of certain persons who lived in the past and revere them by holding as special certain books written by them or sayings attributed to them. The authority of Plato and Aristotle in traditional philosophical thought has been no less significant than the sayings of Jesus, Buddha, or Confucius in traditional religious thought.

But the authority of the past and the sayings of the sages are seriously questioned by modern science and technology. In fact, scientific and technological ways of thinking in the modern world assume that, in principle, everything is open to scrutiny, analysis, and criticism. No text is sacred, no authority remains unquestioned, and no saying is to be accepted until examined according to proper methods. And it is the very method of scientific–technological thinking that demands that all past authorities be so questioned. Revolutions in thinking about the nature of the solar system to revolutions in mechanics have all begun with questioning the ideas of the past.

In his book *The Future of an Illusion,* Sigmund Freud attempted to apply the new way of thinking to the religious doctrines and practices of mankind. Freud argued that the power of religion lies in its assertions about God, which include threats of punishment or promises of rewards. Yet, religious doctrines cannot be shown to be true by means of any scientific tests. Religious ideas do not stand up under modern methods of testing, according to Freud, and the argument used by religious devotees to convince others to believe are weak. The first is that religious doctrines are worthy of belief because great people of the past held them to be true. The second argument is that doctrines are worthy of belief because books written by great people of the past claim to be telling the truth. The third argument is that doctrines should be believed because disbelieving them is wrong.

Freud maintained that all three arguments for religious doctrines must be rejected by those who apply the scientific–technological reasoning. We know the ancients to have been wrong about many things, so unless we have a test to show their views to be correct, we must assume that they could be wrong about religious matters also. Moreover, analysis of the books of old reveals errors. So, Freud argues, traditional religious doctrines must be judged by the scientific–technological method of thinking; then they can be evaluated according to their usefulness, their truth, and their social–psychological function. Freud concludes that most religious doctrines, when subjected to proper scrutiny, will have to be abandoned.

Traditional Theism and the New Faith in Technology

The traditional religious belief most seriously questioned by modern technology is the belief in God. In recent years, talk of Christian atheism, agnosticism, pantheism, and new definitions of God all suggest that even among religious leaders an awareness exists that contemporary experience does not support belief in God. As technological answers are found to many previously perplexing questions, the sphere occupied by God seems to diminish. The assurances and comfort provided by religion that the death of a loved one was "God's will" do not hold well in the face of a technology of medicine that might have prevented the death. As more and more preventions and cures are found for the sicknesses and diseases that formerly killed many, the position of God appears to be ever-weakening in the face of advancing technology. The really important development is that God is being removed from the minds of modern man as technology provides new and more compelling answers to traditionally perplexing questions.

Some religious thinkers believe that the retreat of God from the consciousness of modern man is so complete that technology is functioning as religion. Such technologies as cryonics (the quick freezing of a body for possible resuscitation when cures for the fatal disease are known) and applied behavioral psychology might replace traditional notions of immortality, resurrection, sin, guilt, and punishment. The doctrines of God, notions about the meaning of life and death, and problems of guilt and sin might be displaced by technological innovations that make the older ideas and values meaningless or irrelevant.

However, not everyone is convinced that religion is either on the decline or is radically altered by the technological order. A growing number of sociologists of religion are convinced that basic human religious needs and functions have not changed significantly since the late Ice Age. In fact, some argue that changes that have occurred in the religious consciousness of mankind simply make the fundamental religious questions *more* critical rather than less critical.

Andrew Greeley maintains that "modern man" or "technological man" or "secular man" (whatever name one prefers) is to be found, if at all, only on university campuses, and even there only among some senior faculty members. Students on the secular campuses engage in witchcraft, astrology, and bizarre occult practices. And Greeley notes that available statistical data do not indicate a declining religiousness even in America. The resurgence of curious forms of religious belief suggest the students' fundamental quest for religiosity.

Greeley and many sociologists and religious thinkers, including Robert Bellah, Peter Berger, Clifford Geertz, Langdon Gilkey, Paul Ricoeur, and Thomas Luckmann, assert that human existence is confronted by at least three problems not soluble by technology. The first of these is the problem of "bafflement." When man reaches the limits of either his analytic capacities, or his powers of endurance, or his moral insight, he finds himself doubting the technological assumption that life is comprehensible, and that thought can provide man with proper orientation to life. Bafflement is, then, the threat to peoples' most general ability to understand the world.

The second and third problems facing man are moral evil and human suffering, neither of which can be reconciled through common sense explanations, scientific explanations, or ideological explainations. Suffering and evil persist everywhere in the world, even in technological societies. And while technology may occasionally do something to change the conditions of both, it cannot eliminate either. If religion is understood as man's attempt to deal with human problems of bafflement, evil, and suffering, then a religious dimension of human life apparently does remain. A religion would function in three ways: to provide a "faith" to cope with the question of the final meaning of human existence; to provide a sense of belonging and shared commitments; and to provide a thought system capable of integrating various areas of human life such as art, sex, family, friendship, and order.

Many thinkers claim, therefore, that basic human religious needs persist, although the symbols, rituals, and doctrines surrounding those needs may be forced to change significantly as technology changes the conditions of life. What new directions religious groups might take or what new forms religion itself might take is a matter of continuing interest. That religious interests remain, however, is demonstrated by statistics and scientific observation.

DISCUSSION QUESTIONS

1. What would you expect the future of the "companionship family" to be? Will technology have a greater impact on the family in the future than it now has?

2. By examining a local or national political campaign that you are familiar with, test the assertion that the technology of television tends to reduce political issues to personalities and public relations.

3. What is the value of a humanistic education in a technological society?

4. What do you think will be the future of either capitalism or socialism in technological societies? Does technology tend to support one economic system over another?

5. How does religion change in technological societies? Which of the major religions of the world do you think are most adaptable to technological change?

BIBLIOGRAPHY

Baier, K., and Rescher, N., eds. *Values and the Future*. New York: The Free Press, 1969.

Burgess, E. W., Locke, H. J., and Thomes, M. M. *The Family: From Traditional to Companionship*. 4th ed. New York: Van Nostrand and Reinhold Co., 1971.

Douglas, J. D., ed. *Freedom and Tyranny: Social Problems in a Technological Society*. New York: Random House, 1970.

Freeman, D. M. *Technology and Society: Issues in Assessment, Conflict, and Choice*. Chicago: Rand McNally, 1974.

Freud, S. *The Future of an Illusion*. Garden City, N.Y.: Anchor Books, 1961, 1964.

Greeley, A. M. *Religion in the Year 2000*. New York: Sheed and Ward, 1969.

————. *Unsecular Man: The Persistence of Religion*. New York: Dell Publishing Co. 1972.

Hutchins, R. M. "Science, Scientists, and Politics." In J. G. Burke, ed. *The New Technology and Human Values*. Belmont, Calif.: Wadsworth Publishing Co., 1966.

Rotenstreich, N. "Technology and Politics." *Philosophy and Technology*. New York: The Free Press, 1972.

Singer, M. *When a Great Tradition Modernizes*. New York: Praeger Publishers, 1972.

Wallia, C. S., ed. *Toward Century 21*. New York: Basic Books, 1970.

Williams, N. V. *Factory Employment and Family Relationships in an Egyptian Village*. Unpublished Ph.D. dissertation, The University of Michigan, 1964.

Chapter 4
Technology and the Individual

Technology influences the individual by increasing his probable life span, by extending varieties of expression in the arts, in hobbies, and in communications, and by freeing him from many kinds of work. But technology can also produce social and psychological strains that complicate life. In this chapter we shall look at the role technology plays and might play in the future for individuals.

All human beings have fundamental needs that must be satisfied to sustain life. These basic needs are not, themselves, determined by the social structure, by cultural patterns, or by the socialization process itself. Rather, they are prerequisites to human life. These needs can be considered under two categories: physical needs and self-needs.

Fundamental Human Needs

Physical needs of humans are necessary for the continued functioning of the organism. They include needs for food, water, air, clothing, shelter. Any social environment that is unable to produce these items necessarily ceases to exist. Moreover, if the ecological conditions of an area are such that these needs are difficult to satisfy, these needs will be the predominant concern of almost all members of that society.

Another group of physical needs is the general needs for physical, sexual, and mental activity. These needs can be satisfied in various ways, but the ways in which they are satisfied are generally prescribed by a society and its culture. Thus, sexual needs might possibly be satisfied through masturbation or heterosexual, homosexual, or bisexual activity. The specific forms of permissible sexual activity and the limits placed upon sexual satisfaction vary according to the norms generated by the culture. While all societies recognize the sexual need, the boundaries established for satisfying this sexual need vary greatly among societies. Although needs of physical, sexual, and mental activities are common to all animals, humans differ because there is a wider range of possible ways to satisfy them.

The chief factors that differentiate humans from other creatures of the world are the development of mind and the development of a concept of selfhood. Mind and self are not things; they are processes that arise through the interaction of individuals to the social world in which they live. No human is born with a self; rather, a concept of self develops over a period of time as the human relates to the world of other humans. The crucial element in developing a concept of self is the ability to project an image of a personal self that is distinct from society. The child, for example, interacts with other persons in a social world; while doing so, he develops a sense of self by using others as a mirror through which he sees himself as they see him. He experiences the reactions of others as he behaves. And it is the reaction of others to the individual's activities that provides a self-concept for the individual. The individual gets "outside" of himself to see himself as others perceive him, and by taking the attitude of others toward himself, he forms a self-concept.

The self never exists in isolation from a social environment in which it is found. To have a sense of selfhood requires first, that there be others who can respond or react to the activity of the individual, and second, that the individual be able to get outside or remove himself enough from his activity to take the attitude of others toward his activity.

The most general need of the self is to develop an accurate and acceptable self-concept. That is, a human's socially produced identity must be accurate in that it shows him to be a biological organism with general biological needs to be satisfied. But it must also provide a basis for self-acceptance by indicating what behavior patterns are legitimate in meeting those needs. If social institutions do not provide an accurate concept of selfhood for the individual (that is, if the social institutions demand superhuman behavior), or if the society does not prescribe norms of acceptable behavior, then the self-concept cannot develop. The individual is set adrift; the society expects either too much or too little, or the image of selfhood provided by the society is not accurate with regard to what humans actually need.

An additional self-need is the need to develop or expand the self-concept through continued intimate contact with other human beings. This may be done in a variety of ways—through the family, through friendships, through initiation into tribal groups or classes. Without an opportunity to expand and develop the concept of self, the individual becomes emotionally and intellectually arrested.

It is to be expected that for most of human history mankind has been preoccupied with satisfying basic physical needs. To produce enough food, clothing, and other material items that might insure survival took the major part of time, energy, and abilities of all premodern societies. And while the self-needs are always important, they do not become a primary concern in any society until there is sufficient economic abundance to promise satisfaction of the physical needs.

When a society reaches a point where it can guarantee fulfillment of basic physical needs for humans, then attention shifts to the creation, development, and expansion of the self-concept. Some traditional societies selected a class that devoted itself almost exclusively to matters of the self.

Such aristocratic classes had the opportunity to develop themselves through the arts, through the cultivation of leisure, or through the refinement of the sense in the enjoyment of art and leisure.

Self Needs and Modern Technology

Much contemporary literature is highly critical of modern societies and sees the individual as being abused by new technologies, which relieve people from preoccupation with physical needs without providing them with either the occasion for the pursuit of self-needs or an accurate and acceptable self-image to pursue. Critics of modern societies generally focus on these two problems: Technology does not fulfill the promise that time, space, and resources will be made available for the development of the self; and the image held by modern societies of an acceptable self does not coincide with the realities of the biological conditions of modern man.

Problems with self-development may occur because of two very general developments caused by modern technology. The first development is the modification of the individual's physical environment in which he lives. Because of advanced technology, the environment of the individual is no longer of his own creation. Rather, he is forced to adapt himself to a constantly changing environment that is not under his control. Although, by nature, the human being is made to travel at about five miles in an hour (walking), he can now find himself travelling at six hundred miles an hour. The biological organism is made to eat when it feels hungry and to sleep when it feels sleepy; the new technological milieu makes the organism adjust itself to a clock. The new environment promises grand extensions of the individual's normal powers of sense and reveals to him previously unavailable sights, liberties, and possibilities. But these come about only by a modification of the whole environment normal to the biological organism. Home, furniture, and food all become transformed into something new and often artificial.

The modification of time and motion by technology also tends to complicate the satisfactory creation of a self-image. Time that is marked by the mechanical clock rather than by nature's time (biological time) affects all of the individual's life. Life becomes measured by a machine called the clock. And motion, which is the visible expression of biological life, is modified according to the ever-changing dictates of technology. More precise and efficient human motion is demanded to keep up with the precision and efficiency of the technological environment. The more the machine penetrates the individual's life, the less opportunity the individual has to act spontaneously, unreflectively, or freely. Because human movements must approach perfection to the degree that machines approach it, human movement cannot express individual personalities as it once did. Imperfect motions are no longer tolerated in a highly technologized society. The individual driving an automobile on a crowded freeway must force himself to make the proper movements dictated by the requirements of safe driving. Spontaneity, carelessness, or whim has less and less to do with individual development.

The Human Case Against Modern Technology

The criticism launched against technology on behalf of humanity reads, then, almost like a litany for the estranged. First, it is said that *pressure to conform* is increasing in modern society. To keep pace with society, the individual must act as others act, and all must act according to the dictates of machines. Industrialized production creates a society in which individuals drive the same kinds of automobiles, watch the same television shows, share the same mass culture, and go through the same mechanical motions at work and at home. Groupism, conformity, togetherness are all emphasized at the expense of independence and freedom. Yet, political theory and economic theory common to modern democratic nations project self-images of independence, free enterprise, and individualism. The creation of a healthy self-concept in this contradictory environment is impossible.

A second criticism is *alienation*. In spite of the tendencies toward conformity and togetherness, individuals find themselves alienated from others, from nature, and from themselves. Industrialism, with its factories and factory towns, cut people off from nature long ago. Even though escape to nature by means of the automobile may be an option for some, few people find themselves with any sense of the rhythm of nature's order. Air conditioning, heating, swimming pools, boats, cabins, and manufactured charcoal briquets substitute for nature and nature's ways.

Karl Marx complained a hundred years ago that man was alienated from his work because of technological developments. A person's work in industry does not contribute to the development of a self-concept. Rather, work is something external to the worker, something he does to earn a living. While new developments in the management of personnel relations and unionization may try to humanize work, they do little to solve the problem of alienation. Surveys indicate that most industrial workers dislike their jobs; even increased leisure time is only time off from work. Therefore, workers soon begin to work at enjoying themselves through some means dictated by media advertising. So leisure also becomes an "alienated" form of pleasure.

A third criticism is the *rootlessness* caused by the geographical and social mobility that is peculiar to highly industrialized societies. The opportunity to move from place to place may be welcomed by many as excitement and change to their lives. But the advantages of mobility are tempered by the strain of adapting to new social contexts, new neighborhoods, and new acquaintances. The individual is forced to prove himself in new communities, new jobs, and among new friends. The result is a psychological insecurity unknown to the more stable, premodern societies.

And finally the criticism of *disenchantment* must be noted. Science and technology provide answers to many questions, but they are unable to answer the questions that many individuals find most important: "What shall I do?" and "How shall I live?" Technology provides many means for doing many things; but it does not provide any final answer about the proper goals or ends. Often, then, it is technology that is blamed for not providing the sort of answers people desire. The result is disenchantment.

Blunting the Criticism Against Technology

The criticisms that accuse technology of dwarfing the individual are blunted when we realize that most of them are either so general and could be applied to any society at any time, or they are fuzzy and unfocused. Conformity is, after all, an old story. De Toqueville and Emerson worried about it in America long ago, even before the rise of the industrial society. To blame conformity on modern technology is to ignore the makeup of traditional societies. Every society everywhere forces conformity of some sort.

Moreover, alienation from nature is not a particularly new thing. Previous societies showed no great love or emotion for nature. And most peasant societies live in fear of nature's sometimes catastrophic behavior. And alienation from work is a problem only if one holds to the view that human fulfillment is to be found in work and not in something else. For the majority of humans in history work was for the purpose of survival. And that effort was not always pleasureable.

The alleged alienation of the individual from society is not new either, though its causes may be more subtle today than in earlier times. But from a different point of view, the factors that contribute to a sense of alienation from society are not altogether bad. The impersonal organizations brought about through techniques of management help to make human relations smoother and conserve energy for potentially higher purposes. Finally, the rootlessness and mobility of modern societies do tend to create a more tolerant and open society in such matters as dress, sex, and religion. Technology has its impact upon individuals; but whether it is to blame for what Christian theologians have called "the human condition" is not at all obvious.

The Individual and Technological Possibilities for Change

The direct application of technology to individuals is increasing. Recent developments in pharmacology and neurophysiology focus attention on technological possibilities for controlling behavior and for changing personality in radical ways. Not only is it possible that most forms of disease and sickness might vanish, but deviant and antisocial behavior might also be eliminated through technology.

The current state of the art of applying technology to behavior is still crude, sometimes thought to be unreliable, and still lacking in complete theoretical understanding of processes. Yet, it is possible to alter human behavior by means of drugs, neurosurgical intervention, and systematic stimulus control. Some of the techniques are reversible—that is, behavior can be modified significantly and then brought back to the previous norm. Other techniques are in some sense irreversible; once a technique such as a brain operation is used, a return to previous behavior patterns is often impossible to bring about.

But the major problem with implementing technology to alter human personality is not so involved with the relatively new state of the art as it is with the emotional, moral, and religious considerations. These difficulties will become apparent as we examine some recent developments in the technology of control.

Modification of the Genetic Code

Recent discoveries in the molecular biology of the gene raise the possibility that the DNA code might be radically altered by substituting new genetic material for that already existing in a cell. Since genes make a major contribution to all kinds of behavior, a genetic recombination might provide a method for eliminating undesirable behavior traits among individuals. So far, however, knowledge of the location of chromosomes of genes vital for different types of behavior is scant. Moreover, results of experiments in mammals have been, for the most part, negative. Yet, geneticists continue to work on the exceedingly complicated problem of locating the genetic determinants of human behavior. And in the next fifty to seventy-five years it is certain that control of behavior by manipulation of genetic materials will occur.

Gene Selection by Controlled Mating

Selective breeding of animals has been used for years to produce desired traits, and these techniques are available for application to humans. Significant changes do not occur until several generations have passed. Moreover, opposition to such experimentation on humans is widespread on moral and religious grounds. However, selective breeding of slaves has occurred in human history, and, under certain circumstances, it may occur again.

Nutritional Influences on Human Behavior

The search for nutritional factors that can modify behavior continues. It is well known that a limited diet can lead to deficiencies characterized by abnormal behavior. Precisely what the impact of a carefully controlled diet might be is a matter of speculation and ongoing experimentation. That diet can alter behavior, however, is clear.

Hormones

Recent information indicates that hormones can modify behavior in many different ways. Neural tissues differentiate in one way if certain sexual hormones are present and in another way if they are absent. The influence of hormones often depends on their presence or absence during a particular stage of development, as well as upon the quantity of hormones. In adult life, sexual hormones alter the intensity of drive and modify the reception of stimuli that influence sexual performance. The adrenocortical hormones also modify behavior. Yet, few studies have been completed on humans because the side effects of hormone adjustments are often more interesting to researchers than the behavioral effects.

Drug Research

Drugs such as alcohol have been used for thousands of years to modify behavior. Recently, there has been extensive interest in the chemical organization of the nervous system as a transmitter of information. Researchers are now exploring the synthesis, storage, transport, utilization, and mode of breakdown of many chemical substances in the brain. The relationship of chemicals to mood, to learning, and to physical activity is bound to be a matter of intensified study in the future.

Drugs that expand consciousness, such as LSD and Psylocibin, continue to hold the attention of many. These agents produce a subjective experience that combines an intensification of sensation with a heightened emotional state combining elation and fear. They have been used in psychotherapy to treat various disorders of the mind. The most dramatic aspect of these drugs is their use by subcultures within many societies of the Western hemisphere. Research on LSD, however, has recently been curtailed because of some evidence that prolonged mental disorders can be produced by even a single, small dose of such drugs.

Neurosurgical Interventions

Surgical operations on the intact brain for the relief of undesirable symptoms have been carried out since the 1930s in Europe and in America. During the 1950s, frequent use of psychosurgical techniques to modify abornmal mental and physical behavior began in mental hospitals. The major operation was the lobotomy, the severing of the connection between the frontal lobes and the rest of the brain.

Recently work has been done to modify behavior in animals by inserting electrodes into the brain. Currents are passed through the electrodes while the subject is awake and behaving normally. The current flow stimulates some neurons to produce nerve impulses which produce, modify, or arrest behavior. These experiments in animals have been used to produce alertness, drowsiness, and sleep, to arrest some behavior, to modify the urgency of some biological drives such as sex and maternal tendencies, and to increase or decrease aggressive behavior. The technique suggests that certain centers of the brain elicit pleasant or unpleasant sensations. To stimulate these centers as reward or punishment could provide a way to control behavior in a fairly rigid way.

Other Surgical Procedures

The removal of glands alters the endocrine system, and behavior changes follow. Also, the attachment of mechanisms to the body to increase the efficiency or effectiveness of certain organs is an expanding technology. For example, the surgical implantation of a pacemaker to control heartbeat is now common. Research on mechanisms for other organs continues.

Environmental Manipulation: A Technology of Behavior

For some time Harvard psychologist B. F. Skinner has argued for a technology of behavior. According to Skinner, modern society's major problems are caused by human behavior. Population control, nuclear arms proliferation, the threat of atomic warfare, problems of housing, transportation, health, and sanitation are all problems of human behavior. Yet, present attempts to solve the problems concentrate only on new technologies such as contraceptives, nuclear deterrents, new architectures, faster and more efficient transportation, or better medicines.

But new technological hardware does not solve human problems. In fact, medicine and sanitation become more sophisticated and efficient only to produce greater population problems when more people live and live longer. The application of "hardware" to the social sphere does not really solve problems; sometimes it even complicates them. Housing, medicine, agriculture, transportation are all areas of great technological innovation in the last one hundred years. But unless people can be induced to use the new hardware, no problem can be solved. Contraceptives are abundantly available throughout the world; but unless people begin to use them, they will not help to solve the population problem.

In short, what is required is a technology of human behavior. Human behavior must be changed before any technological hardware can solve pressing problems. New advances in technologies related to the human body and the physical world are widespread, but no comparable advance in modifying behavior can be noted. In fact, crime seems to be on the increase, and fear of nuclear war haunts all the so-called developed nations.

Skinner insists that theories about human behavior that are being used in the courts, in schools, in industry, and in religious institutions are horrendously inadequate and out of date. No physicist today reads Aristotle for help in his work. Yet students of the humanities still read Plato, Confucius, and other sages of the past in order to gain some insight into human behavior. While Aristotle would not understand one page of a modern physics text, Socrates and his friends would have little difficulty following most discussions about human affairs in our time. When it comes to human behavior, modern people still operate with theories generated twenty-five hundred years ago.

The problem is that while the sciences long ago abandoned explanations for natural events that appealed to spirits, wills, impulses or feelings, people still try to explain human behavior by talking about a person or a personality independent of the body that behaves. According to Skinner, it is only the behavior that matters. The spirit, the will, the impulses, the feelings, and the intentions do not have to concern anyone who wants to change behavior. In fact, to talk about motives, intentions, and feelings is to talk about something other than the actual behavior that might need changing.

Students of human behavior must take the same step as the natural scientists took long ago and abandon the idea of an inner man, an agent apart from the physical body. They must concentrate, instead, on the environment and the relation that exists between behavior and its consequences in a particular setting. Physics did not advance by trying to discuss the jubilance of a falling body. And the study of human behavior will not advance so long as people continue to search for more information about feelings, plans, purposes, intentions, and emotions of some spirit that is thought to exist distinct from the body that acts. In the modern world, it will do no good to discuss the supposed intentions or motives guiding the person who might obliterate the earth by starting a nuclear war. It is the behavior, the act, that must be studied and prevented.

Skinner maintains that the key to a technology of behavior is to focus on the environment in which an individual is behaving. The Russian scientist Pavlov first showed the importance of the environment in determining behavior when he showed how a stimulus (food placed before a hungry dog) could bring about regular and predictable consequences (salivating). Skinner calls for a more sophisticated appreciation of the environment on behavior than Pavlov was able to formulate. According to Skinner, the environment needs to be studied, not only because of what it does to the organism (that is, forces the organism to act in a certain way), but also because of what takes place in the environment after the organism acts.

Skinner believes that behavior is shaped and maintained (stimulated and reinforced) by its consequences. If the hungry dog is allowed to eat the food placed before it, the behavior observed (salivating) is positively reinforced. If the dog receives an electric shock when it tries to eat the food, its behavior is negatively reinforced, and it will act differently in subsequent situations with food. Once the role of the environment on behavior is recognized, the interaction between the organism and the environment can be clarified and formulated into a theory of behavior.

Implications of the Behaviorist Technology

Two results of Skinner's theory follow: First, behavior can be studied in terms of the environment and its relationship to consequences of behavior. Second, environments can be manipulated to bring about desirable behavior. Once the function of the environment and the action of the organism have been understood, a technology of behavior is possible. No one need talk about states of mind, feelings, or character traits to explain behavior. It is an analysis of the interaction between organism and environment that explains behavior and provides a technique for changing behavior.

Such a technology of behavior as Skinner advocates calls for a revolution in thinking about the individual human being. In the traditional view of man, the individual is assumed to be free. He is autonomous in the sense that his behavior is thought to originate from within himself. Therefore, human behavior is, in a sense, free and uncaused. The individual can be considered to be responsible for what he does and can be justly punished if he does what is offensive.

A technology of behavior, however, would operate on the assumption that the individual is neither autonomous nor free. Rather, individual behavior is controlled by complex relations built up between action and environment. Thus, all talk of freedom, responsibility, and motives for behavior must be abandoned, as well as such concepts as praise, blame, dignity, and dishonor, in their traditional meanings. A technology will shift both responsibility and achievement to the environment. We cannot praise a person for doing something that an environment has rewarded him consistently for doing. Neither can we blame a person for doing what an environment has previously indicated is acceptable behavior. Praise and blame must be taken from the individual and transferred to the environment since it is the environment that controls behavior.

A second result of adopting Skinner's behavioral technology is the creation of a new problem: If the emphasis shifts to seeing environment as determining individual behavior, who should control and manipulate environments for people? How will "good" be defined by those who are in control? And is it right that a technological elite should exercise complete control over the lives of others? These questions are value questions relating to individual and social life. According to Skinner, the environment always determines behavior; it is not a question of whether or not it ought to be allowed to determine behavior. It already does. Rather, the important question is whether or not society will recognize the role of the environment and use such insight to change human behavior for the better.

Skinner maintains that by examining the interaction between individuals and the environment, it is possible to formulate and carry out the means by which to control personal and social development systematically. Individual freedom is irrelevant; a choice can and must be made concerning a technology of behavior. The power exists. It may be used or abused. Humans can either mold themselves into model personalities or they can pay no attention to what is already happening.

Toward the Creation of Technological Man

Neither the technological society nor the technological human being presently exists. Societies are increasingly influenced by inventions, machines, and techniques. But age-old problems continue and become even more complicated than they were in previous generations. The problems include not only war, overpopulation, pollution, and famine, but also problems of social adjustment, crime, and mental disorders. In most highly industrialized countries, prisons and mental hospitals are overcrowded at the same time that major technological efforts are made to automate industries, transplant human organs, and fly people to the moon.

It appears that individual humans are out of harmony with the technological order they themselves help to create and maintain. Many social psychologists insist that a fundamental disparity exists between modern societies dominated by technology and individual aspirations for security, stability, and safety. Although much government money in America is spent to provide national security, most Americans feel less safe than they did fifty years ago. America's nuclear arsenal, the guns under millions of pillows, and the multiple locks on city doors all indicate that a disparity exists between the individual and his society. What, then, is required to bring about harmony between the individual and his world? How can technological man be created to live in a technological society?

Skinner's technology of behavior is one proposal for remaking humans. Victor C. Ferkiss suggests what sort of ideas and attitudes, short of a controlled technology of behavior, might help bring about behavior and attitudes that will help individuals survive physically and emotionally in a society dominated by technology.

The first requirement for the creation of a technological person is the recognition that he or she does not yet exist. This means that we must recognize the existing disparity between the present technological order and the individual. To say that there is no problem for the individual in contemporary societies is to deny a reality. Humankind still operates with old ideas, values, and solutions that stem from old problems and old societies. Creeds, whether religious or political, must be examined in terms of their relevance to present conditions. Some problems of the individual may stem from commitments to old ideas, methods, and values that no longer work.

A second requirement for the creation of a technological person is to instill into the minds of people the idea that humankind and nature are one.

This, Ferkiss calls a "new naturalism." All social policies must be ecological in character—that is, they must be based on the recognition that individuals are totally interrelated with other people and with the natural environment. Any single decision is going to affect the total system. And nature has certain rights, too, since it is inextricably bound to people and the people are bound to it.

A third requirement is to recognize that individual decisions can no longer be made. No individual can consider himself or herself independent of the whole-world process. Thus, a new holism must be absorbed into human thought. No individual exists in a vacuum; all decisions are linked to other decisions.

A fourth requirement is the notion of immanentism—the view that order in the world is not imposed from outside but consists in the structure of relationships created through the constant activity of all elements composing the world. So long as the whole survives, there is a pattern to its activity. The individual must live and learn and act in terms of that pattern. To try to act against the pattern or to ignore the pattern is to court disaster.

And finally, the individual must come to be seen as a part of nature, not as its conqueror. His or her values, morality, and decisions must be seen as affecting the whole of the natural order. To know oneself is also to know nature; and to know nature is to know humankind.

Students of oriental thought might see the prescriptions of Ferkiss to read much like the advice found in such ancient texts as *Tao Te Ching* or the *Saddharmapundarika*. But Ferkiss is advocating neither Taoism nor Buddhism. He is joining with Skinner in maintaining that the reality of the technological society demands an end to traditional notions of freedom, autonomy, and individualism. And it is for the student of humanity, society, science, and technology to judge the implications of such a proposal.

DISCUSSION QUESTIONS

1. To what extent does the technology you are familiar with meet physical needs but neglect self-needs?

2. Can technology adequately fulfill self-needs? What sorts of technology might do so?

3. How much conformity is good and necessary in a society?

4. Do the advantages of mobility (both social and geographical) outweigh the disadvantages?

5. What moral and religious problems face societies that develop new technologies of behavior control?

6. What happens to the individual in Skinner's technology of behavior? Does it require a drastic change in thinking about morality, free will, and responsibility?

7. Do individuals have a real choice about individual behavior in the complicated technological order that dominates many modern societies?

BIBLIOGRAPHY

Baier, K., and Rescher, N., eds. *Values and the Future*. New York: The Free Press, 1969.

Berger, P. L., Berger, B., and Kellner, H., *The Homeless Mind: Modernization and Consciousness*. New York: Random House, 1973.

Braden, W. *The Age of Aquarius*. Chicago: Quadrangle Books, 1970.

Burke, G., ed. *The New Technology and Human Values*. Belmont, Calif.: Wadsworth Publishing Co., 1966.

Dorf, R. *Technology, Society, and Man*. San Francisco: Boyd & Fraser Publishing Co., 1974.

Douglas, J. D., ed. *Freedom and Tyranny: Social Problems in a Technological Society*. New York: Random House, 1970.

Ferkiss, V. C. *Technological Man: The Myth and the Reality*. New York: George Braziller, 1969.

Kelly, K. D. *Youth, Humanism, and Technology*. New York: Basic Books, 1972.

Mayer, E. "Biological Man and the Year 2,000." In D. Bell, ed. *Toward the Year 2000: Work in Progress*. Boston: Beacon Press, 1967.

Muller, H. J. *The Children of Frankenstein: A Primer on Modern Technology and Human Values*. Bloomington, Ind.: Indiana University Press, 1970.

Pirsig, R. M. *Zen and the Art of Motorcycle Maintenance*. New York: Bantam Books, 1974.

Skinner, B. F. *Beyond Freedom and Dignity*. New York: Bantam/Vintage, 1971.

Slater, P. *The Pursuit of Loneliness: American Culture at the Breaking Point*. Rev. ed. Boston: Beacon Press, 1976.

Chapter 5
Levels of Technological Development

Historically, technological development is a continuous process. Historians have traced the development of technology from prehistoric times to the present and have labeled the important stages on the continuum the Stone, Bronze, Iron, Dark, Industrial Revolution, Atomic, and Space Ages. In general, these ages are chronological, but they are not mutually exclusive. Technological development is a fluid, continuous process that cannot be divided into distinct stages.

When we look at the world as it exists today, the problems of categorizing technological development into various ages become apparent. Not all of civilization is in the Space Age. Indeed, the technological development of some tribal societies has not moved beyond the Stone Age. Many of the developing nations of the world are currently passing through various stages comparable to those of the Industrial Revolution. Some developing countries have atomic power at their disposal, while some so-called developed nations do not. Only a few highly developed nations of the world are truly in the Space Age. But even in these countries, pockets of lesser developed areas exist. Therefore, to say that technological development has reached the Space Age accurately identifies it for only a small segment of the world's population.

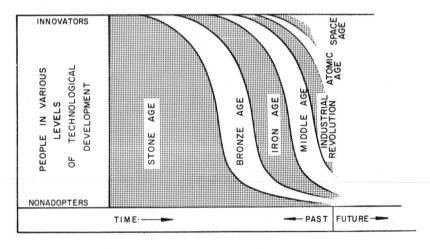

CONTINUUM IN TECHNOLOGICAL LEVELS

How, then, can the levels of technological development be meaningfully categorized? All the various levels of technological development currently witnessed can be placed into three general categories—low-level technology, intermediate-level technology, and high-level technology. But it must be remembered that the divisions among these broad categories are arbitrary. The purpose of condensing the number of categories to only three is to make easier the task of identifying the broad levels of technological development currently attained by various societies throughout the world.

As was seen in Chapter 1, there are many definitions of technology. Therefore, before we can define levels of technological development, technology, itself, must be defined, and for this particular chapter, William Gunston's description is most appropriate.

> At first [a human's] technology was a few bits of wood, stone, and animal skin. He learned to fashion these into useful shapes and then opened a new door by mastering fire with which he not only kept warm and cooked food but also hardened wood and extracted and used metals. As he learned to build houses, farm land and domesticate animals his technology advanced in parallel, until in historic times he learned to transport himself in every environment on, under, above and remote from the earth. Today his technology includes not only his hardware made from tangible materials but also his analytical techniques, his mathematics, his computer programs and even his thinking processes. Together these tools form an impressive armoury with which to meet the formidable tasks of the future. (De Bono, 1971, p. 60)

In short, then, technology is the accumulation of artifacts and mental processes used by the human race in its attempt to create a better life environment.

Low-Level Technological Development

Low-level technological development ranges from the human being's first attempt at toolmaking to primitive, animal- and human-powered machines; it transcends the age from prehistoric to the present; and it is the foundation upon which virtually all future technological developments were built.

If we accept the simple definition of a human being (family *Hominidae*) as being "a toolmaker," then low-level technological development must be as old as the human race. And how old is the human race? While we have no way of knowing exactly, the famed British archaeologist and anthropologist, Dr. Louis B. Leakey, discovered in Africa's Olduvai Gorge a humanlike fossil and accompanying tools that have been dated at more than 1,750,000 years old. Based on the discovery of the *Zinjanthropus,* or East African man, the generally accepted age of the human race is said to be at least two million years.

One other definition needs to be added to this description of low-level technological development—the definition of a tool. Anthropologist Philip

K. Bock classifies a tool as a subclass of artifact. He states that "an artifact is any portion of the material environment that has been deliberately used, or modified by man," and, "a tool is an artifact that is used to supplement or augment man's ability to act upon the physical world."

Primitive Tools

As noted earlier, low-level technological development encompasses the primitive tools and primitive machines used by humans. Primitive tools may be further delineated into natural, adapted, and manufactured tools. A natural tool is an artifact upon which the user has made no modification —that is, the tool is used as it is found in its natural state. Examples of a natural, primitive tool include the stone used to break open a nut; the fallen tree branch used to knock fruit from a tree; and a large animal bone used as a club. Undoubtedly these were the first tools used by humans; however, they can be and still are used today.

The use of natural phenomena such as fire, wind, tides, and gravity is not included in this classification because they are forces and are not really part of the material environment. Thus, even though humans use these phenomena to act upon the physical world, they cannot be classified as tools, as we have defined the word.

An adapted, primitive tool is an artifact which the user has modified, but only in size and shape. Examples of an adapted, primitive tool include: stones that have had pieces chipped or flaked off so that one edge is sharpened for cutting, scraping, or clubbing; an animal antler, horn, or bone that has had one edge or end sharpened for cutting or piercing; a wooden stick sharpened to a point and used as a spear; and a piece of wood carved into a flattened semicircle for hunting (boomerang).

Many adapted, primitive tools must be joined with other adapted or natural, primitive tools before they can be used effectively. But then they are no longer adapted, but are manufactured. A manufactured, primitive tool is an artifact created by the user's combining two or more natural or adapted artifacts to form a new artifact. A fishhook carved from animal bone is an adapted tool, but it is of little use until combined with a piece of vine or animal sinew. Other examples of primitive tools are bows; arrows, spears, and harpoons with bone or stone heads; a stone hammer or axe with a wooden handle, tied together with animal sinew; and a bone needle and thread of sinew.

To the best of our knowledge, the development of the primitive tool technology took place during the Paleolithic and Mesolithic periods, a span that encompasses about 1,995,000 of the approximate two million years, or 99.8 percent of the period of human existence. It should not come as a shock, then, to discover in Chapter 6 that some societies have progressed hardly at all from this level of technology. What is amazing, however, is the tremendous development that has taken place throughout much of the world in the last five thousand years or so.

LEVELS	OF DEVELOPMENT		TOOL USE
LOW	INTERMEDIATE	HIGH	
NATURAL HAMMER STONE	HAMMER	PNEUMATIC HAMMER	HAMMERING
ALTERED STONE KNIFE	METAL BLADE KNIFE	ELECTRIC KNIFE	CUTTING
MANUFACTURED HORN PICK	METAL HOE	HYDRAULIC PLOW	CULTIVATING

TECHNOLOGICAL   DEVELOPMENT

The "beehive" oven and the stick used to put in and remove items from the oven are examples of adapted and natural primitive tools, respectively. Photo by Mark Lund.

Primitive Machines

The primitive machines in low-level technological development are the six basic machines—lever, wedge, inclined plane, pulley, wheel and axle, and screw—and a few of the simpler two-machine combinations. The majority of these basic machines were developed during the Neolithic and metal periods (Bronze and Iron) of civilization, or from about 3500 B.C. to about 1000 B.C. Undoubtedly, the lever and the wedge, and perhaps even the inclined plane devices were used prior to the Neolithic period, but there is little or no evidence to support the use of the other basic machines. During the Neolithic period also humans began to change from nomadic packs of hunters and gatherers to more settled animal domesticators and cultivators. It was this animal domestication that allowed for the development of animal-powered machines for transportation, for irrigation purposes, for plowing fields, and so on.

A machine is an object that modifies the force applied to it by a human, an animal, or another machine. Usually the modification is in the form of an increase in the force applied to the object, allowing the human to do things he was unable to do when using only his own strength or the strength of his animal. The development of the more complicated of the six basic machines during the Neolithic period was revealed in several ways: by stone implements with holes bored in them, an indication of the development of the screw; the use of the wheel and axle for transportation and for making pottery; and the development of the lathe for wood turning, an indication of the development of the pulley.

A special group of primitive machines is the slightly more complicated ones that employ natural-force prime movers. Roger Burlingame defined a prime mover as "an automatic machine which moves other machines without the intervention of animal or human power." Windmills, tidemills, and water wheels are examples of natural-force prime movers.

Intermediate-Level Technological Development

Intermediate-level technological development represents the second-stage development of our civilization's artifacts. The primitive tools and machines from low-level technological development are improved upon, combined, and altered to make them do a better, more selective, and/or more complicated job. They are catalysts used to promote new discoveries and inventions. The intermediate level of technological development can also serve as a transitional stage for technology passing from the low level to the high level.

Intermediate Level Tools

Intermediate-level tools are hand tools that were basically developed at the low level of technological development and that have since been modified. This modification might mean that the tool is now made from different materials and/or perhaps the tool design is altered so that it can be used for different purposes. A hypothetical development of the prehistoric stone axe–hammer illustrates how a tool is modified as it passes from low-level technological development to intermediate-level technology.

The first hammer that a human being ever used was probably just a rock that fit nicely into the person's hand. So we will call it a "hand hammer." The hand hammer was probably multipurpose—to crack open such things as nuts and shellfish and to bludgeon to death animals and perhaps even other humans. One day the human discovered that when certain other rocks were struck with the hand hammer, chips came off the struck rock, and a fairly sharp edge was formed. This sharpened edge could be used for scraping animal skins and for cutting things. But now our ancestor had to carry around two rocks—a hand hammer and a hand axe. Because, when the blunt end of the hammer was used to bludgeon an animal or another person the sharp side of the sharpened rock cut into the hand holding it.

The next step in this development probably came many years later when someone discovered how to make a handle by forcing the center of the sharpened rock into a split piece of tree limb and then tying the split ends of the limb around the rock with animal sinew. Both ends of the rock could now be used without cutting the user. When the hand axe and the hand hammer were combined into a single tool with a handle, the inventor soon discovered that one did not have to exert nearly as much force to crack nuts, shellfish, or even heads. So the inventor discovered not only a new tool (the combination axe–hammer), but also one of the six basic machines, the lever. Once more, many years passed, and as hunters became less nomadic and more settled, they had time to sharpen, grind, and even polish their stone axe–hammer more carefully. They could now even cut down small trees for fencing to pen up their animals.

Then, after still more years passed, came the discovery of metals—first copper, then bronze, and finally iron. Not only could the metal tool be sharpened to a much finer edge than could any stone axe–hammer, but the new metal edge also remained sharp much longer and absorbed blows that would smash even the best stone axe–hammer to smithereens. But even more important was the fact that now there was a way to vary the size and shape of the tool. As a result of the discovery of metals, the axe and hammer divided into two major specialized tool categories, each having a variety of sizes, shapes, weights, lengths and handles, each made from a variety of materials, and each having a specific purpose.

The dividing point in the hypothetical story between the low-level tool and the intermediate-level tool is between the polished-stone axe–hammer and the metal tool. Once the change in materials and specialization begin, the axe–hammer is no longer a low-level tool, but is instead an intermediate-level one. Most basic hand tools follow this pattern of development, except that for most other tools, the development usually did not start until metal was discovered. Nevertheless, the development from a single, primitive model to multiple, specialized models for specialized uses is the same.

Intermediate Level Machines

An intermediate-level machine can be defined as a compound or complex machine (combining two or more basic machines) that has interrelated parts with separate functions. An intermediate-level machine can be powered by humans, animals, or any of the prime movers, including natural forces.

It is the prime movers that become especially practical in intermediate-level technology. The steam engine, for example, is said to have been the catalyst for the Industrial Revolution, which began in England during the middle of the eighteenth century. In 1698, Thomas Savery developed a device that used a steam-created vacuum to pump water from coal mines. This steam pump led to Thomas Newcomen's invention of the first practical steam engine, which he and Savery put into operation in Stratfordshire, England in 1712.

The first steam engine, like the first steam pump, was used to pump water from coal mines, but the geniuses of the day soon realized that the steam engine could do much more than just pump water. As noted earlier, when the steam engine was connected to the manufacturing machinery of the eighteenth century, the Industrial Revolution was born. But equally important was the steam engine's contribution to transportation. The steamship made the sail obsolete, and for more than one hundred years the quickest means of ground transportation was the steam-powered railroad car. It took the combined efforts of three new devices to dethrone the steam engine as the king of the prime movers: The electric motor (invented by Michael Faraday in 1821) replaced the steam engine as the prime mover of manufacturing machinery; and the steam turbine (invented by Charles Parsons in 1884) and the internal combustion diesel engine (invented by Rudolph Diesel in 1893) replaced the steam engine as the major power source for sea and rail transportation, respectively.

The first compound machine was probably the loom. Its discovery is reported to have been around 3500 B.C., or some fifty-five hundred years ago. The significance of this technological development was emphasized by Australian archaeologist and scholar V. Gordon Childe when he wrote: "The invention of the loom was one of the great triumphs of human ingenuity. Its inventors are nameless, but they made an essential contribution to the capital stock of human knowledge."

Intermediate-level technology, then, transcends a period in our civilization of some fifty-five hundred years—from around 3500 B.C. to the present —and spans a multitude of tools and machines, encompassing the earliest developments made from the basic tools and machines up to the development of the tools and machines of high-level technology. It is at the intermediate level where the majority of the human inhabitants of this earth are found. As noted earlier, there are still a few tribal societies of the world using only low-level technology, and we shall soon see that there are only a few societies of the world that have reached the high level of technological development. Nearly all the remaining societies are at some stage included in the intermediate level.

Development Strategies

Societies in the intermediate level of technological development are often called "developing" or "Third World" nations. Their developmental process is one of moving from the more primitive steps of intermediate-level technology to a higher step, or even into the high level of technological development. The manner and rate of speed at which these nations move through the intermediate level of technological development have been areas of disagreement among development specialists since the birth of the developing nations. (Most developing nations are former colonies that have gained their independence since the end of World War II.)

The controversy stems from one basic question: How can a Neolithic peasant farmer, carpenter, or laborer who has no mechanical knowledge be transformed into a modern progressive farmer, carpenter, or laborer who properly utilizes all the scientific knowledge and technology available in today's world? The debaters have taken two points of view: One group maintains that it is best to develop in small, slow, and carefully planned steps; while the other group strongly favors development that makes one big, transitional jump from intermediate-level technology to high-level technology.

Quick Transition Strategy. The proponents for making one big jump claim that the time required to solve the world's problems is rapidly running out and that there is not enough time for every society to make the same gradual transition that the developed world made. Nor could the environment tolerate the same mistakes repeated over and over again. The global problems of overpopulation, food and nutrition, energy, health, and pollution must be solved on a macroscopic scale immediately or there will be no tomorrow for mankind.

The position held by the one-jump group is illustrated in the results of a UNESCO-sponsored conference held in 1968 in New Delhi, India. The purpose of the conference was to determine how to apply science and technology to the development of Asia. The conferees concluded that among the prerequisites for the application of science and technology to development were: (1) that the role and responsibilities of the universities must be to advance, communicate, and apply scientific knowledge at the highest level; (2) that priority must be given to increasing the numbers of technicians and subprofessional personnel, teachers of science and engineering in universities, graduate engineers and scientists, managerial and executive personnel, clerical and secretarial personnel, and craftsmen; (3) and that technological sciences and applied research be promoted. Further, these development specialists concluded that there was an urgent need for "technology transfer and information centers [to] be set up . . . in order to provide assistance to enterprises in identifying their technological needs, ascertaining the availability of the necessary technology abroad, and the negotiation of agreements." (UNESCO, 1970, p. 216)

Slow transition strategy. However, the development specialists who favor a slow, more gradual transition argue that economically, sociologically, and psychologically such rapid development as prescribed by the big-jump advocates can only lead to major disasters. Societal infrastructures must precede development, the gradual-transition proponents claim, and they must be the first step in a natural technological development setting. They question how an illiterate farmer can be expected to grasp the intricacies of modern technology. But even if some farmers do manage this improbable feat, the specialists still raise complex questions that are interrelated: Why increase the farmer's production if a means for transporting his excess crop to market is not available, if no market system is available, if there are no means for storing the crop, and if, as modern farming implies, thousands and perhaps millions of people are no longer employable since agriculture can no longer be a labor-intensive industry?

Finally, the slow-transition proponents question the ability of the heavily populated Third World to cope with a rapid and drastically changed lifestyle. They point to Alvin Toffler's work, reported in his book *Future Shock,* which indicates that too much change too fast can lead to sociological and psychological problems for people who live in developed countries where rapid change is a way of life. Think, then, of the sociological and the psychological effects of rapidly changing a human being from a Neolithic farmer to a modern one.

A member of the slow-transition clan, Richard Farmer, suggests that gross general misconceptions are responsible for Third World nations' seeking the wrong solutions to the wrong problems. Among the misconceptions listed by Farmer are: (1) management is unimportant and irrelevant; (2) planning and economy are easily controlled; (3) population control is either irrelevant or easy; (4) agriculture can take care of itself; (5) educational and behavioral problems are not serious. The results of these misconceptions are grandiose plans with huge projects that are rarely fruitful; a large workforce in capital-intensive situations that are unrealistic for the existing economic situation; inept marketing of the meager product that is produced; and administrative hierarchies of great complexity and little productivity.

Farmer believes that Third World nations should seek much simpler technologies and get rid of the highly technical and complex ones they have tried to implement so unsuccessfully. In his opinion, the people of the developing world must first acquire a sense of mechanical things before they can fully understand the complex workings of contemporary Western technologies.

Which group of development specialists is right? Perhaps both. Perhaps neither. It is difficult to say that one theory is right and the other wrong, because both views are right under some circumstances and wrong in others. What both sides seem to ignore is one of the major characteristics of developing nations: Although all these nations are indeed at the inter-mediate level of technological development, the stages of this level vary so widely that they encompass development from barely above the Stone Age to development barely below high-level technology. How, then, can any one development plan work for all developing nations under all circumstances? Obviously, no single plan can. Therefore, what seems to be needed is a variety of plans, developed especially for each given situation, so that in some cases rapid development would be used, and in other situations, a slower, more gradual change would take place.

High-Level Technological Development

High-level technological development is prevalent in only a few, mostly Western, societies. It includes only the more sophisticated tools and machines, but its roots are planted in a surprisingly distant past.

The tools described in the low and intermediate levels of technological development all functioned with power supplied by a human user. Tools of high-level technological development, however, no longer use human power, and thus, have really become hand machines. But in order to maintain a parallel structure for all levels, and because these hand machines are commonly called "hand power tools," we shall continue to call them "tools." High-level technology tools, then, can be defined as hand-held machines that essentially duplicate the job of an intermediate-level tool and that have a source of power other than the user's power.

The jackhammer and the riveting gun are examples of high-level tools. In both, the source of energy is usually pneumatic power created by an internal combustion engine. They duplicate the intermediate-level tools, the pickaxe and the ball peen hammer, respectively. Other examples of high-level tools are the electric-powered hand drill, the electric-powered hand-saws (of which there are many), the electric-powered hand plane, and so on.

Machinery included in high-level technology may be defined as those complex machines whose functions are combined with special facets of human activity to form a unique third process. High-level technology occurs, as Gunston stated, when technology includes not only the hardware produced, but also the analytical, mathematical, and thought processes of the human mind. The result is usually large-scale mass production of goods and materials or the rapid solution of problems that otherwise would take years of human effort to solve.

Burlingame credits the invention of a single, automatic machine as the start of the whole evolutionary process leading to what he calls the Industrial Age.

> It gave . . . a new sense of continuity. It laid a basis for standardization, first in performance, later in its construction. Later it provided a reference point for precision both of thought and of practical techniques. Last of all,

it suggested the interchangeability and random assembly of its component parts. In itself it produced nothing.

Unlike other early mechanisms, it assisted the mind, not the body. It did, indeed, a job of which the human mind, by itself, was incapable. The material it worked in was beyond man's control. Its function was in the realm of natural forces, interpreting the celestial movement. It appeared to stand, like a priest, midway between man and God. (Burlingame, 1949, p. 15)

It is an instrument for measuring time—a clock. Like so many other inventions, the creation of the first mechanical means for keeping time and the person or persons who created it are clouded by history. *Clepsydras,* or water clocks, were commonly used as early as 250 B.C. The purist, however, one who insists that a *clepsydra* is not a true mechanical clock, prefers to date the clock's emergence between the years 1000 and 1335. (The former is the date a mechanical clock is suspected to have been displayed in England, and the latter is the date of the first confirmed existence of a mechanical clock constructed in Milan, Italy.) No matter which date is preferred, if Burlingame's thesis is accepted, high-level technological development had its origination, at the very latest, more than six hundred years ago.

The Assembly Line

The unique processes resulting from combining mind and machine functions can be placed into three general classifications—the assembly line, automation, and cybernetics. The assembly line is a group of complex machines working in conjunction with the following concepts:

1. Interchangeability or standardization of parts.

2. The division of labor.

3. Synchronization.

4. Quality control.

5. Precision.

6. Continuity.

7. Integration.

Interchangeability, or standardization of parts, was an idea that allowed for mass production; so did the concepts of quality control and precision. The division of labor meant that instead of an individual worker being responsible for the construction of an entire product, he was responsible for assembling only a part of the total product. The concepts of synchronization and integration allowed the worker to be at the right place, with the right parts and equipment at the right time, and the product being assembled to be at the right place, at the right time, so that it was assembled in the right sequence. The concept of continuity allowed the product being assembled to move constantly along the line so that each added part contributed to the total product.

One of the first applications of the modern moving assembly line was this magneto operation at the Ford Motor Company Highland Park plant in 1913. Magnetos were pushed from one workman to the next, reducing production time by about one-half. Photo courtesy of Ford Motor Company.

Contrary to a popular American myth, the assembly line was not invented by Henry Ford when he began operation of his moving chassis-assembly line at Highland Park, Michigan, in 1914. What Ford did do was to prove, through the use of time and motion studies and the effective use of available technology, that the assembly-line process was the most efficient method for manufacturing automobiles. The first recorded use of the assembly-line process dates back to 1438. Burlingame cites a report by Pero Tafur, entitled *Travels and Adventures, 1435–1439,* translated in 1926 by Malcolm Letts. In his report, Tafur describes a scene he witnessed at an arsenal in Venice in 1438.

> And as one enters the gate there is a great street on either hand with the sea in the middle, and on one side are windows opening out of the houses of the arsenal, and the same on the other side, and out came a galley towed by a boat, and from the windows they handed out of them, from one the cordage, from another the bread, from another the arms, and from another the balistas and mortars, and so from all sides everything which was required, and when the galley had reached the end of the street all the men required were on board, together with the compliment of oars, and she was equipped from end to end. In this manner came out ten galleys, fully armed, between the hours of three and nine. I do not know how to de-

scribe what I saw there, whether in the manner of its construction or in the management of the workpeople, and I do not think there is anything finer in the world. (Burlingame, 1949, pp. 57, 58)

What Tafu saw was a moving assembly line.

The modern assembly line, despite its contributions to the mass-production manufacturing process, has been the target for much recent criticism. Since the automobile industry has had the greatest publicity, we shall use the problems confronting it as an example. Because of new, automated processes, it is now possible for completely assembled automobiles to come off assembly lines at a rate exceeding one every two minutes. The workers on the line claim that the constant pressure of maintaining this rate of speed and the menial tasks they are required to perform over and over again are responsible for the high incident of such stress-related sicknesses as ulcers, alcoholism, and drug abuse found among these workers. A high rate of absenteeism, sabotage to the line, and unfinished or sabotaged automobiles coming off the line have been the workers' methods of retaliation.

Numerous solutions to the major problems involving the assembly-line worker have been proposed, and management and union leaders are currently cooperatively adopting some of them on a trial basis. Some examples of techniques implemented by various companies are: four-day, ten-hour workweeks; job shifting on a periodic basis; group work, as opposed to individual responsibilities; more decision-making situations for the worker; and greater worker–management interaction. The problem continues to be a major one. Despite the fact that the recession of the mid-

A part of the Ford Motor Company's first moving assembly line for producing automobiles. Circa 1913–14, picture shows the exterior use of the building for lowering the auto body onto the chassis. Photo courtesy of Ford Motor Company.

1970s has reduced the number of publicized incidents, the causes of the problem remain, and, if not eliminated, will resurface again and again.

Automation

We noted earlier that neither Henry Ford nor the Ford Motor Company invented the assembly line, but that Ford was the first to recognize

Whether in Japan or the United States, modern automobile assembly lines can be boring and frustrating places to work. Photo courtesy of Consulate General of Japan, Chicago. Photo courtesy of Ford Motor Company.

the commercial value of the process. It was also the Ford Motor Company that built the first completely automated manufacturing system. Once again, it cannot be said that Ford invented automation because automation is not a single invention, but a conglomeration of many machines and processes combined to produce a product in the total absence of human beings. In 1946, Delmar S. Harder gave the name "automation" to the humanless process he devised to manufacture automobile engines at a rate of one every fourteen minutes. Prior to Harder's process, it took human labor twenty-one hours to manufacture a single engine.

The major characteristic of automation is that it is self-regulated and self-controlled through a feedback system that is sensitized to the output of the processes within the major system. By comparing the output to a desired norm, the system can automatically adjust itself whenever the norm is not reproduced. A self-regulating system of this type that seems to "think" for itself is also known as a "cybernetic" system, which we shall discuss shortly.

To many industrial workers, the word "automation" is as foul a word as could possibly be uttered. To them, automation means layoff, unemployment, loss of security, a feeling of not being wanted, or worse, not being needed. Whenever a mass-production industry begins to automate, the ranks of the unemployed semiskilled production worker fill rapidly. It is the semiskilled worker who is usually the most affected. There are always "broom-pushing" jobs for the unskilled, and the skilled worker is often not affected. But if he or she is affected, the person usually has enough experience and education to retrain for a different position.

Proponents of automation, however, claim that the effects of automating an industry are minimal. For example, David Hamilton, in his book *Technology, Man and the Environment,* states that "there is no evidence from the experience of the last 150 years that, in the long run, increasing mechanization brings anything but shorter hours of worker and higher living standards." Other advocates of automation point to the industries that have developed as a result of automation—the electronics industry, for example—and claim that for every person automation puts out of work it creates a new job for someone else. What automation has really done, they continue, is to make life easier and more enjoyable for the worker by eliminating the difficult, dangerous, and boring jobs in industry.

Cybernetics

A recently developed phase of high-level technological development is cybernetics. The word, coined by M.I.T. Professor Norbert Wiener, refers to the act of piloting or steering. When discussing automation, we referred to the controlling mechanisms as being cybernetic in nature. Wiener defines control as simply the sending of messages that alter the behavior of the receiver, and cybernetics as the study of the effective messages of control. "Society can only be understood," Wiener emphasizes, "through a study of the messages and the communication facilities which belong to it; and . . . in the future, development of these messages and communication facilities . . . are destined to play an ever increasing part." He visualizes cybernetics as the eventual emancipator of humans from the repetitive, trivial, and degrading tasks related to mechanization.

As the scientific field of cybernetics aged, however, its definition began to change. Ashby, for example, claimed that cybernetics "is a 'theory of machines,' but it treats, not things but *ways of behaving,* . . . [and] might, in fact, be defined as *the study of systems that are open to energy but closed to information and control*—systems that are 'information tight.' " He felt that cybernetics offered the opportunity to study and control systems that were intrinsically complicated.

In 1972, Ralph Parkman, in *The Cybernetic Society* stated:

> Cybernetics may be described as the study of brainlike processes or equilibrium-seeking processes and in these kinds of terms it is subject to very broad and often disparate interpretations. It overlaps such fields as general systems theory, theory of automata, semantics, information theory, logic, and invades important areas of the physical, natural and social sciences. There are those who prefer to use cybernetics narrowly as a synonym for the applied science of computerized engineering control systems, and others who feel cyberneticians have cast their net so broadly that they have forfeited any right to claim for it the status of a separate discipline at all. (Parkman, 1972, p. 205)

Finally, in 1974, Stewart Brand, in *Two Cybernetic Frontiers,* said of cybernetics:

> The field of cybernetics is still finding out what it is. Our comprehension has grown used to the concepts of matter and energy, but the burden of cybernetics—information—continues to boggle us. Weightless energyless *differences* fly about making patterns which are apparently nothing but will move some things with mysterious regularity. Meat learns; machines learn. An absence is as significant as a presence. The rules of articulation of a system are inarticulate within that system, which makes things difficult for a cybernetician, who has no way of standing outside of his science. It is a science of essences, a slippery business. Information, energy, and matter (and life) make an inseparable whole, but there is yet no theory to link them formally. (Brand, 1974, p. 7)

We have, in cybernetics, a case in which the more a subject is studied the less seems to be known about it. The further technology progresses, the more complicated becomes the definition of cybernetics. In short, the formulation of a definition is not yet possible.

Computers

The most well-known machine related to cybernetics is the computer. As expressed earlier, some consider cybernetics to be the study of *only* applied computer systems. The computer is a real-life model of the magic wand in fairy tales. Given a proper program, the computer can calculate in split seconds what it would take a team of mathematicians months to work out; it can have an unforgettable, instantaneous memory; it can solve problems as rapidly as they are fed into it; it can diagnose illnesses and act as a nurse; it can do virtually anything we want it to do, more quickly and easily than anything else can do it.

The modern era of the automatic, digital computer began during World War II. Between 1939 and 1947 three major developments in the computer occurred. The first was the construction, between 1939 and 1944, of the Automatic Sequence Control Calculator (Mark I) by Howard Aiken at Howard University. The Mark I followed a programmed sequence of instructions contained on punched tape. It was the first automatic, digital computer, but it could not branch and its speed was limited because its operation was electromechanical.

The second major breakthrough in the development of the computer was the construction of the Electronic Numerical Integrator and Calculator (ENIAC). It was completed in 1946 by the Moore School of Engineering, the University of Pennsylvania, and the U.S. Army. ENIAC, the first fully electronic computer, weighed thirty tons, occupied fifteen hundred square feet, and required about eighteen thousand vacuum tubes. Taking into consideration the average life of the vacuum tube and the heat it produces, work on the electronic computer probably would have ended there but for the development of the germanium transistor in 1947. The use of the transistor in the computer greatly reduced its size and heat output and eliminated the almost constant replacement of burned-out vacuum tubes.

The third major development, also in 1946, was the concept of the stored program. The idea was to store in the memory of the computer codes that would represent the basic instructional operations. Then, since the instructions and the data were now stored in the same manner, the machine could automatically execute coherent commands given to it. This made branching possible—that is, if the results of an execution were positive, the machine continued its normal processing, but if the results were negative, the machine branched to a different set of commands or instructions. This branching operates on a 0–1 binary coding system.

The father of the computer was Charles Babbage, a nineteenth-century English mathematician. Babbage first attempted to make a steam-powered calculator, which he called a difference engine. The development of this machine, which could only add, was thwarted by the level of metalworking technology in the 1820s and the fact that Babbage's ideas were constantly changing. In 1834, Babbage proposed to the English government that he try to develop an analytical engine that would not simply add, but would also perform all arithmetic calculations. Government officials wrongly judged Babbage's new plans as being nothing more than an elaboration of the unsuccessful difference engine and rejected the proposal.

In reality, Babbage's plans contained the basic elements that later proved necessary for the development of the modern computer, including the memory and the arithmetic unit. The key to Babbage's plan was the incorporation of an automatic loom-controlling device invented by the Frenchman Joseph Marie Jacquard in 1801. Jacquard's system was designed to allow for the large-scale manufacture of goods containing complex weaving patterns. Jacquard's technique used a punched card system, which Babbage is reported to have converted to a punched-tape design. The punched tape would contain a coded program not unlike the ones used to run modern computers.

Babbage's machine probably would not have worked even if he had been supported by the English government, for the same reasons his difference engine did not work—his ideas were too far advanced for the level of technology of the times. But the concept of the functions of a computer undoubtedly was his.

Summary

All the societies in the world today, regardless of whether they are a modern nation–state, a primitive tribe, or somewhere in between, are functioning at one of three broad levels of technological development—low level, intermediate level, or high level. These levels are overlapping, both in current use and in chronological development; therefore, their boundaries cannot be clearly identified and must remain somewhat arbitrary. On the other hand, for the levels to have any meaning, clear, distinct definitions for the terms "technology" and "tools" must be formulated.

In broad, general terms, low-level technological development may be defined to include those tools and machines developed by the earlier human beings. These were the basic tools and simple machines that served as the foundation for all other tools and machines and may be subdivided into natural, adapted, and manufactured tools, and human- and animal-powered machines. The period during which this development took place is considered to be from when the human being developed, about two million years ago, until approximately 3200 B.C.

Intermediate-level technological development includes all the diverse, human-powered tools developed from the primitive ones, and nearly all the machinery developed throughout history that does not have incorporated within its function human, thought-like processes. The majority of human beings now on this earth live at this level of technological development. The intermediate level encompasses a time period from approximatly 3200 B.C. to the present.

High-level technological development, obviously, includes machines utilizing human thought-like processes within its functions. It also includes hand tools, or more technically, hand machines, which are no longer powered by the person using them. Subdivisions of high-level technological development are the assembly line, automation, and cybernetics. Only a few societies have reached this level of technological development since it is the most recently developed. The assembly line was described more than six hundred years ago, but the first fully automated manufacturing system was not developed until 1946, and the word "cybernetics" was first used to describe a unique system in 1948.

DISCUSSION QUESTIONS

1. Machines run by natural-force prime movers were categorized as low-level technological development in this chapter. Why was this done? Can you develop a case for placing natural-force prime movers in the intermediate level of technological development?

2. Discuss the similarities and differences among the assembly line, automation, and cybernetics.

3. Offer some ways to alleviate "future shock" in a society undergoing rapid technological change.

4. Remote farming villages in India are, or will soon be, receiving information via television beamed from a satellite. The majority of the peasants in these villages are subsistence farmers using practices not very different from those used two thousand years ago. What technological "age" are these farmers in—space, iron, Industrial Revolution, other? Explain your choice. At what level of technological development, as defined in this chapter, are they? Explain your answer.

BIBLIOGRAPHY

Ashby, W. R. *An Introduction to Cybernetics.* New York: John Wiley & Sons, 1958.

Bateson, G. *Steps to an Ecology of Mind: Collected Essays in Anthropology, Psychiatry, Evolution, and Epistemology.* San Francisco: Chandler Publishing Co. New York: Ballantine Books, 1972.

Bock, P. *Modern Cultural Anthropology: An Introduction.* New York: Alfred A. Knopf, 1969.

Brand, S. *Two Cybernetic Frontiers.* New York: Random House, 1974.

Breyer, H. [*Columbus was Chinese: Discoveries and Inventions of the Far East*], S. Attanasio, trans. New York: Herder & Herder, 1972.

Brumbaugh, R. *Ancient Greek Gadgets and Machines.* New York: Thomas Y. Crowell Co., 1966.

Burlingame, R. *Backgrounds of Power: The Human Story of Mass Production.* New York: Charles Scribner's Sons, 1949.

Childe, V. G. *Man Makes Himself.* New York: New American Library, 1951.

De Bono, E., ed. *Eureka!: An Illustrated History of Inventions from the Wheel to the Computer.* New York: Holt, Rinehart, & Winston, 1974.

———. *Technology Today.* London: Routledge & Kegan Paul, Ltd., 1971.

Derry, T. K., and Williams, T. I. *A Short History of Technology. From the Earliest Times to A.D. 1900.* New York: Oxford University Press, 1960.

Dover, E. *Charles Babbage and His Calculating Machines.* New York: Morrison, Phillip & Morrison, 1961.

Farmer, R. N. *Benevolent Aggression.* New York: David McKay, Co., 1972.

Forbes, R. J. *Studies in Ancient Technology.* 2d rev. ed., 9 vols. Leiden, Netherlands: E. J. Brill, 1964–1972.

Gunston, W. "Technology for Man's Survival." In E. de Bono, ed. *Technology Today*. London: Phoenix House, Ltd., 1961.

Larsen, E. *A History of Invention*. London: Phoenix House, Ltd., 1961.

Parkman, R. *The Cybernetic Society*. Elmsford, N.Y.: Pergamon Press, 1972.

Susskind, C. *Understanding Technology*. Baltimore: The Johns Hopkins University Press, 1973.

Toffler, A. *Future Shock*. New York: Random House, 1970

Tunis, E. *Colonial Craftsmen and the Beginning of American Industry*. Cleveland: World Publishing Co., 1965.

UNESCO. *Science and Technology in Asian Development*. Switzerland: 1970.

Wiener, N. *Cybernetics: Or, Control and Communication in the Animal and the Machine*. New York: John Wiley & Sons, 1948.

————. *The Human Use of Human Beings: Cybernetics and Society*. Boston: Houghton Mifflin Co., 1950.

Chapter 6
Levels of Technological Societies

Introduction

In the previous chapters, the various aspects of the interface, or relationship, between society and technology were discussed. In Chapter 1, for example, the terms "science," "culture," and "technology" were defined. In Chapter 3, we developed the general interactions between technology and the family, politics, education, economics, and religion. In Chapter 4, we considered the impact of technology upon human needs. Finally, in Chapter 5, we discussed methods of discerning the general levels of technological development. But a level of technological development is only one of many indicators used to describe the different levels of technological societies. In fact, all the previous chapters discuss major indicators for determining at which level a technological society exists.

Why is it so important to determine the levels of technological societies? The first reason is academic: Since there are wide variations in technological societies throughout the world, the societies should be identified and classified. The second reason is more practical: Because the variations do exist, humanists in every discipline in both developed and developing societies are constantly trying to lessen societal differences by increasing the technological level of the lesser endowed societies. As we shall see in this chapter and in Chapter 7, the methods of transferring technology and/or increasing development must vary according to the needs and level of the society being aided. Hence, we need to know at which stage of development, or technological level, the society is presently functioning.

Three general levels of technological societies can be identified—tribal, transitional or emerging, and highly developed or postindustrial. In many instances, a transitional or highly developed society is identified with the political boundary of a nation. For the sake of convenience and clarification, we, too, shall make such identifications. It must be remembered, however, that the identification of the United States, for example, as a highly developed technological society does *not* mean that *all* peoples within its boundaries are highly developed. There are societies within the political borders of the United States that are close to being (or are) tribal and, by definition, there are many societies that are transitional or emerging. But since the majority of the societal indicators, and hence the majority of the people, fall into the highly developed category, the entire country is considered highly developed.

The same set of circumstances holds true for many transitional or emerging technological societies. If the society is identified by political borders, and it almost always is, then the majority of the societies within those boundaries are transitional; but there certainly are some highly developed societies within those borders, and perhaps a few tribal societies as well.

The differences between levels of technological societies can be identified by observing certain common characteristics of specific sectors within the society. The sectors identified and discussed in this chapter are: the methods of education and food production, the political and economic structures, the levels and methods of communication, and the levels of technological development.

Tribal Societies

Tribal societies, the lowest level of technological society, are often referred to as primitive societies. These societies are in remote areas that are difficult to reach. The peoples of these societies, therefore, have had little, if any, contact with the outside world and may prefer their isolation (as demonstrated by the hostility sometimes shown intruders into their territory). But there have also been those tribal societies that have so enthusiastically welcomed the incursion of the outside world that they have become assimilated into a larger, emerging or highly developed society, causing their own society to nearly vanish.

These two reactions have created opposing theories of why and how societies developed in such isolated places. One theory states that because they just happened to develop where they did, the tribal societies had no way to interact with the outside world. As a result, they could not benefit from the discoveries and inventions made in other societies and therefore remained in a tribal state, developing at a naturally slower pace because of the limitation of their small numbers.

The other theory is that the tribal societies were once living on the periphery or were part of a larger society. As this larger society began to develop, some members found the new direction abhorrent and wanted things to remain as they were. Therefore, they deliberately sought out and retreated into the most remote areas in which to live. As a result of this history, when modern society contacts them, they react with violence.

The two opposing views also raise these questions: Should we try to modernize the tribal societies by assimilation and, for all intents and purposes, destroy forever their unique society? Or should we leave them as they are—a tribal, but unique, society—to fend for themselves, even though we may have the means for providing them with a better life?

Characteristics of a Tribal Society

Education. Frequently, no major educational process with specific daily periods is set aside over a long period of childhood for either teaching, learning, or acquiring knowledge. Skill training is accomplshed through observation and mimicry either over an extended period or for a short but intensive period, and is usually a case of the son learning from the father and the daughter learning from the mother. Children's games often reflect the practice of a needed societal skill, as in the example of the boys of a society shooting small, toylike bows and arrows when "play hunting." Heritage, superstition, rites, and so on may be passed on from generation to generation in the form of verbal stories, songs, dances, and artwork. Since there is rarely, if ever, a written language beyond a few symbols, most members of tribal societies can neither write nor read their spoken language.

Food Production. Most tribal societies acquire their food by hunting animals and by gathering wild fruits, nuts, and berries. However, some tribal societies do cultivate small plots of land on which they grow their main, nonmeat food staples such as taro, cassava, corn, rice, and wheat. Their cultivation methods are barely advanced beyond those used by the Neolithic farmer and usually consist of a superficial digging of the ground prior to planting the seed or plants. These gardens are rarely fertilized, weeded, or irrigated. Depending upon the society, the plots may be owned either individually or communally. Small herds of animals may also be found occasionally.

Politics. In general, the political structure of a tribal society is autocratic; a single chief, leader, or headman has total power. There may also be an advisory person, such as a shaman, a medicine man, or a magician, or an advisory group, such as a tribal council, the elders of the group, or the leader's family. But their role is strictly an advisory one, with final decisions being made exclusively by the leader. The leadership is sometimes handed down through a royal family, which may be either matrilineal or patrilineal; it may be won by challenge or some other means; but rarely is the leadership acquired through an election process. Usually the leader completely controls the actions of the members of his society, and opinions are voiced and decisions made during public audiences. Individual freedom of choice rarely exists in a tribal society.

Economics. The attitude toward ownership of material goods varies widely among the tribal societies. Some of these societies regard highly the acquisition of material goods, some feel that owning material goods is bad, and other societies depend on communal ownership of material goods. Tribal societies are those that have, at best, a barter economy. If trade of excess commodities exists, it is extremely low level—sometimes intratribal and sometimes intertribal, but rarely beyond a local level. And the trade usually consists of simple exchanges of a single or group of articles for another single or group of articles. Formal marketing systems or structures are almost never found in tribal societies.

Communications. Short-range communications consist almost entirely of the spoken word. However, for periods requiring total silence, such as hunting, or times when a common language is not known, elaborate hand signals or voice signals resembling bird or animal calls may be used. Long-range communications, if they exist, may be loud shouting, the beating of drums, the use of runners, smoke signals, and so on. As stated earlier, hardly ever does a written language go beyond a few symbols.

Technology. Low-level technological development is prevalent in tribal societies. Their tools are usually basic hand tools of the adapted class; the limit of their tool and weapon sophistication is usually the bow and arrow. To find a machine more complicated than the six basic machines is also very rare. This lack of technological development might be due to the natural, slow progress of invention by small groups of people and also the fact that there does not seem to be a place for the development of technology or the inventor within the society. An invention developed within a tribal society is more often ridiculed and rejected than accepted. Certainly no reward for the innovator is built into the tribal society.

Case Studies

Amazon Indians

The specific society of Amazon Indians described here are the Camayurá,[1] a tribe with a 1971 population of about one hundred ten, equally divided between males and females. The Camayurá live in the Upper Xingu River basin in the Brazilian state of Mato Grosso and are members of a group of eleven tribes whose total population is approximately seven hundred fifty.

Education. Formal training for the Camayurá children begins at puberty. For three to four months, and under strict discipline, the children concentrate on the essential skills they will need during their adult life. The female spends her time learning spinning, what medicines to use for abortion, what to do during pregnancy, and in general, how to treat her future husband. The males, in the meantime, are learning how to make bows and arrows and how to play the flute. They are also instructed by their fathers and the other elder male members of the tribe in tribal history and beliefs, the performance of important rituals, correct behavior in a raid, and other essential aspects of the male role.

---

[1] Based on data from B. J. Meggers, *Amazonia: Man and Culture in a Counterfeit Paradise.* AHM Publishing Corp., Arlington Heights, Illinois, 1971. Reprinted by permission.

Food Production. The major portion of the Camayurá tribe's food is derived from slash-and-burn farming, a primitive method that requires an area to be cleared of all vegetation and burned. The land is then planted with a crop for several growing seasons until the soils gives out and/or the jungle reclaims the land. (Contrary to popular belief, jungle soil is poor.) The villagers then choose another parcel of land and clear it and repeat the entire process. If the tribe is large and/or the soil is particularly poor, the slash-and-burn method often requires that the tribe move to a new area every ten to twenty years since the land cannot recover fast enough. The major food crops grown by the Camayurá are: manioc, from which they make their staple food (cassava bread), sweet potatoes, maize, and peanuts. The major nonfood crops are: cotton, tobacco, achiote, gourds, and calabashes (in which they store food).

Piquis, a large oily fruit, and the mangabas, an apricotlike fruit, are gathered in season, as are palm nuts, coco bobão, and palmito. Few wild vegetables are consumed. Although wild game abounds in the jungle, only birds are commonly eaten. Monkey and ocelot are hunted for their bones, which are used as arrow points. Fish, a major food of the Camayurá, are caught using bows and arrows, weirs and traps, and by damming streams to form pools that are then poisoned with rotenone from crushed vines. Turtles and turtle eggs are also hunted, gathered, and eaten. Delicacies among the Camayurá tribes are two species of ants. Only the head of one species is eaten; only the larvae of the other ant species is eaten. The Camayurá have no domesticated animal herds.

Politics. The Camayurá villages are governed by a council composed of a tribal chief, the house chiefs, and other elders of the village. The tribal chief is selected by the other council members from among the male relatives of the previous chief. Their selection is based upon such criteria as knowledge of customs and ritual, skill at arbitrating disputes, and ability to perform the rituals of a shaman. A house chief is the person who organizes the labor to construct a communal house. The council meets each evening in the plaza formed by the village houses. The tribal chief organizes community activities—land clearing, fish poisoning, trading, moving to a new site, receiving visitors, and so on. However, the tribal chief is not the leader when the Camayurá go to war.

Economics. The Camayurá are an unusual primitive group in that they have incorporated specialists in the manufacture of certain articles into their village life. Only four men, for example, make bows, and all the other tribesmen trade for them. As a result of this specialization, a primitive marketing system has developed; a house group, whenever it has accumulated a surplus of items, announces during the evening get-together that their articles are available. The next morning, the house displays its items and a buyer may exchange something of his for one of the house items. Intervillage trade is also carried out in a similar manner. Some of the items commonly traded are pottery, flutes, shell necklaces, canoes, and bows. A standard scale of trade has also been developed, particularly for intervillage and intertribal trade, in which, as an example, a shell necklace is worth two bows.

Communications. The Camayurá speak Tupi-Guaraní. Of the eleven Amazon Indian tribes inhabiting the Upper Xingu River basin, only one other tribe speaks that language. Six of the remaining nine tribes speak Carib, two speak Arawak, and one speaks Trumai. With the exception of Trumai, which is an isolated language, the other languages are related. Therefore, intertribal communication is not as difficult as would first appear. Communication is restricted to speech and sign language; the tribes are unaware of modern, mass-communication systems.

Technology. The Camayurá live in thatched, communal houses with parallel sides and rounded ends. They range from 30 x 55 feet to 34 x 66 feet, with a center ridge pole about twenty feet high. Male clothing consists of a fine, fiber cord worn around the waist. The females add to their cord a small triangular ulurí, made from a specially folded leaf, which covers the pubic area. The principal weapon of the Camayurá, and probably the artifact that signifies the height of their technology, is a six and one-half-foot bow. As mentioned earlier, the Camayurá subscribe to the theory of division of labor; as a result, only four men make all the bows for the male population. The arrows are five feet long and have a cane shaft, a hardwood foreshaft, and a head made from either a stingray spine, a splinter of bone from a monkey arm, or the rib of a tapir or jaguar. Their accuracy with these weapons is about one hundred feet.

The Tasadays

The Tasadays are assumed to be the most primitive of all of the world's societies.[2] Living in the rain forest of the southern end of the Philippine Island of Mindanao, their existence was unknown until June 1971. The population of the Tasaday tribe in 1972 was only twenty-four—ten males, five females, and nine children, mostly male.

Education. The lifestyle of the Tasadays is so simple and natural that there seems to be little need for a formal educational period or process; at least none was observed by Mr. MacLeish during his visit with them. When Dofal, the Filipino who first made contact with the Tasadays, attempted to show several of them the process for extracting natok (an edible substance contained in the heart of certain palm trees), he had to repeat the

---

[2] Based on data from Kenneth MacLeish, "The Tasadays: Stone-Age Cavemen of Mindanao." *National Geographic* 142, no. 2 (August 1972): 219–49. Reprinted by permission.

fairly simple process four times before the Tasadays were able to carry out the task by themselves.

Food Production. The Tasadays have no agriculture, and prior to their contact with the outside world, they subsisted exclusively on food gathered from the local environment. They gathered and ate wild yams and bananas, berries, flowers, and a vine root called "biking." They also caught and ate tadpoles, frogs, crabs, small fish from local streams, and grubs from rotting logs. These foods are so plentiful that the Tasadays rarely forage more than five miles from their cave home. They did not hunt or trap the plentiful game animals until Dofal showed them how to construct and set traps. As a result, the Tasadays have added deer, pig, monkey, and mouse to their diet. They are not very committed to their traps, however, since they view the meat as a luxury, not a necessity. Dofal was responsible for adding ubud and natok to their diet. Both are the pith from palm trees and were inaccessible to the Tasadays until Dofal acquainted them with the new delicacies and provided a bolo knife as a means for extracting them. The Tasadays still do not hunt and do not find a bow given to them to be very useful.

Politics. The Tasadays claimed that they had no leader and that decisions were made by the entire group. However, one Tasaday male acted as the chief spokesman, and perhaps tacitly this same person influenced the actions of the rest. No division of labor was observed; nor was preferential treatment accorded to a special group. Each Tasaday did what he could do best, and all shared equally in the results of the actions taken.

Economics. The possession of material goods holds no interest for the Tasadays; all things, including food, are shared equally. Consequently, they have no economic system since they have no way of placing a value on anything. Again, their lifestyle is so simple that all their needs are provided by nature. When the Tasadays were given enough bolo knives for each male member of the tribe, plus one extra, no one claimed the extra knife. In fact, all the knives were stored together, so no one claimed any particular knife.

Communications. The only communications observed by Mr. Mac-Leish were verbal communications. The Tasadays had no way either to send or receive mass communications.

Technology. The technology of the Tasadays is truly Stone Age technology. Until they were presented with bolo knives and bows, the tools of the Tasadays consisted of stone axes, digging sticks, stone scrapers, sharpened bamboo knives, bamboo tongs (for turning roasting food), and a wooden fire drill. They store and carry their water in hollow bamboo stems. The Tasadays have three stone axes—each made from a split rock polished along the cutting edge, fitted into a notched stick handle about a foot long, and tied with vine. The axes are used to crush hard fruits and to smash open rotted logs in search of grubs. The axes are not used as weapons; in fact, the Tasadays have no weapons of any kind, nor do they have a word for warfare. The entire Tasaday tribe lives in a complex of three caves (one unoccupied), high on the side of a steep ridge. They have no woven cloth, no pottery, no pipes, no tobacco. The Tasadays quite possibly may be the only society in the world to which tobacco is unknown.

The Hottentots

Driven off their pastoral lands by both white settlers and Negroid African tribes, murdered, enslaved, assimilated into other tribes, and deprived of their unique culture, the Hottentots have almost become extinct. Only a few small groups living in the Kalahari Desert and the Okavango Swamps of southern Africa are said to have true Hottentots as members and to follow the Hottentot traditions.

Education. The children of the Hottentots learn necessary living skills by observing their parents and other elders. The tribal traditions and history are contained in songs and dances, but the Hottentots remember little personal family history beyond four generations. Their lack of educational practice and experience becomes evident when they are pressed into trying to remember things for an extended period of time. When this happens, the Hottentots' answers become increasingly hazy and incoherent. They also find it difficult to concentrate on a mental problem for a long period of time.

Food Production. Although the Hottentots once had large herds of cattle, plus some sheep and goats, today's survivors are primarily hunters and gatherers. The male, desert Hottentots stalk game animals, mostly antelope, while the females gather different types of edible nuts, berries, bulbs, tubers, seeds, melons, and wild vegetables. Those Hottentots who sought refuge in the Okavango Swamps quite naturally have become adept as fishermen. They also hunt impala, lechine, kudu, buffalo, wildebeast, tsessbe, reedbuck, and wart hog. The women of the swamp Hottentot gather marula fruit, magom (palm heart), nakwa fruit, the pith from papyrus stems, ilala palm nuts, dates, waterlily bulbs, and other edible vegetation. In addition, these women have planted small crops of pumpkin, watermelon, sugarcane, maize, and sorghum—the first known agriculture engaged in by a Hottentot tribe.

Politics. Each small family group has the senior male member of the family as its leader. If several family groups form a larger but local group, the head of this local group is usually a member of the tribal council, which is comprised of a number of such heads and presided over by the paramount chief. All leaders, heads, and chiefs are hereditary through the male line. Their rule is absolute, and decisions are followed unhesitatingly.

Economics. Although it varies from tribe to tribe, the economic level of the Hottentots is at the bare subsistence level. Other than the clothes on their backs, a few household utensils, and their hunting equipment, they are virtually without possessions. Some trade is done with the Negroid tribes who barter Western clothes, iron pots and spear tips, zinc buckets, mugs, tin trunks, blankets, and mosquito nets for animal skins.

Communications. The Hottentots have no written language. Their vocal language is a strange and unique combination of normal words or sound expressions and clicking sounds. The Hottentot language is very difficult to learn because only pitch differentiates some words, and there are as many as four click sounds in a single word. The Hottentots have no knowledge of mass media.

Technology. The technological development of the Hottentots is low level and almost entirely associated with hunting. The desert Hottentots' chief hunting weapons are the bow with poisonous arrows and the spear. The bow is strung with sinew, but both the arrow and spear tips are made of iron that is acquired in trade with the Negroid tribes. The swamp Hottentots have four different spear heads to use, depending upon the type of game pursued, but they do not use bow and arrows. However, they have developed the technologies for building canoes, basket traps, and reed fences used for catching fish, while the desert Hottentots have developed noose snares and pitfalls for catching game animals. The fire drill is also a common artifact of the Hottentots.

Transitional or Emerging Societies

The majority of the world's societies fall into the second societal level—the transitional or emerging society. It includes all societies between the primitive level and the highly developed level. Obviously then, the transitional or emerging societal level is not a single level but rather a large group of sublevels collected under a single heading because they share common problems and common goals. Transitional or emerging societies are also known as underdeveloped, developing, lesser developed, and Third World societies.

As stated earlier, transitional or emerging societies are not usually discussed individually, but instead are discussed collectively as a nation or a country. For example, the Indian subcontinent is comprised of a multitude of distinctive societies. Even though habitants can be generally identified by the regions in which they live and by the differences in their language, customs, culture, religion, and so on, and even though a few of these societies are at the tribal level and a few others are at the highly developed level, all these societies are usually collectively discussed as the transitional or emerging countries of India, Pakistan, and Bangladesh. Our case studies will follow this common procedure and will discuss transitional or emerging nations as a whole, rather than extract a single society within a nation and exemplify it. In general, transitional or emerging nations can be described as being traditionalist and overpopulated, with low economic productivity and a slow rate of technological development.

Transitional or emerging societies differ from tribal societies by having developed an intermediate level of technology, by having progressed economically beyond bartering and agriculturally beyond hunting and gathering, and by having created at least the foundations and structure necessary to carry out formal education. Transitional or emerging societies differ from highly developed societies in that they are less technologically developed, less industrialized, economically less productive, and politically less stable. Transitional societies are almost always located in the poorly developed rural areas and in the slums of large cities.

Characteristics of a Transitional or Emerging Society

Education. Although an infrastructure for a formal educational process exists in most emerging societies, the literacy rate is usually very low. This situation exists for several reasons: (1) Parents fail to see the need for education beyond the reading and writing of a person's name; (2) Although attendance is usually mandatory by law, few school systems pay attention to truancy; (3) The teachers, skillwise, are the poorest and the least motivated in the education system; and (4) Consequently, the children are not motivated to stay in school or to learn when they are there.

The educational systems of transitional or emerging nations are almost always based upon a European school system, which emphasizes educating the affluent, often at the expense of the poor.

Food Production. Most people in transitional or emerging societies are members of subsistence farm families—that is, they have enough land, water, seed, and fertilizer to grow enough food to survive, barely. Any food left over from an unusually good harvest or any cash crop grown must be sold to provide money to buy next year's seed and fertilizer, to pay the taxes or rent, and to meet other expenses. Usually one major food crop is raised from which the families receive the bulk of their diet. Cereal grains such as rice, corn or maize, and wheat, legumes, and starchy roots and tubers such as cassava, sweet potato, yam, and white potato are examples of the food crops raised by transitional societies throughout the world.

Some of the more progressive farmers of these societies are beginning to practice modern methods of agriculture, but the majority still prefer the traditional methods. A small number of livestock are also common in emerging societies, but their use as a major food source is not common. Usually the animals are work animals and are used for cultivating, for supplying the power to pump irrigation water, and for transportation. Any additional food they may provide, such as milk or meat, is a bonus for the family. Many emerging or transitional nations consider their number one goal to be increasing their country's food production and have given it the highest priority.

Politics. As indicated earlier, transitional or emerging nations are politically more unstable than the highly developed nations. At the societal level, however, this is not the case. In fact, subjection to traditional political powers is one of the reasons many of these societies are still in the transitional stage. They often have two leaders—their traditional one and one supplied by some government agency. The leaders often have conflicting objectives and consequently disagree about many issues, with the societal members caught in the middle. It is common for transitional-society members to feel that they have no control over their destiny and that the government and its agents must be blindly obeyed or they will suffer dire consequences—and that is often the case.

Many transitional or emerging nations have set up political infrastructures in which the members of transitional societies can democratically choose their representatives. However, quite often their choices are limited, and after the election, they have little or no contact with the representatives.

Economics. The economic level of emerging societies is low, but not as low as that of the primitive societies. For instance, business is usually transacted with money as the medium of exchange, rather than through simple bartering. However, the economic productivity of transitional societies is quite low. As mentioned earlier, the inhabitants are primarily subsistence farmers and, as such, contribute little if anything to their nation's overall economy. Those members of a transitional or emerging society who are not engaged in agriculture are almost always unskilled and are at the very bottom of the economic productivity scale. Unemployment and underemployment are major problems in most transitional societies.

A marketing infrastructure exists in most transitional or emerging nations, but it commonly favors the urban consumer rather than the rural farmer. For example, storage facilities for surplus or perishable crops are often inadequate or even nonexistent. As a result, the farmers must sell their products immediately upon harvesting them, in an already glutted market when prices are at their lowest. Another major problem for many emerging nations is their trade deficit. They are exporting too little, usually cheap, raw materials, and importing too much, usually expensive, manufactured goods.

Communications. Although an infrastructure exists within the emerging nation, the emerging societies within that nation rarely benefit from it. For example, major newspaper circulation is confined to the larger cities; local newspapers do not exist because most of the people are illiterate. Television, uncommon even in the large cities, is usually confined to one or at most two government-controlled stations. Radio is the most common means of mass communication available to emerging societies. Even in the poorest rural villages and city slum streets, at least one transistor radio can be found. However, programs are rarely educational; they consist primarily of entertainment and controlled news broadcasts.

Technology. Intermediate-level technology is predominant in transitional or emerging societies. Manufactured goods and supplies are available to most members of these societies, as are labor-saving machinery and modern means of transportation. Their economic ability to purchase these items, however, is limited. Some of the basic services available to highly developed societies, such as electricity and running water, are also beginning to reach many transitional societies. But even when a society has access to these services, few can afford the individual services. Therefore, the water service may consist of a single tap replacing the village well, and the electric service may be limited to running the irrigation pump or to lighting a few weak bulbs in the church or mosque, the local store, and perhaps several homes of the more affluent villagers.

Transitional or emerging nations are being forced to choose between expanding their current level of intermediate technology both horizontally and vertically, or bypassing the intermediate level of technological development to begin using the technology developed by the highly developed nations. The major argument against bypassing the intermediate technological level is that high-level technologies are capital intensive and labor saving, just the opposite of what seems to be needed for these countries with a dearth of capital and a surplus of labor.

Case Studies

India

Education. India has a constitutional goal to provide free and compulsory education for all children up to the age of fourteen. The responsibility for this goal has been given to the state governments, and it is expected to be reached sometime during the early 1980s. In the meantime, the country's education system is severely strained to provide for this large expansion program while maintaining a quality educational process. An estimated annual expansion rate of 6–7.5 percent will be required to meet population increases, to overcome the existing backlog of underdevelopment, and to complete the desired expansion on schedule. The literacy rate for India is estimated to be about 25 percent. Since it was a British colony from the late eighteenth century until 1947, India's educational system, quite naturally, is based upon the English educational system. Like the English system, the Indian system has separate divisions for the potential scholar and the potential vocational trainee, starting at the preschool, or kindergarten, level.

Chemistry class in a women's college in New Delhi. Attaining this education level is out of the question for most Indians. Photo courtesy Information Service of India, New York.

Food Production. More than 70 percent of the total labor force of India is employed in agriculture. Almost three-fourths of these farmers own less than five acres of land each; the ratio of total cropped area to total population is 0.8 acres per person; the agricultural yields are among the lowest in the world; and fertilizer usage is approximately one-fifth of what is minimally required. As a result of these situations, the productivity of the farmers of India is estimated to be about 37 percent of that of all others in the Indian workforce. Approximately 75 percent of all the cultivable land is used to grow food grains such as rice, wheat, grain sorghum, millet, and various pulses.

The United Nations estimated that in 1973 fewer than 70,000 tractors were in use in India. Although bullocks and buffalo are the major power sources available to the Indian farmer, they also supply him with several other necessary commodities: food in the form of milk and its by-products; fuel and fertilizer from the dung; and hides and skins that are salable. Sheep and goats are also kept, primarily for their meat but also for their milk, wool, and skins. Poultry is a relatively minor area, but seems to be increasing in importance. The fishing potential for India is tremendous because of an extensive coastline, 70,000 miles of irrigation canals, and its large major rivers. However, only a small portion of this potential has been realized because priority has been given to developing other food source areas.

The traditional method for transplanting rice is similar for subsistence farmers throughout the world. Photo courtesy Information Service of India, New York.

Research conducted in such places as the Central Rice Research Institute, Cuttack, has led to increased yields in recent years, but much work must still be done for India to become self-sufficient in food. Photo courtesy of Information Service of India, New York.

Politics. The government of India is both parliamentary and republican, with a federal system operating under the Constitution of 1950. The president is the titular head of state, and the prime minister has the power role, serving as the chief executive of the union. The Parliament consists of two houses—the Lok Sabha (House of the People) and the Rajya Sabha (Council of States). The members of the Lok Sabha, a maximum of five hundred, are directly elected in the states. An additional twenty-five members are either elected or appointed to represent the Union Territories. The members of the Rajya Sabha, a maximum of two hundred fifty, are elected by the state legislatures, except for twelve, who are appointed by the president. India is comprised of seventeen states, ten Union Territories, and the territory of North-East Frontier Agency. States are divided into districts, and local governments are subject to district authority. The Constitution of 1950 guarantees all the basic freedoms, except in time of war or a national emergency called by the president.

Economics. With its economic planning based upon the popular five-year-plan system, India has become one of the top ten nations in the production of goods and services. However, it is also among the bottom ten nations in per capita output. In 1974, the nation's per capita gross national product was estimated to be around $150. The exact figures vary, depending upon the source quoted, but India's annual trade deficit has consistently exceeded $1 billion. Within the past ten years, some sources have quoted this annual deficit to be as high as $10 billion.

India's major exports are jute products, tea, iron ore, and cotton textiles. The nation's major imports are footdstuffs (consistently amounting to more than 30 percent of the total), machinery, fertilizers and chemicals, and

Steel plants such as this one in West Bengal are being constructed by the Indian Government in an attempt to reduce its steel imports. Photo courtesy of Information Service of India, New York.

iron and steel. Regarding domestic trade, since more than 80 percent of India's people live in rural villages, approximately 80 percent of the country's marketable produce is sold locally. It is estimated, however, that as much as 25 percent of the food produced is never consumed because of the extremely poor systems of marketing, storage, distribution, and food processing prevalent throughout much of the nation.

Communications. Although there are nearly eight hundred daily newspapers in India, they reach only about 6 percent of the total population of more than six hundred million. The major languages of these papers are English, Hindi, Bengali, Malayalan, Marathi, Tamil, and Telegu. (More than eight hundred distinct languages and dialects are spoken in India.) The approximate one hundred forty Indian radio stations operated by the Ministry of Information, Broadcasting, and Communications reach fewer than one-half of all the rural areas. In 1973, UNESCO estimated that there were twenty-three radio receivers for every one thousand persons in India. Although educational programs aimed at the nation's farmers are increasing, almost half of the air time is spent broadcasting music. Another 25 percent is devoted to news programs broadcast in eighteen languages and twenty-four dialects. The remainder of the air time is spent broadcasting dramas, talk shows, specials and features.

Television is confined to only a few of the major cities, with air time limited to a two- to three-hour period each day. India, however, is currently establishing an experimental television system that will beam its signal from a satellite to the country's rural areas. The primary purposes of the broadcasts will be to promote the nation's birth control programs and to increase the farmers' awareness of modern agricultural techniques.

Technology. India has within its borders all the levels of technological development. There are primitive tribes in the south-central highlands whose technology is low level; the majority of Indians are using primarily intermediate technologies; and there are a few modern industrial sites where high-level technology is utilized. Although only about one-third of India's industrial operations are considered large scale—that is, fifty or more employees with an outside power source or one hundred employees without an outside power source—they account for approximately 85 percent of the nonfarm employment as well as approximately 85 percent of industry's gross value of output.

In per capita consumption of energy, one of the indicators of industrial production, India ranks low on the list. Despite this fact, because of its food production and population problems, many observers felt that India was placing an inordinate emphasis on developing the industrial sector during the 1950s and 1960s. Recent development programming seems to show an increasing emphasis toward the transfer and diffusion of technology that addresses itself to the population and food production problems. The latest United Nations figures show that in 1972 India had more than 103,000

Much of India's industry is small scale. Here Indian craftsmen create murals using techniques that have been handed down for generations. Photo courtesy of Information Service of India, New York.

scientists, engineers, and technicians engaged in research and experimental development, and the nation's total expenditures for these activities in 1970 was just over $225,000.

United Republic of Cameroon

Education. Cameroon was founded in 1960 with the decolonization and reunification of the two former African colonies of British Cameroons and French Cameroon. As a result, their national educational system is an integration of the British and French educational systems, which emphasized African cultural heritage. The levels of the education system range from preprimary education through university although the preprimary education is available in only the larger cities. Despite an impressive effort on the part of the Cameroon government to increase the number of schools, the number of new teachers, and the enrollment, the literacy rate is still only about 15 percent. Even though approximately 70 percent of the school-age population attend the primary- and secondary-school systems, for example, only one in ten students entering the primary schools ever completes the sixth, or final, year. This unusually high dropout rate is attributed primarily to the still extreme shortage of qualified teachers. About half of those who teach at the primary level fill positions for which they are unqualified. Currently, there are strong movements for increasing both the vocational–technical training at the secondary level and the enrollment in the national university. The latter movement is aimed at diminishing the number of students who attend foreign universities, many of whom fail to return to Cameroon upon completing their degree.

Food Production. More than 75 percent of the population of Cameroon is in the rural sector; the majority of these people are small farmers with holdings of about six and one-half acres. Generally, about 40 percent of this land is used for growing food crops, with the remaining 60 percent devoted to a cash crop, usually cocoa. Plantation agriculture, mostly foreign owned and raising export crops of palm oil, bananas, rubber, and sugarcane, uses only about 5 percent of the total land under cultivation. It was estimated that only fifty-two tractors were operating in Cameroon in 1973. Principal food crops grown by Cameroon farmers include millet and sorghum, maize, cassava, sweet potatoes, yams, and rice.

Extensive lands are devoted to pasture for raising cattle, sheep, and goats; along with pigs and poultry, these comprise the major types of livestock raised in Cameroon. The productivity of both the crop farming and livestock raising is poor when compared to Western countries, but it is better than average for African countries. Although it was virtually self-sufficient in food production during the 1960s, Cameroon has recently been forced to import rice and meat because of a rising urban population.

Politics. Like the educational system, the Cameroon governmental system is a combination of French and British systems. The Constitution of 1972 specified the right to the basic freedoms of religion, expression, press, assembly, and so on, only vaguely alluded to in the 1961 Constitution. The government of Cameroon is headed by an elected president who wields great power. He is head of state, government, and the military, and personally fills all cabinet, military, civilian governmental, and judicial posts and also has the right to declare a state of emergency and suspend all civil rights. The National Assembly is an elected, unicameral body consisting solely of members of the ruling presidential party, even though the new constitution allowed for the formation of opposition political parties. The new regulation was circumvented by the ruling party's declaration that the entire country was one big electoral district and, therefore, the party that received the most votes would fill all the seats in the National Assembly. Regionally, Cameroon is divided into seven provinces, each administered by appointed governors. The provinces are divided into thirty-nine departments, and all but three departments are further divided into districts, or arrondissements. Three federal courts were created by the first constitution, the most important being the Federal Court of Justice, which made final decisions on cases concerning conflicts between constitutional and state regulations.

Economics. Economically, Cameroon is one of the most stable and most advanced nations in Black Africa. It ranks fifth in the world production of cocoa, which, along with coffee, accounts for better than one-half of the nation's total exports. In fact, raw and slightly processed agricultural products account for more than 90 percent of Cameroon's total export sales. In exchange, it imports machinery and equipment for agriculture, transportation, and communications (accounting for more than 50 percent of the total imports); materials and equipment for industry; and the food-stuffs mentioned earlier. Cameroon has been holding its own as far as trade deficits and the balance of payments are concerned, thanks mainly to its large aggregate of agricultural exports.

Regarding domestic trade, Cameroon's industrial products can be found in the remotest villages, and the barter system has virtually been eliminated. However, the three-quarters of the population engaged in agricultural production are responsible for only about 35 percent of the total gross domestic product. Transport, power, and service contribute about 45 percent, and manufacturing and construction are responsible for the remaining 25 percent or so. The per capita GDP for Cameroon is around 200 U.S. dollars. The internal market of food crops is handled primarily by African merchants.

Private enterprise and foreign ownership dominate the commercial sector. Export crops are controlled by an official marketing board in the western sector of the country and by five official stabilization funds in the eastern sector. These funds and the board were set up to protect the small farmers and businessmen from the fluctuations in the world market prices of cocoa, coffee, cotton, groundnuts, and palm kernels.

Communications. Although twenty-four major languages and numerous dialects are spoken in Cameroon, the two official languages are French and English, with French dominant in government, commerce, and the mass media. The traditional channel of communication was and still is word of mouth. In 1973, according to UNESCO, eight radio stations in Cameroon, all government controlled, served over 216,000 sets, or thirty-seven for every one thousand inhabitants, most of which were located in the urban areas. The three daily newspapers, one French-speaking and two English-speaking, were published and distributed in the larger cities. Their total circulation was less than twenty-five thousand copies. Six weekly newspapers are published in Yaoundé and distributed almost exclusively within the French-speaking areas of the country. A government regulation requires a copy of each newspaper be submitted to the ministry of interior prior to publication. As of 1973, there was no television in Cameroon.

Technology. Since so much of Cameroon's agriculture is carried on by the small farmer, the major tools used are the hoe and the machete. Agricultural development projects emphasizing intermediate technologies such as animal-drawn plows seem to be having much greater success than those projects that attempted to introduce modern agricultural equipment. In 1973, Cameroon's modern, capital-intensive, industrial capacity was the third largest in French-speaking Africa. However, a sizable contingent of intermediate-level, labor-intensive, manufacturing enterprises still operated as well.

Peru

Education. School attendance is required by law for all Peruvian children between the age of seven and fourteen, but as few as 50 percent of the students in this age bracket may actually attend school for the entire seven years. Classes are held for six hours a day, six days a week. The educational system includes the preprimary level to the university level; however, only primary schooling is available to much of the rural populus. Even then, students may have to walk several miles to attend a school whose facilities are small, poorly developed, and run by a single teacher who instructs in a language that is foreign to them. Although Spanish is the official language of Peru, the inhabitants of many rural areas speak only Quechua or Aymara. In 1970, only about ten thousand of the estimated 2.73 million primary-school child attended bilingual schools. Included in a broad reform of the educational system instituted in the early 1970s were attempts to decrease academic material being taught and increase the amount of technical and practical information. Estimates of the literacy rate of Peru range from a high of 77 percent to a low of 45 percent. In 1970, the Pan American Union estimate was 71 percent. The highest literacy rate was among the urban males, estimated at slightly more than 90 percent. The lowest literacy rate was among the rural females, estimated at slightly less than 25 percent.

Food Production. Because of an ever-widening gap between food production and population growth, major reforms are taking place in the agricultural sector of Peru. The government has become intimately involved, sometimes alone and sometimes as a partner with private enterprise. Land reform has made millions of acres of land available to formerly landless peasants; major irrigation projects have added or will soon add thousands of acres of cultivable land; and the small farmer is being provided with increased economic and technical assistance. Yet, in 1970, only 5.4 million acres, or 1.7 percent, of the total of Peru's 317.4 million acres were under cultivation. The size of land holdings varies from small acreages to large plantations, but approximately 60 percent of the farmers hold slightly more than four acres each. Roughly 50 percent of the Peruvian labor force is engaged in agricultural or food producing activities. The major cash crops are sugarcane and cotton, and the major food crops are potatoes, bananas, sweet potatoes, the indigenous potatoes known as oca and olluco, manioc, corn, rice, barley, and wheat.

Livestock is raised primarily in the Sierra region of Peru, and the major food producing animals are cattle, sheep, hogs, poultry, and guinea pigs (a major source of meat in the rural areas). In addition, Peru's fishing industry is among the five largest in the world.

Politics. In 1968, a military coup overthrew the government of Peru; since then, the country has been ruled by a military junta consisting of the president and the commanders of the army, navy, and air force. The former president was removed from office, the legislature was dissolved, and the cabinet ministers were removed and replaced with military personnel.

Peru is divided into twenty-three departments plus the constitutional province of Callao. Each department is divided into one hundred forty provinces, which in turn are divided into 1,554 districts. Each department and the constitutional province are controlled by an appointed prefect, each province by an appointed subprefect, and each district by an appointed governor. The prefects and subprefects are usually from outside the area of their control, but the governor normally is from his own district. Communities officially recognized by the junta are permitted to elect their local leaders. The National Justice Council, created in 1969, appoints all judges and has the power to investigate and remove from office those guilty of improper conduct. The judicial system includes, in order of importance, the Supreme Court of Justice, nineteen superior courts, the provincial courts, and, finally, the local justices of the peace in almost every village and town.

Economics. Although Peru is rich in natural resources, many of its people living on subsistence-level farms and in urban slums and are among the poorest in the world. Unemployment and underemployment are chronic problems, with the former hovering consistently around 30 percent. Prior to the military coup in 1968, the distribution of wealth was inequitable, with only one-fourth of 1 percent of the population receiving almost 35 percent of the nation's total income, and 80 percent of the population sharing about 20 percent of the income. The estimated 1972 per capita gross domestic product was about $380 and has continued to rise on the strength of Peru's mining, manufacturing, and fisheries industries. However, despite the government's intervention into what was once almost exclusively private enterprise areas, the inequities in the distribution of wealth can still be detected, as seen in the following statistics: Only about 5,200 of an estimated 25,000 industrial establishments are rated higher than artisan or craftsman establishments; yet these 5,200 firms are responsible for 98 percent of Peru's total industrial production, excluding mining. Although agriculture employs almost 50 percent of the population, it contributes less than 15 percent to the gross domestic product. The manufacturing, mining, and petroleum sectors contribute more than 30 percent to the total gross domestic product.

Peru's balance of payments fluctuates radically each year because its surplus or deficit is largely dependent upon the international prices of various metals and fishmeal, the country's major exports. The major imports are foodstuffs (since Peru's food production is not keeping up with its population expansion), machinery for various mining and manufacturing enterprises, and chemicals for both agriculture and mining concerns.

Communications. As was mentioned earlier, Spanish is the predominant language of Peru, but local Indian languages are common in rural areas, the two most widely distributed being Quechua and Aymara. Five daily newspapers, all published in Lima, share the bulk of the newspaper circulation within the country. Although the papers have provincial circulation, the majority of their sales are within Lima's urban area. Information is disseminated to an estimated twelve million receivers, largely through Peru's more than three hundred radio stations. Even the rural areas benefit from this mass media method, for nearly 85 percent of the provincial families own a radio. By law, each station is required by the government to devote one hour each day to airing cultural and educational programs. According to UNESCO figures, there were fifty-two television stations and more than 400,000 receivers in Peru in 1972, with the government owning a controlling interest in all of them.

Technology. The technological development level of Peru fluctuates greatly, depending upon the situation presented. In agriculture, for example, the subsistence farmers continue to practice methods not unlike those practiced by the Incas when the Spanish first entered the country. On the other hand, the commercial plantations' methods rival those of any modern farming enterprise. For example, Peru had more than 12,500 tractors operating in 1973.

The industrial sectors have similar contrasts. Many small artisan and craftsmen-type manufacturing enterprises use tools and methods bordering on the primitive, while the larger manufacturing and processing firms employ modern equipment and methods. The mining and fishing industries also have enterprises that employ widely contrasting technologies. According to United Nations statistics, in 1970, Peru had more than eight hundred fifty scientists and engineers and almost eleven hundred technicians engaged in research and development, but total expenditures for those activities were just over $8,000.

Highly Developed or Postindustrial Societies

A standard benchmark for highly developed or postindustrial societies is those societies living at or above the economic middle-class level of a particular nation. However, if only this criterion is used, a person can move from a highly developed societal level to a transitional societal level, and vice versa, simply by leaving one country and entering another since the economic level of countries may vary so greatly. Therefore, other criteria are needed. A highly developed society has a strong economic and industrial base from which to operate; it is highly mechanized; the majority of the people are *not* engaged in agriculture; emphasis is placed upon improving the status quo (especially economically); mass communications are available to all members; a strong and stable governmental structure exists; and education is truly mandatory for the children.

Although it is not a true indicator by itself, the economic level of a society does indicate that a better standard of life is available to its members than that which is available to economically lesser endowed societies. The economic resource base enables the highly developed society to have better facilities and to utilize more efficiently the educational, industrial, and research facilities that lead to further technological advancements. These, in turn, lead to greater economic productivity; hence, the cycle is repeated.

The members of the highly developed societies, in all but a few cases, rule or at least control developing nations even though they are in the minority. Consequently, many of the developmental improvements instituted seem only to increase further the economic level and general lifestyle of the already wealthy portion of the country, sometimes even at the expense of the transitional societies. One can determine the real concerns of a country's government by looking at several aspects: the percentage of mass media devoted to educating the transitional societies; the amount of capital invested in nonlabor-intensive industry, in increasing military might, and increating edifices; and the lip service paid to increasing the economic, educational, and general lifestyle of the poorer societies. Of course, these criteria also hold true for the governments of the highly developed nations.

Highly developed or postindustrial nations are those in which the majority of their population lives at the highly developed or postindustrial societal level. They also contain, however, transitional, and in some cases, even tribal, societies. Highly developed and postindustrial nations are also sometimes labeled developed, highly mechanized or industrialized, Westernized, and First World countries. Nations that have a communist-type of government are often called Second World countries. However, we prefer to refer to the communist-bloc countries as either highly developed or transitional, depending upon their overall status.

Characteristics of a Highly Developed or Postindustrial Society

Education. Education is emphasized in a highly developed society. In general, the higher the educational attainment of an individual, the more respected he or she becomes. Although classical or straight academic education was once lauded over technical education, currently, and particularly at the postsecondary level, technical education is given equal status with academic education. In fact, technical education in some instances has become even more prestigious than academic education. Compulsory, free, public education for all children up to the approximate age of sixteen is available to almost all highly developed societies, and the regulation is generally strictly enforced. Some members of these societies, however, consider public education to be inferior and enroll their children in private institutions, even though public educational institutions are available from the preprimary through the postdoctoral university level. The literacy rate for a highly developed society is rarely below 90 percent and often encompasses the entire society.

Food Production. Food production is *not* the major employment of the members of a highly developed society. The agricultural sector of most of these nations has become so highly mechanized that relatively few persons are required to produce all the necessary food. Surplus food storage facilities, as well as ingenious techniques for preserving certain perishable foods, allow the highly developed societal members to enjoy a variety of foods throughout the year. These facilities also allow the farmer to store some of his crop so he is not forced to sell it cheaply at harvest time. The farmers of a highly developed society are as much businessmen as they are agriculturalists. They usually own large holdings of land; utilize large amounts of mechanical equipment; are cognizant of the latest technological developments in cultivation and planting techniques, herbicides, pesticides, seed, and fertilizers; and have access to sources of credit and professional assistance when problems arise. Animal production is more commonly accomplished in feed-lots, where the animals' movements are restricted, and where they have a constant supply of feed, rather than on ranges or in pastures. Hunting and gathering are performed primarily for the sport or enjoyment rather than for the acquired food.

Politics. Although it is usually more liberal than traditional societies, the political structure of highly developed societies is really still quite conservative, which partially accounts for their strength and stability. Once again, it is a case where, collectively, the persons in power wish to retain the status quo even though some individuals might be quite liberal. Leadership roles are held by persons from within the society. In fact, most national leaders are members of the highly developed societies, regardless of the level of the nation as a whole. It is generally agreed that the members of highly developed societies enjoy considerably more benefits than do the members of other societal levels. The right to enjoy the basic freedoms is considered mandatory by members of highly developed societies. Some of the greatest conflicts between the political structure and the members of a society, including the communist ones, have occurred over the issue of the basic freedoms.

Economics. Economic strength and stability are the foundations upon which highly developed societies are built. A combination of factors results in high economic productivity on a national level: Many sectors make substantial input into the gross domestic and gross national products so that the economy is not dependent upon a single sector; there are large internal and external markets for the goods and services produced; foreign trade usually results in a surplus in the balance of payments; and generally speaking, capital is available for development and expansion. The free enterprise system is commonly practiced in all but the communist countries, so that an individual member in a highly developed society may purchase land, buildings, stocks and bonds, or engage in any other industrial or entrepreneurial enterprise he wants.

Communications. The level of mass communications practiced within the highly developed societies is the highest in the world. Nearly every member has access to all types of mass-communication information. In addition, a great variety of each type of mass media is available to the individual. The electronic media, combined with satellite technology, have been developed to the point where they can provide almost instantaneous information from anywhere in the world.

Technology. Highly developed societies make almost exclusive use of high-level technology. The members of these societies employ computers to help solve their problems and use machinery to do work that is menial, difficult, hazardous, and repetitious. Through interpreters and translations, high-level societal members can use knowledge acquired from developmental projects around the world, as well as from their own. Research, development, and invention are recognized as important developmental tasks, and thus persons working in those fields are rewarded with prestigious positions and high salaries.

Case Studies

Union of Soviet Socialist Republics (U.S.S.R.)

Education. The educational system of the Soviet Union ranges from preschool through the postgraduate university level and includes nursery, kindergarten, primary, secondary, technical and vocational, special education, adult education, part-time, correspondence, nondegree schools, and institutes. There are insufficient numbers of preschool, nursery, and kindergarten schools to enroll all the younger children, but primary- and secondary-school attendance is reported to be around 95 percent. The Soviet Union has a compulsory ten-year attendance requirement that is strictly enforced, and, as a result, the literacy rate is almost 100 percent. The curricula of the Russian schools are heavily weighted toward technical, scientific, and communist doctrine courses, with the latter even further emphasized by required extracurricular activities. The school week is commonly six days long with five to six hours of class each day. The administration, planning, teacher training, curriculum, and textbooks are controlled by the state organizations—the U.S.S.R. Ministry of Higher and Specialized Education and the U.S.S.R. Ministry of Education. Education in the Soviet Union was developed to include all segments of the population, but minor rumblings of discontent about education are still heard in the rural areas. Some critics feel that rural education is inferior to urban education and that an upgrading of the rural education system is required.

Food Production. The majority of the Soviet Union's agriculture is conducted on the nation's 37,000 collective and 13,000 state farms. The state farms are managed by the state, while the farmers themselves manage the collective farms. A small, individual, private plot is allotted to each state farmer and collective farmer for growing his personal, subsistence food crop. Although the gross productivity of the agricultural sector has doubled in the past twenty years and despite the fact that it has more land under cultivation than any other nation in the world, the Soviet Union must still import vast amounts of grain each year, usually from Canada and the United States.

Unusual as it is for a highly developed nation, and even though it is heavily mechanized with over two million tractors and nearly 600,000 combines, Russia still employs about one-third of its labor force in the agricultural sector. The value of the agricultural products is almost equally divided between crops grown and livestock raised. Principal food crops grown are grains—primarily wheat, barley, rye, and corn—legumes, potatoes, and other vegetables. The major types of livestock raised are cattle and sheep, with goats and hogs declining in number. Roughly 30 percent of all the crop acreage is devoted to growing feed grain. According to the Food and Agricultural Organization (FAO) of the United Nations, the Soviet Union was second only to Japan in 1973 in total tonnage of fish caught. It is estimated that Russia has nearly one million agricultural specialists with secondary or higher education degrees engaged in agricultural production or in some supportive area.

Politics. The U.S.S.R. consists of twenty republics, eight regions, and ten national areas. The nation's highest and most powerful body is the Supreme Soviet—a bicameral parliament consisting of the Soviet of the Union and the Soviet of Nationalities. Members of the former chamber are elected to their seats by popular vote on a basis of one deputy for every 300,000 persons; the latter chamber, whose members are also elected by popular vote, contains thirty-two deputies representing union republics, eleven representing the autonomous republics, five from each region, and one from each national area. The Supreme Soviet not only makes the laws but it also carries them out. The Supreme Soviet elects the members of the Presidium, which consists of a president, fifteen vice-presidents, twenty members, and one secretary.

The Presidium is the body that actually carries out the government's business since the Supreme Soviet meets only twice a year for a few days. The Presidium is, however, responsible to the entire Supreme Soviet. Republic Supreme Soviets run the republic governments and local Soviets the local governments. Each is also elected by popular vote, the republic Soviet members for four-year terms and the local Soviet members for two-year terms. The Soviet Union has been notorious for its rigged elections, the tight control over its citizens, and the neglect of the rights to the basic freedoms. At times, attempts have been made to ease these restrictions, but often the temporary freedoms were replaced by even harsher restrictions. However, the overall general lifestyle and freedom of the Russian people seem to be improving.

Economics. In the Soviet Union, all economic planning is conducted by the state, which also controls the supply, production, and distribution of all materials, commodities, and products. There is no private sector of the economy since all production is publicly owned. Heavy industry has been the nation's major economic emphasis for many years, but recently consumer goods and services have been receiving increased attention. Domestic trade, however, is also a virtual state monopoly, with only the collective farm markets not completely under their jurisdiction. All other retail sales outlets are either state owned and operated, or communally owned and operated but state controlled. Market prices for almost all goods are set by the government. Since its inception, the Soviet Union has been an economically independent nation. Foreign exports, for example, consumed only 3 percent of the nation's industrial and agricultural output in 1970. Also a monopoly, the Soviet Union's foreign trade has consistently led to a positive balance of payments. Major exports from Russia consist of machinery and equipment, metal ores and their products, fuels, and forestry products. Major imports are machinery, equipment, and consumer goods (primarily foodstuffs).

Communications. The official and major language of the Soviet Union is Russian, but there are thirteen other languages, each having more than one million native speakers. Mass communications are entirely state controlled and under strict censorship. The newspapers are divided into four levels—all-union, republic and region, city, and local. Of the approximate 8,500 newspapers published in Russia, only twenty-six are all-union, but together they amount to almost one-half of the total circulation. The majority of the papers, nearly 7,500, are local papers, but they comprise only about one-fifth of the total circulation.

The radio network of the Soviet Union extends to even the remotest of areas; UNESCO statistics state that three thousand stations transmit to over one hundred five million receivers. The radio programs of the Soviet Union are not meant to be entertaining, and the majority of the programs are devoted to news and educational and cultural topics. The television network is also widely distributed throughout the country with over 1,400 stations broadcasting to some forty-five million receivers. Also like radio, the television programming is not centered on entertainment, but rather on political, social, and cultural ideologies. The major problem of the mass media area is a shortage of television receivers. Many of the television receivers have controls for selecting one of the several simultaneous language transmissions broadcast by Russian television stations.

Technology. The Soviet Union is one of the few nations of the world truly in the Space Age and currently engaged in a space race with the United States to determine the leadership in space exploration. The nation places a high priority on science, research and development, and inventive endeavors. As noted earlier, science and technology dominate education. Students who receive the highest honors are employed in many research institutes located throughout the country, where varieties of topics are being researched and studied. The nation's industries employ the latest automated and computerized techniques; the agricultural sector is also highly mechanized. Therefore, the conclusion is drawn that much of the Soviet Union is at the high level of technological development. In fact, the nation employed over one million scientists and engineers and spent over $17 million on research and experimental development in 1972.

United Kingdom of Great Britain and Northern Ireland

Education. The United Kingdom requires that all children between the age of five and sixteen receive a full-time education. Some 95 percent of these children attend publicly funded schools from nursery through the university. The compulsory attendance law is strictly adhered to, and, as a result, the nation's literacy rate is about 100 percent. Bureaucratically, the education system is controlled at the ministerial level of the four state comprising the United Kingdom—England, Wales, Scotland, and Northern Ireland. The public schools are administered either by central government departments, local educational authorities, or voluntary organizations, usually religious. In England, Scotland, and Wales, the curricula come under the jurisdiction of the local education authorities, although Her Majesty's Inspectors advise and review. Assistance with the curricula is also received through the Schools' Council for Curriculum and Examinations. In Northern Ireland, the curricula are the responsibility of the School's Curriculum Committee, with assistance from the Schools Council. Special problems currently being given priority attention include poverty, overcrowding, and antiquated facilities within the school system. Apparently, all areas of the curriculum are equally emphasized, with no one area receiving more attention or considered more prestigious than any other. This observation is supported by the fact that at the university level about 45 percent of the students are taking arts or social studies courses, while just over 40 percent are taking science and technology courses. The remaining students are concerned primarily with medicine and agriculture. Higher education is expanding rapidly in Britain; the number of universities has increased to forty-five from seventeen in 1945. The number of students attending higher education institutions more than doubled in the ten years between 1961 and 1971, increasing from just under 200,000 students to almost 475,000 students during that period.

Food Production. The total land mass of Britain is relatively small for the nation's population. As a result, the nation must import nearly half its food, despite the fact that nearly 80 percent of the land is devoted to agricultural enterprises. One of the problems lies in the quality of the land. Much of it, nearly three-fourths in Scotland for example, is suitable only as grazing or pasture land. Less than 3 percent of the population is engaged in agriculture—the lowest percentage in the world—and the sector contributes less than 3 percent to the gross national product. There are over 290,000 farms in the United Kingdom, but only about 165,000 are full-time enterprises. The average size for the full-time units is 232 acres. Each year Britain loses more of its land to urban expansion, but so far, increased yields have compensated for the loss. The major crops grown in the country are wheat, barley, oats, potatoes, sugar beets, fruits, and vegetables. The major types of livestock raised include sheep, cattle, pigs, and poultry. Britain's agricultural production is highly mechanized; it has one of the highest tractor densities in the world—one for every thirty-five acres of cultivable land, or an estimated 465,000 tractors in use.

Government involvement in the agricultural sector is realized through ministries and departments of agriculture in the individual states. It consists of such areas as: annual reviews to ensure common agricultural policy and set price guarantees; providing for and/or guaranteeing credit for agriculturally related improvements; legislating various land tenure systems; regulating the markets of selected products; and contributing to research and education related to agriculture. The value of the United Kingdom's fishing industry harvest in 1972 totaled over one hundred million English pounds. But even then, they had to import another one hundred million English pounds worth of fish to fill the demand.

Politics. The United Kingdom is a monarchial state and an independent member of the Commonwealth, a body of nations all of whom recognize the Queen of England as titular ruler. The power of the throne is no longer a major political force, however; the government of the United Kingdom is run by the prime minister, his cabinet, and Parliament. The prime minister heads the government, has the right to select his ministerial cabinet, and traditionally heads the political party that seated the majority in the House of Commons—one of the two houses of Parliament. The other house is the House of Lords, whose members consist of all hereditary lords over twenty-one, those peerages conferred by the Crown, the Archbishops of Canterbury and York, the Bishops of London, Purham, and Winchester, and the twenty-one senior bishops of the Church of England. An average of one hundred fifty lords attend the parliamentary proceedings daily. The House of Commons is an elected body, and in 1974 had 630 seats—511 for England, 71 for Scotland, 36 for Wales, and 12 for Northern Ireland.

The Parliament is the main legislative body of the nation and sits for five years although it can be dissolved and a general election called for any time prior to the expiration date. Local government is headed by a secretary of state in both Wales and Scotland. Northern Ireland is currently in a transitional period at best, and a state of turmoil at worst, and therefore its local government is difficult to define. Lesser local governments, usually in the form of councils for controlling county, district, city, and so on, are all elected by the populace. The civil service of the United Kingdom numbers close to 700,000 persons.

Economics. The major factor in the United Kingdom's economy is its foreign trade; it ranks fourth in the world behind the United States, West Germany, and Japan. The nation is responsible for more than 6 percent of all the world's trade, importing over 10 percent of the world's exports of primary products and, in return, exporting over 10 percent of the world's total exported manufactured goods. Obviously, the manufacturing sector is a major factor in the economy; it contributes more than 30 percent to the nation's total gross domestic product.

Major imports are foodstuffs, raw materials for manufacturing, and processed goods needed in manufacturing activities, mainly textile yarns and chemicals. Major exports are transportation vehicles, electrical equipment, machinery, and textiles. Governmental control of the economy is administered through the Treasury, the Departments of Trade and Industry, Employment, Environment, and the Ministry of Agriculture, Fisheries, and Food. Britain's railways, coal, steel, gas, and electricity industries are under government control, and, in 1975, Parliament nationalized its aircraft and shipbuilding industries. The major advisory group is the National Economic Development Board, which consists of members of government, management, and the unions.

The United Kingdom has a graduated income tax structure, the purpose of which is to help lessen disparities of wealth among its citizens. The private sector of the British economy has major involvements in world banking, it supplies capital for development to the industrial sector through three separate private corporations, it controls a major stock exchange, and it provides economic opportunities through investment trust companies and unit trusts.

Communications. The vast majority of the United Kingdom's approximately fifty-six million people speak English, the official national language. However, Welsh is the first language of about 20 percent of the people in Wales, and some Gaelic is still spoken in Scotland. Britain publishes approximately one hundred thirty daily and Sunday newspapers, which have an average daily circulation of about 1.8 million, and over 1,100 additional weekly newspapers. Nine of the papers are national, all of which are published in London, although they also have regional editions published elsewhere. There are over eight hundred regional papers in England, about one hundred fifty in Scotland, over sixty in Wales, and just forty-five in Northern Ireland. Private corporations and individuals own the papers, and freedom of the press is a guaranteed right of the nation.

Radio and television programming is regulated by the Minister of Posts and Telecommunications. Two public independent organizations, the British Broadcasting Corporation (BBC) and the Independent Broadcasting Authority (IBA) together control the country's nationwide television and radio networks. These two communication bodies are required by constitutional law to provide informational, educational, and entertainment programs to the populace. Television programming averages about twelve hours a day, and radio programming ranges from nine to twenty hours a day, depending upon the station. In 1972, the United Kingdom had, according to UNESCO, 397 radio stations and 401 television stations broadcasting to over thirty-seven million radios and almost seventeen million television receivers.

Technology. Many of the societies of the United Kingdom are at the high level of technological development, and, as a whole, the nation is highly mechanized. Technological and scientific research and development receive much support, with funds being supplied by the government, public corporations, private industry, and independent trusts and foundations. Government-sponsored research is being conducted in such diverse fields as the military, medicine, space, agriculture, communications, pollution, nuclear energy, and transportation.

Dissemination of research and development information, as well as some direct research itself, is conducted primarily under the auspices of Britain's Royal Societies, of which the most prominent are The Royal Society of London for Improving Natural Knowledge; the Royal Society for the Encouragement of Arts, Manufactures, and Commerce; the Royal Institution; and the British Association for the Advancement of Science. The latest available United Nations figures show that in 1968 the United Kingdom employed over 43,500 scientists and engineers and over 106,000 technicians in research and development activities. In 1970, expenditures for research and development were over $2.5 million.

Japan

Education. Japan established a compulsory, three-year, primary education system in 1871, and by 1906 it had an estimated 95 percent attendance rate. After World War II, the free, compulsory education years were extended to nine—six at the primary level and three at what is now commonly called the junior high-school level. The percentage of students reported to be continuing their education beyond the compulsory age of fifteen varies greatly depending upon the source. Somewhere between 60 percent and 85 percent of the students complete an additional three years of secondary school, and from 10 percent to 25 percent enter a college or university. An

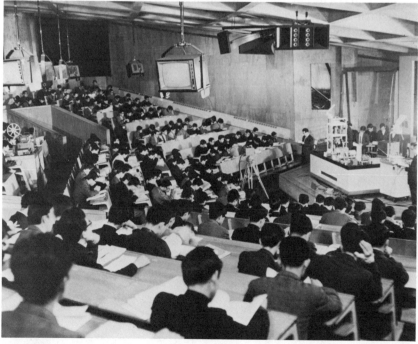

Primary, Secondary, and University classes in Japan. Note the apparent extensive use of television in all three classrooms. Photo courtesy of Consulate General of Japan, Chicago.

estimated 99.9 percent of the nation's children attend the educational facilities, and, therefore, the literacy rate is said to be nearly 100 percent.

Approximately four hundred four-year colleges and universities and
almost five hundred two-, or three-year junior colleges comprise Japan's
higher education system. A half dozen of the universities, however, enjoy
especially high prestige since admission to one is seen as the first stepping-
stone to an ultimate high-level position in the government, or industry, or
both. Preparation and competition for entrance into one of these highly
rated institutions are so intense for Japanese students and their families
that the period has been given the name "examination hell."

Virtually all of Japan's primary and secondary schools—over 95
percent of them—are free, public, coeducational, and locally administered
by a school board, whose members are selected by the local elected official.
The Ministry of Education is primarily responsible for national coordination,
budgeting of national government funds to education, and for legislature
regarding education.

Food Production. Less than one-third of Japan's total population lives
in rural areas, and approximately 14 percent of the nation's labor force is
employed in agricultural production. Some 90 percent of the land holdings
used for agriculture are privately owned, but extremely small; the average
holding is less than three acres. This has caused the rapid mechanization
of the farm sector to emphasize small, often hand-operated machinery,
rather than the giant tractors and harvesters prevalent in most other highly
mechanized countries; however, about 283,000 tractors are being used in

Large-scale farming such as shown in this picture is extremely rare in Japan.
Photo courtesy of Consulate General of Japan, Chicago.

Japan. Examples of the small machines include rice threshers, hullers, and polishers, cultivators, power insecticide sprayers, milking machines, and irrigation pumps. Accompanying the mechanization were an increased use of fertilizers, herbicides, insecticides, and improved seed, all leading to a large increase in the productivity of the agricultural sector.

However, foodstuffs remain a major import. Rice is the major food crop, but other. cereal grains and soybeans have been declining in total acreage under cultivation because of an increased demand for fruits, vegetables, and dairy products. Few pastures are available for livestock grazing, and few acres are devoted to feedgrains. Consequently, commercial livestock raising of dairy cattle, hogs, and chickens must rely upon commercial feeds. Japan's fishing industry—over 50 percent of which consists of small, family units and whose tonnage of catch in 1973 was the highest in the world—adds much to the nation's food production. Fish is commonly eaten at most meals; served in a variety of ways, including raw, it contributes a substantial portion of the protein in the Japanese diet. The fishing industry, along with the nation's other food production industries, can produce more than 80 percent of the required food.

Politics. Japan is a constitutional monarchy with a bicameral parliament elected by the populace. Since the end of World War II, the role of the emperor has been reduced to a ceremonial one, but he continues to assert a stabilizing influence on the Japanese people. The Diet consists of a House of Representatives, which has 486 members, and the House of Councillors, with 250 members. Both houses are elected by popular vote, but the House of Representatives is the dominating body. It has the right to dissolve the cabinet with a vote of no confidence, and its viewpoint becomes the one followed in the event of irresolvable disputes between the two houses. The House of Councillors must also act upon budgets and treaty ratifications within thirty days of their receipt, or the decisions of the House of Representatives are retained.

The prime minister, the executive head of the government is selected from the members of the Diet. The prime minister selects his own cabinet, but the majority are required to be members of the Diet. Local governments exist at the prefect, city, town, and village levels. Japan is divided into forty-six prefectures, with each prefecture administered by an elected governor and a unicameral assembly. The terms of office for both the governors and the assembly are four years. City governments are controlled by an elected mayor and his assembly, whose number might range from thirty to one hundred depending on the population of the city. Town and village governments are headed by a mayor and a town or village council. These officials are also elected to four-year terms.

Economics. Japan specializes in heavy industry, as well as being a heavily industrialized nation. Its steel production ranks third behind the United States and the Soviet Union. It is the world leader in shipbuilding, an enterprise undertaken initially to provide transportation for the nation's large import–export business. As the number one producer of motorcycles

Building housing the Japanese Diet. Photo by Edward C. Pytlik.

and bicycles in the world, it is second, behind the United States, in automobile production. The domestic sales of these cars have generated an extensive road building program throughout the nation. Japan is also a major world producer of such diverse things as petrochemicals, synthetic fabrics and leather, electronic equipment, cameras, aircraft, and space technology.

This heavy industrial development has not been without its consequences, however. Currently, one of Japan's major problems is the pollution of its air and water, caused primarily by the industries and secondarily by the nation's rapid urban sprawl. Japan's major exports are machinery, chemicals, textiles, ships, cameras, automobiles, and synthetic fabrics. The major imports to Japan are foodstuffs, raw materials for manufacturing, petroleum, and petroleum products. The United States has been Japan's favorite exporting country, as well as its favorite importing country, with nearly 30 percent of each total either going to or coming from the United States. Since 1965, Japan traditionally has had an export surplus—the total value of its exports has exceeded the total value of its imports—obviously a favorable position. Japan's per capita gross domestic product in 1973 was $3,782, according to U.N. statistics. Also in 1973, Japan's gross national product was the third largest in the world. Private enterprise dominates both the industrial and the economic sectors of Japan.

Communications. Japanese, the official national language, is used and understood by all native Japanese. Other major languages spoken in Japan are Ryukyuan, Korean, Chinese, and English. Approximately seventy mil-

Japan is the world's largest shipbuilder, an industry created to provide transportation for its vast trade industry. Photo courtesy of Consulate General of Japan, Chicago.

lion radios can be found in Japanese homes, tuned to one of some 890 public and private stations, whose networks completely cover the nation. In 1973, there were over twenty-four million television sets in Japan; approximately 97 percent of the households contained one of these sets. The country has more than four thousand television stations. Japan's radio and television operations are controlled by the NHK—a semiautonomous government agency. The majority of Japan's radio stations are members of one of three networks, one of which is concerned primarily with news, entertainment, and programs of general listener interest. The other two networks concentrate on educational and cultural programs, although all three networks broadcast all types of programs. Daily air time is between eighteen and nineteen hours. The television stations are similarly organized into networks. One network emphasizes news, entertainment, and cultural programs, while the other two networks broadcast programs that are more than 80 percent educational. Air time for the three television networks ranges from twelve to nineteen hours.

Five national newspapers dominate the printed news media—each has a circulation exceeding one million; three of the papers have a general format, and the other two concentrate on economic news. Modern micro-

Japan's large electronics industry provides much of the paraphernalia for the nation's vast electronic communications network. Photo courtesy of Consulate General of Japan, Chicago.

wave transmissions facilities permit the publication of these five papers in several locations simultaneously. Local newspapers, published in almost every metropolitan area and prefecture capital, are devoted primarily to local and regional news rather than to the national and international news covered extensively in the national papers.

Technology. The majority of Japan's societies, both rural and urban, are at the high level of technological development. In fact, it is well within the ranks of the ten most technologically developed nations in the world. Japan is well aware of the value of modern science and technology and the role they have played in its resurgence as a major world power. Both the government and private industry have built new universities, new research institutes, and new research facilities. However, poor facilities have still forced many Japanese researchers abroad to seek a better environment in which to work, particularly in basic research studies. Even so, Japan's research expenditures run into the millions of dollars, and the nation is a world leader in computer usage as well as in research for peaceful uses of nuclear energy. In 1972, Japan had some 314,000 scientists and engineers working in research and development projects amounting to $4.80 million.

Summary

The levels of technological societies are especially important to those persons concerned with increasing the development of a lesser developed society, regardless of whether the development be in the economic, the technological, the industrial, or in any other societal sector. Before such assistance can be useful, the current levels must be established to serve as a foundation from which the development can evolve. If the society being aided is at a level far below or far above that which is assumed, then the assistance provided will be valueless. Three general levels of technological societies have been identified—the tribal, the transitional or emerging, and the highly developed or postindustrial levels.

Six sectors were selected to provide the information for placing a society at one of the three general levels: education, food production, governmental or political, economic, communications, and technological sectors. Each of these sectors is in some way related to each of the other sectors, and, therefore, by researching six sectors instead of just one, a more concise picture of the real level emerges. Also, we can establish a more exact location of the society within its general societal level. Further, since the sectors are all related, assistance to one area will affect the other areas as well, but the effect is not always positive. Thus, knowing the levels of the other five sectors, we can more easily anticipate problems and more easily try to solve them.

Tribal societies, also known as primitive societies, are the lowest technological societies. Generally, their educational system is limited to the basic "life" skills and traditions; their food production practices involve everyone, and are not unlike those of the Neolithic farmer of three thousand years ago; their leadership is usually tyrannical and local; they have a barter economy; their communications are verbal and local; and they possess a low level of technological development.

Transitional or emerging societies are the most common level of the technological societies. Generally, a transitional or emerging society has a formal education system, but less than 50 percent of the society's children attend for any useful length of time. Agricultural production employs a large portion of the labor market and is mixed, with many farmers practicing traditional techniques, but many others using at least some modern methods and technologies. Leadership and control often come from outside the society, even at the local level. A monetary system has usually replaced the bartering system, but other economic factors such as trade, markets, and ownership are low. Radio and word of mouth provide the principal means of communications, with newspapers ranking third because of a generally low literacy rate. And technologically these societies are at the intermediate level.

Highly developed or postindustrial societies are the highest level of the technological societies. Generally, these societies have a compulsory, free, public education system for all children from the approximate ages of five to fifteen. Food production is highly mechanized and employs only a small amount of the total labor force. The government is structured in such a manner that everyone has a voice at all levels, from local to national. Economic productivity is the highest in the world. Communications are virtually total, with modern mass-communication systems relaying world information almost instantaneously. They are at the high level of technological development.

DISCUSSION QUESTIONS

1. Did tribal societies just happen to have developed in remote areas, did people choose to live there, or were they driven by enemies? Give reasons for your answer.

2. Should today's world attempt to "free" tribal societies from their traditional way of life by exposing them to modern technologies? Or should they be left to their own private world? Explain your answer.

3. Six societal sectors were chosen as prime indicators for establishing the level of a technological society. Discuss alternative sectors that could or should have been used. Discuss alternative methods for establishing the level of a technological society.

4. The case studies ·in this chapter were designed to illustrate various levels in the development of technological societies. A common definition for development is progress. If you agree with this definition, then what is progress? If you disagree, then what is development?

5. As noted in the text, transitional and highly developed societies are often discussed in terms of whole nations. What are the advantages of discussing the societies in this manner? What are the disadvantages?

BIBLIOGRAPHY

Aurell, G. E.; Barth, H. A.; Chaffee, F. H.; Cort, A. S.; Elam, D. W.; Fasano, V. J.; Forker, S. C.; Moeller, P. W.; and Weaver, J. O. *Area Handbook for Japan*. Washington, D.C.: U.S. Government Printing Office, September 1969.

Beasley, W. G. *The Modern History of Japan*. 2d ed. New York: Praeger Publishers, 1974.

Bishop, J., Jr.; Carroll, R.; Steele, R.; and Van Voorst, D. "To Have and Have Not." *Newsweek,* September 15, 1975, pp. 37–40, 45.

Black, J. K.; Blutstein, H. I.; McMorris, D. S.; Munson, F. P.; Townsend, C.; and Weil, T. E. *Area Handbook for Peru*. Washington, D.C.: U.S. Government Printing Office, March 1972.

Boucher, A. A.; Elpern, S. J.; Giloane, W.; Keefe, E. K.; Moore, I. M.; Ogden, T. L.; Peters, S.; Prevas, J. P.; Walstrom, N. E.; and White, E. T. *Area Handbook for the Soviet Union*. Washington, D.C.: U.S. Government Printing Office, 1971.

Britain 1974: An Official Handbook. London: Her Majesty's Stationery Office, 1974.

Byford-Jones, W. *Four Faces of Peru*. New York: Roy Publishers, 1967.

Cowley, C. *Fabled Tribe: A Voyage to Discover the River Bushmen of the Okavango Swamps*. New York: Atheneum, 1968.

Cunningham, G. *Britain and the World in the Seventies: A Collection of Fabian Essays*. London: Weidenfeld & Nicolson, 1970.

Dobert, M.; Marvin, B.; McDonald, G. C.; McLoughlin, J.; Moeller, P. W.; and Nelson, H. D. *Area Handbook for the United Republic of Cameroon*. Washington, D.C.: U.S. Government Printing Office, 1974.

Folan, J. B.; Hopkins, M. G.; Parker, M. B.; Shinn, R.; and Younglof, R. L. *Area Handbook for India*. Washington, D.C.: U.S. Government Printing Office, May 1970.

Georgiyev, M. [*Soviet Union Today*], J. Riordan, trans. Moscow: Progress Publishers, 1971.

Isenberg, I., ed. *Japan: Asian Power*. New York: The H. W. Wilson Co., 1971.

Just, P.; MacDonald, J. E.; Martindale, K. W.; Record, J.; Shinn, R; Townsend, C.; Vreeland, M.; and Whitaker, D. P. *Area Handbook for Japan*. 3d ed. Washington, D.C.: U.S. Government Printing Office, 1974.

Lathrop, D. "The Upper Amazon." *Ancient Peoples and Places* 70, G. Daniel, gen. ed. Southampton, England. Thames & Hudson, 1970.

LeVine, V. T. *The Cameroon Federal Republic*. 2d ed. Ithaca, N.Y.: Cornell University Press, 1971.

MacLeish, K. "The Tasadays: Stone Age Cavemen of Mindanao." *National Geographic,* 142 no. 2 (August 1972): 219–49.

Meggers, B. J. *Amazonia: Man and Culture in a Counterfeit Paradise*. Chicago: Aldine-Atherton, 1971.

Nance, J. *The Gentle Tasaday: A Stone Age People in the Philippine Rain Forest*. New York: Harcourt Brace Jovanovich, 1975.

Shaw, E. M. *Man in Southern Africa: The Hottentots*. Cape Town, S. Africa: The South African Museum, 1972.

Tomlin, E. W. F. *Japan*. New York: Walker & Co., 1973.

UNESCO Statistical Yearbook, 1973. Paris: The UNESCO Press, 1974.

United Nations, Department of Economics and Social Affairs. *Population and Vital Statistics Report* (Series A), 24, no. 4 (Oct. 1, 1972).

United Nations Statistical Yearbook, 1974. New York: United Nations, 1975.

Chapter 7
The Transfer of Technology: An Overview

Introduction

Technology may be transferred in many ways and for a variety of reasons, but the three most prominent situations are the following:

1. Technology may be transferred within the realms of science and technology, themselves, to further the causes of those disciplines.

2. Technology may be transferred within a societal level from one geographic location to another, usually for economic gain.

3. Technology may be transferred from one societal level to another societal level, both internationally and intranationally, ostensibly for development.

But once again the questions must be asked, What do we mean by technology? And what does "transfer of technology" really indicate? What about the steps from invention to innovation, from "technology" to a "state of the art"? Do we concern ourselves with whole, all-encompassing technologies, or specific, single-unit ones? How does the *human factor* enter into the technology transfer process? Assuming there is a difference, does the communication gap between science and technology need to be considered? How do the processes of adoption and diffusion interact with technology transfer?

To the casual observer, the transfer of technology from a highly developed society to a transitional society might seem like a simple procedure —a technology in the form of a process, a product, and/or technical manpower is sent from the highly developed society to become incorporated into the transitional society. As Pearson observed, "Donors and recipients alike tend to view modernization and development . . . as an attempt to repeat the Industrial Revolution in quick time."

The questions presented above, however, seem to indicate that the transfer process itself is not really that simple. But now we have added yet another variable: development of a transitional society. This variable brings its own set of questions, starting with the seemingly easy question, What is development? An intriguing question is, Where in the development process does technology transfer belong? Also, what areas or sectors of development are the most critical to a transitional society and therefore should receive priority? Are there specific, formal models of the transfer process that can be applied universally and internationally? Or must each transfer be treated as a unique undertaking? How are we to deal with the vast differences between the educational, economic, and communication levels of the highly developed and transitional societies? And certainly not the least important, how are people involved?

These are only a few of the many questions that can be asked about the transfer of technology. Few, if any, answers to these questions will be found in this chapter or in this text, for that matter. Development experts from all disciplines and from all societal levels have been seriously studying the transfer process and its relationship with development since the end of World War II, and although many theories, models, and projects have developed, hard and fast answers are not forthcoming. This chapter, then, will not seek solutions. Rather, it will attempt to acquaint the reader with the technology transfer process and its relationship to development.

Technology Transfer: The Process

Assumptions

Several general assumptions can be made about the transfer of technology. First, it is assumed that any technology may be transferred, regardless of the definition used for the term "technology." If it really is a technology, then it can be transferred. Whether or not it *should* be transferred, however, is an entirely different matter. For example, if technology is defined as the application of scientific principles to the production of goods and services, then the transfer of the scientific principles from one circumstance to another institutes a transfer of technology. But no judgment is made regarding the correctness or applicability of the scientific principles to the new situation or to the involved society.

Second, it is assumed that, regardless of the purpose of the transfer, a technology transfer always involves the introduction of a new technology to an area, place, position, process, and so on, where it was not currently being applied. It does not necessarily mean that the technology had been applied to the situation for the first time; nor does it mean that the technology was a new or even a recent creation. It very well could be a reintroduction of an old technology that, under the present circumstances, will create the best desired result.

Third, by its very definition, a transfer of technology will always result in a change—in process, in product, in power, in attitude, in wants and desires, and/or in situations that are either political, social, economic, or environmental. Something will change. It is the magnitude of this change, discussed in Chapter 5 and later in this chapter, that has become the most debated issue in discussions of strategies for the development of transitional countries.

Fourth, for a technology transfer to be viable in the new situation, a process of adoption and diffusion is necessary. This interrelated process is crucial to the acceptance of the new technology even though the transferred technology may clearly be superior to the old. The adoption–diffusion process must work in close tandem with the process of technology transfer in order to achieve the desired results.

Adoption and Diffusion

The adoption and diffusion of a technology transfer is not unlike the introduction, adoption, and diffusion of a new technology into a society. In many ways they are the same. In researching the adoption–diffusion process of various technological innovations on U.S. farms, Beal and Bohlen concluded that the process was not a single act, but rather a series of complex acts or stages through which an individual progressed. In addition, they further concluded that the adoption–diffusion stages had a specified order—namely, awareness, interest, evaluation, trial, and adoption (see Table 7.1).

TABLE 7.1 The Adoption Process and Sources of Information

Awareness	Interest	Evaluation	Trial	Adoption
Knows about it; lacks detail	Develops interest; gathers general information and facts	Mental trial; application to personal situation: Can I do it?	Small-scale, experimental use: How to do it!	Large-scale, continued use; satisfaction
(1) Mass media: radio, TV, newspapers, magazines	(1) Mass media	(1) Neighbors, friends	(1) Neighbors, friends	(1) Neighbors, friends
(2) Government agencies: extension agencies, vocational agencies, and so on	(2) Government agencies	(2) Government agencies	(2) Government agencies	(2) Government agencies
(3) Neighbors, friends	(3) Neighbors, friends	(3) Mass media	(3) Mass media	(3) Mass media
(4) Salesmen, dealers	(4) Salesmen, dealers	(4) Salesmen, dealers	(4) Salesmen, dealers	(4) Salesmen, dealers

Source: Reprinted by permission from *The Diffusion Process* (Special Report No. 18) by G. M. Beal and J. M. Bohlen, published by Cooperative Extension Service, Iowa State University, November 1962.

The awareness stage is the period when the individual first becomes aware of the new technique, idea, or technology. The individual has heard or read about the innovation but lacks specific information. This first stage is particularly critical to the adoption–diffusion process because of the natural human inclination to reject or at least downgrade unfamiliar things. Therefore, an individual's first contact with a new or transferred technology must be positive or else the process will be halted even before it begins. In fact, a positive feedback is critical to all stages of the process. If a negative response is received, the individual will probably end the process since few persons continue to investigate a subject that produces negative feedback.

The interest stage begins when the individual seeks further information about the new or transferred technology. This information gathering may be formal, informal, or a combination of both. Friends, neighbors, government officials, and salespersons may be questioned; data from newspapers, journal and research reports, and product manufacturers may be solicited. The evaluation stage—the mental ingestion of the information gathered—constitutes the decision-making process: How valuable is the new or transferred technology to the individual's personal situation?

If the decision at the evaluation stage was positive, the individual will proceed to the fourth, or trial, stage. Few individuals have enough confidence in the mental evaluation process to accept totally the new or transferred technology at that stage. Therefore, a pilot study, a trial run, or some small portion of the overall situation is "sacrificed" to study the effects of the new or transferred technology in a real-life situation. A complete understanding of the trial technology is vital at this stage because an incorrect application will result in poor trial results and probable rejection of the innovation even though the poor response may have been the fault of the individual and not the technology.

A positive trial, however, will usually result in a large-scale use of the new or transferred technology. This brings us to the fifth stage—adoption. The rate at which an individual progresses through the adoption–diffusion process depends upon the individual himself and the complexity of the new or transferred technology. Beal and Bohlen categorized individual differences in accepting a new idea into five general groups and superimposed them onto an adoption-time curve. They titled these five groups of individuals the innovators, early adopters, early majority, majority, and non-adopters. Profiles of these individual groups of adopters follow:

1. Innovators. These are the first individuals to adopt the new or transferred technology. A community rarely has more than two or three individuals in this category. They are the pillars of their society—the aristocrats —they are active in the community and are often powerful beyond the local society because of professional membership and even leadership in regional, state, and national organizations. On the other hand, being considered somewhat aloof, they are rarely considered as "friends and neighbors" by most of the local society. The innovators search out information from individuals and keep current in the literature published in their field. This group of individuals is often wealthy and has the financial resources to experiment with a new or transferred technology.

2. Early adopters. This second group of individuals, younger and more educated than the average member of their local society, dominates the local leadership of church, school, political, and social organizations. Like the innovators, the early adopters keep abreast of happenings and changes in their profession by reading current literature. An individual in this group is often referred to as a go-getter, a person on the move, or a person who is going places.

3. Early majority. This first large group of adopters represents the upper middle class of a local community; they are those individuals who are considered the informal leaders of a local society. These individuals may not make a decision quickly, but when they do, they are usually right. Consequently, they are respected and looked to for informal guidance. Their prestige, however, rarely goes beyond the local society.

4. Majority. This group represents the middle class of a local society and constitutes the followers rather than the leaders. They are the individuals who accept a new or transferred technology only after it has been established as significantly better than the older technology. As a group, they take few risks, are relatively inactive in the community, and do not keep up with the current literature in their field.

5. Nonadopters. Frequently these individuals are outside the mainstream of the society. They steadfastly adhere to the old methods even though another may be an undeniable improvement.

When we add the adoption–diffusion process to the process of transferring a technology, it becomes evident that the combined processes constitute a very complex situation, even if the transfer takes place within a society or between two societies at the same technological level. However, when the technological transfer takes place between different technological levels (almost always this involves a transfer from the highly developed level to a lesser developed level) as we shall see next, so many additional variables must be considered that the already complex transfer process becomes virtually unworkable.

Technology Transfer and Development

Like so many other terms in this text, "development" has been defined in innumerable ways. These definitions range in length from a single word ("progress") to paragraphs, and from the purely physical to the totally ethereal. To say that any one definition is more nearly right than all the others would be folly. However, for the sake of convenience in discussing the subject, we propose the following definition of development: *Development is a process of improving the capability of a society and its institutions to meet the increasing and changing needs and demands of the total population.* This, then, requires that a society's institutions emphasize human development—seeking social change to meet social goals rather than seeking economic, political, and/or technological development as ends in themselves.

In the past few decades, however, most of the transitional or developing countries have emphasized economic development and growth, or industrialization. Using Moore's definitions, industrialization is "becoming a part of the industrial system at least in the utilization of products"; economic development implies "structural change in addition to mere increase in output," a structural change that is political and social as well as economic. Thus, when developing nations follow a course leading toward modernization by seeking technological solutions to their national problems, they are confronted not only by technical constraints, but also by behavioral and organizational adjustments and constraints.

The purpose of this part of the text is to explore the scope of activities involved in the transfer of technology to transitional societies, to realize the complexities of the process, and to understand the magnitude of this dynamic force that is literally shaping much of the world and greatly changing the social structures.

Successful absorption of a technology transferred from one technological level to another depends, not only on the transfer of technical knowledge, but also on the ability to introduce changes in the administrative, financial, and social systems. Further, in order for successful technology transfer to occur, the right balance of these changes must be achieved. For example, the six main elements of an industrial technology can be outlined, showing the major functions of each:

1. Research: new specific and technical knowledge; ideas and innovations; research facilities.

2. Production: techniques; equipment; production control; scale of production.

3. Materials: specifications; quality control; control of supply.

4. Marketing: management of marketing and selling; characteristics and control of markets.

5. General management: business know-how; management techniques.

6. Finance: control of access to finance.

Modern industrial technology requires a complex support system of medium and small firms, each highly efficient in its own specialty and able to react to changes in the economic and technological climate. This implies that for the transfer of an industrial technology to be effective, the key elements of the technology must either be present or readily absorbed; that the enterprises engaged in the transfer must be compatible; and that managerial skills, markets, and so on must be available to support the transfer.

Hawthorne claims that the transfer process is an integral part of the overall development of industry and society. Some of the technical factors that development planners must contend with are: feasibility; selection of basic or nonbasic industries; choosing the best techniques or technical processes, levels and type of investment, marketing, management and staff development, labor market, material supplies, distribution and sales; as well as other infrastructure factors such as transportation, communication, research and development, and so on (see Figure 7.1).

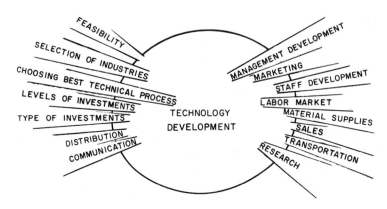

TECHNICAL FACTORS INFLUENCING TECHNOLOGY
TRANSFER FOR DEVELOPMENT

In the planning stage, all these aspects need to be explored in considerable detail. Further, such studies cannot be conducted in a vacuum; rather, they must be undertaken in light of local and national political intrigues, involvement of vested interests, myths and misconceptions, the vagaries of international politics, condition of world markets, and so on. But the most important challenge facing the developing nations is to bring into their decision-making process a social consciousness and an awareness of the social accountability of the transfer of technology.

How should this social consciousness and awareness of social accountability be channeled into the transfer of technology and, thus, into development in general? This question is the heart of the current debate among persons who are concerned with development throughout the world. Recently, for example, many development planners have been emphasizing the need to develop the rural societies rather than modernize the industrial sectors of transitional societies. The advocates of rural development base their arguments on the following factors:

1. To date, the modernization of the industrial sector of transitional countries has failed to aid the total population.

2. Modern industry is capital intensive rather than labor intensive and, therefore, is not useful to countries that have a surplus of labor and a shortage of capital. This condition identifies the plight of nearly every developing nation.

3. The failure of agricultural production to keep pace with population expansion is approaching the critical stage throughout the world.

4. An emphasis on rural development would: (a) serve the total population either directly or indirectly, (b) provide rural jobs and help eradicate mass migrations to urban areas, (c) increase food production, and (d) stimulate the overall national economy.

Schumacher, for example, emphasizes that "development does not start with goods; it starts with people and their education, organization, and discipline. Without these three, all resources remain latent, untapped, potential." He further states that technologies introduced into a society will be beneficial and thrive only if they are compatible with the educational level of the people, and would be truly valuable to that society only if they promoted the further advancement of education, organization, and discipline.

Schumacher disagrees with the basic format of the vast majority of the past developmental schemes, that were aimed at modernizing the industrial sector of developing nations. He contends that since the vast majority of the population of developing countries lives in the rural areas (70–80 percent is not an uncommon figure), then the major goal of development should be the creation of an agro-industrial structure that bypasses the big cities and maximizes work opportunities for the rural unemployed and underemployed. Schumacher explains his reasoning:

> The technology of production by the masses, making use of the best modern knowledge and experience, is conducive to decentralization, compatible with the laws of ecology, gentle in its use of scarce resources, and designed to serve the human person instead of making him the servant of machines. I have named it intermediate technology to signify that it is vastly superior to the primitive technology of bygone ages but at the same time much simpler, cheaper and freer than the super-technology of the rich. (Schumacher, 1973, p. 145)

Owens and Shaw agree with Schumacher that labor-intensive, intermediate technologies are needed rather than the development of large, capital-intensive industries. When discussing the agricultural sector, Owens and Shaw claim that "the kind of machines needed in small farm, labor-intensive agriculture are those which complement human effort rather than replace it, that is, the Japanese rather than the United States style of farm mechanization."

In discussing the industrial sector of a developing nation, Owens and Shaw suggest that, from an economic standpoint, emphasis should be placed on output per dollar invested rather than output per worker. They state that "industrial development policy . . . should be redesigned in favor of . . . labor-intensive industries" and that "whenever there is a technological choice for a factory, the poor countries should encourage the system of production which uses the fewest machines and creates the most jobs."

Case Studies

Thus far in this chapter we have been concerned primarily with theoretical frameworks and models. The following two case studies, however, describe actual attempts at development and technological transfer. The first[1] out-lines the purposes, organizational framework, major components, and results of three integrated rural development projects in Ethiopia. The second is an in-depth look at an attempt to introduce farm tractors in rural Pakistan.

A Comparison of Three Major Integrated Rural Development Projects in Ethiopia

Introduction. Ethiopia is a nation of subsistence farmers. Approximately 90 percent of the labor force is employed in agriculturally related activities, and about 85 percent of the country's twenty-five million people are engaged in subsistence-level or near-subsistence-level farming. Prior to the Land Reform Proclamation in March 1975, the average land holding per rural resident was less than one hectare (2.47 acres). Ethiopia is also a nation whose economy is firmly entrenched in agricultural production. The agricultural and agriculturally dependent sectors account for nearly 90 percent of the gross domestic product, and 95 percent of the value of the country's exports are agricultural products. The estimated per capita income is $75 (U.S.) per year.

Despite these rather overwhelming statistics and the fact that Ethiopia has been engaged in comprehensive economic planning since 1958, it was not until the third five-year plan (1968–1974) that the small farmer became a focal point for agricultural development. It was decided that a "package" approach should be undertaken in those specific areas of the country that hold the greatest potential for success. The package approach was defined as ". . . concentrating the relevant elements of development within a clearly defined geographical area in a coordinated manner."

The first three projects implemented under the third five-year plan were the Chilalo Agricultural Development Unit (CADU), begun in 1967, the Wolamo Agricultural Development Unit (WADU), started in 1970, and the Ada District Development Project (ADDP), which began operations in 1972. The goals of these three integrated rural development projects were:

1. Raise the real incomes of small farm households, mainly [those] with holdings of twenty hectares and less . . . .

2. Elicit participation of small farmers and local government authorities in their development efforts.

---

[1] Based on data from Tesfai Tecle, "The Evolution of Alternative Rural Development Strategies in Ethiopia: Implications for Employment and Income Distribution," African Rural Employment Research Network. Published by Department of Agricultural Economics, Michigan State University, East Lansing, Michigan, 1975. Reprinted by permission.

3. Control adverse employment effects and . . . generate new additional employment opportunities.

4. Narrow the prevailing income disparities by directing efforts mainly toward farmers in the lower brackets.

5. Search continuously for suitable methods for furthering rural development nationwide.

6. Provide data for formulating better projects in the future.

Organizational Framework. The CADU project, begun as a joint Swedish–Ethiopian government project in 1967, operated as an autonomous section of the ministry of agriculture until the formation of the Extension and Project Implementation Department (EPID) in 1971, at which time it shifted to EPID's jurisdiction, but retained much of its autonomy. CADU is administered by an executive director who reports to the head of EPID.

The project's programs are implemented through four major departments—experimentation, extension and training, infrastructure, and common services—and three autonomous divisions—marketing, seed, and cattle breeding. In addition to implementing those functions, a planning and evaluation unit conducts feasibility studies for potential future activities and develops feedback systems to improve the management of the project.

WADU is financially backed by a five-year loan, effective in April 1970, from the World Bank. The loan was issued because there were indications that the local administration was ready to support the project without reservation, and because there was a belief that the population to be affected was very enthusiastic about the plan. Like CADU, WADU is an autonomous unit of EPID and is administered by an executive director. Major components of the project are administered by the planning and evaluation, and trials units, and the development, livestock, marketing, credit and cooperatives divisions.

The ADDP program was initiated in 1972 as a joint Ethiopian government and USAID project, designed to serve primarily as an area in which to experiment with rural development approaches that had not yet been attempted by either CADU or WADU. The project was developed to serve as a catalytic innovator, utilizing and coordinating the facilities and programs of local and national government and private agencies.

Originally, the ADDP was also an autonomous unit of EPID that was administered by a project manager and that had adapted a framework similar to both CADU and WADU to provide the farmers with information on agricultural extension, some economics, credit, marketing, cooperatives, promotion, road building, and rural water supply. However, a 1974 evaluation resulted in a major revision of the project's planning. ADDP's autonomy has been greatly reduced; it is now closely controlled by EPID. Its high-level staff and budget allocations have been significantly reduced, and the experimental portion of its activities and the aim to serve as a testing ground for a variety of rural development approaches have been de-emphasized.

Major Components. CADU has emphasized three areas: agricultural extension, specifically the development of an improved technological package and the dissemination of new practices; input distribution, specifically in establishing farm credit and lending policies and procedures; and output marketing.

The improved technological package research was conducted emphasizing wheat and barley crops, livestock production, and improved, labor-intensive, farm implements. The latter research developed prototypes of ox-drawn plows, harrows and carts, as well as stationary threshers and cleaners. However, the adoption of the prototypes by small farmers has been extremely poor because of environmental variations between localities, cost, and farmer preferences toward the shape and weight of the implements. For example, they find the plow too heavy to carry on their shoulders. A notable exception to this rejection has been the ox-drawn harrow; about seven hundred harrows were sold in 1974 alone.

The livestock research program has focused on upgrading the local breeds of dairy cattle through artificial insemination with European breeds. As a result, the average yield per lactation has increased from about three hundred liters to nearly one thousand liters. Research in beef cattle production has so far been neglected because there is only a very limited domestic market and the export potential seems equally poor.

CADU's crop production research, focusing on variety and fertilizer trials, has produced notable results. On the better farms in the CADU, wheat yields have been tripled from 1967 to 1973 by using improved seed varieties, fertilizer, and improved cultivation practices.

Dissemination of the new practices is conducted through a model-farmer scheme and demonstration plots. The chosen model farmer works closely with the extension agent, using new practices as they become available and serving as a demonstrator for the other farmers in the area. Field days, when processes and experiments are described to all the farmers, are frequently held in the model farmers' fields as well as on demonstration plots strategically located near major roads, market places, and churches.

Based on the number of farmers it has assisted in using improved agricultural practices, CADU fell a little short of its target for 1971–1974. From a peak of 14,164 in 1971, active participation declined to 12,644 in 1972, and 13,302 in 1973, before jumping to 25,205 in 1974, even though the project area was expanded during that time. It has been suggested that the declining participation was caused by fluctuations in the price of wheat, the risk associated with credit, problems related to land tenure, and weaknesses in the dissemination strategy. Regarding the latter reason, it was found, for example, that some farmers believed that one fertilizer application was enough for several seasons; others believed that inputs provided by CADU were not adaptable to other local conditions, and therefore not profitable.

There is a nationwide lack of public and private credit for small farmers in Ethiopia. Even the Agro-Industrial Development Bank, established in 1970 to help meet the credit needs of *all* farmers, has neglected the small farmer. It is not surprising, then, to learn that during the first two years of CADU's credit program, the larger land owners were the major beneficiaries. There are several strict requirements: All creditors must secure two guarantors, one of which must be the landowner if the farmer is a tenant; they must produce down payments and a signed lease agreement; and, to further ensure repayment, all participating farmers in a model area are held responsible as a group to ensure that the annual repayment is never below 90 percent. These credit eligibility requirements, plus the fact that tenant farmers found it less rewarding financially to adopt the new technologies (since as much as one-half of the gross output went to the landowner), seem to be the two major reasons for the poor rate of small-farmer participation in the credit program.

WADU's major components consist of the dissemination of new practices, farm credit, output marketing, and its settlement scheme. WADU's program on adaptive research is very limited. It relies on CADU, the Institute of Agricultural Research, and the Debre Zeit Agricultural Experimentation Station for the major part of its needs in new inputs, although it does have a small trials unit that works primarily on cereals.

WADU opposes the centralization of dissemination activities around the model farmers. It believes that the model-farmer approach results in only a few farmers benefiting from the demonstration process, and it seems to give preferential treatment to a selected few. WADU's process involves specific demonstrations that take place directly in the field of a specific farmer who is selected by a joint effort of the extension agent and a committee of area farmers. The extension agents, incidentally, had been selected from within the local committee they were expected to serve, were trained at the training center, and were then returned to the local area. WADU's target was to reach six thousand farmers by 1975. By 1973, it had already reached seven thousand farmers, and it was anticipated that a total of ten thousand would have been reached by the end of 1975.

WADU's lending policies for its credit program are significantly different from CADU's. First, WADU does not explicitly restrict eligibility in terms of tenancy and farm size. Second, signed leases are not required for tenant farmers. The only requirement is two guarantors. Third, WADU provides cash loans for consumption purposes to eliminate the need for local farmers to borrow from local moneylenders, whose interest rates are exhorbitant.

Unfortunately, the results of the two credit programs are the same. Like CADU, only a small percentage of small farmers are benefiting from the credit program, with the majority of the loans going to the large landowners. It is theorized that even though the credit eligibility and collateral requirements are more lenient, the tenant farmers decided it was still not worth taking the risk. WADU has had an exceptionally high repayment rate, 97 percent for its first three years of operation. As is the case with CADU, the WADU small farmers and/or tenants have a better repayment record than the large landowners.

The WADU marketing, credit, and cooperative division handles both cash crops and subsistence crops. WADU's marketing strategy is to let the farmer participate in any risk of unexpected price declines. This is accomplished by making first payments amounting to 60 percent of the anticipated sale price when a farmer submits his crop to WADU. A second payment is made if gains made selling the crop exceed the storage and selling costs. Since this is not often the case, the farmers were beginning to become disillusioned with the plan until a government-sponsored price freeze was declared in 1975.

One of the major government objectives in initiating WADU was to develop the cheapest means of undertaking viable planned settlement programs. The plan for the first five years of WADU was to reorganize the settlement plots of the seven hundred households already settled and to settle another 1,050 highland families on five-hectare plots, two hectares of which were to be readied for planting before the settlers moved in. Although the reorganization took place on time, only 747 new families had been accommodated by mid-1975.

The presence of the old settlers has been a hindrance to the project since they had become accustomed to grazing their livestock on the unoccupied land surrounding their settlements. Since the loss of this land meant they had to reduce the number of their livestock, the old settlers were opposed to a planned layout of settlement plots. The reorganization would also disrupt social and cultural structures that had been carried along with their original migration from the highlands.

Unlike the other integrated rural development projects, ADDP is fortunate in having an agricultural experiment station operating within its area —The Debre Zeit Agricultural Experiment Station. ADDP has worked very closely with the station in developing technological packages for farmers suitable for the varying ecological zones of the region. To disseminate to the farmers the packages of innovations tested and/or developed by the station, ADDP has adopted CADU's model-farmer and demonstration-plot strategy.

ADDP has a credit program open to all project area farmers cultivating less than ten hectares. Like CADU, it required that tenants had to sign a lease agreement with their landlords to be eligible for credit until the Land Reform Proclamation in 1975. Unlike the results of CADU, however, have been the positive results of the ADDP credit program. For example, in 1974 the goal was set of extending credit to 256 farmers, but a total of 412 received such aid. In 1974 the goal was 512, but 1,085 farmers were extended credit. In addition, more than 58 percent of the borrowers were small tenant farmers.

Nonmajor Components. We should examine the nonmajor components of the three integrated rural development projects that directly or indirectly reinforce development. In the CADU program, 165 assistant extension agents, 35 home economists, and 179 marketing agents have been trained. Extensive surveys of surface and underground water sources have been made, and an overall master water development plan has been adopted. The rural health services program has been integrated with the provincial health department to utilize efficiently the resources. The road-building program has completed about 46.5 km. of all-weather roads at a cost of about Eth. $20,000 per kilometer.

WADU's nonmajor components include soil conservation projects in which nearly one hundred thirty kilometers of contour terraces, protecting about seven hundred hectares of land from water erosion, have been completed using a voluntary local labor force. Its training center has provided short-term training (four to eight weeks) to many of its demonstrators and a few selected farmers. However, WADU's projects in rural water supply, consolidation of holdings, and destocking of highlands have shown little or no progress.

ADDP has programs in home economics, road building, and rural water supply. To date, five home economics agents in five different development centers have been giving classes in gardening, poultry raising, child care, and nutrition. Surveying for road and water supply construction programs have been completed. Five deep wells have been drilled, and 30 kms. of feeder roads have been constructed at a cost of Eth. $500 per kilometer.

Summary and Conclusions. CADU, WADU, and ADDP provide a number of lessons for designing and implementing rural development projects in other parts of Ethiopia. Before the adoption of the package approach as the major approach to rural development, Ethiopia had a limited number of extension agents to provide technical advice to farmers with neither the financial backing to get the required inputs nor the means to acquire them. Consequently, they were ineffective in assisting small farmers. With the establishment of CADU, the effectiveness of the package approach in reaching small farmers was demonstrated.

The importance of establishing small research units within regional, intensive package projects cannot be minimized. These small, local units need to focus their attention on the special needs of the small farmers so that research will benefit the poor sections of the population as well as the rich. This will help to eliminate or ward off research that could lead to the eviction of tenants, to landlessness, and to unemployment.

The provision of services like credit and marketing should be undertaken after examining how essential these are to the overall project. In extending credit, the two important problems are providing facilities to all segments of the rural population and ensuring repayment of the credit. However, these two objectives quite often form a paradoxical situation. Providing credit for only the credit-worthy, who are able to provide security, often eliminates the poorest section of the population, which is most in need of the service.

The operation of ADDP, which was set up to test rural development approaches not included in CADU and WADU by mobilizing available resources from local and central government agencies, has shown the difficulty of mobilizing resources and coordinating the efforts of the various government agencies to promote rural development effectively.

Finally, when considering the limitations of replicability of innovation

developed by the projects, the high cost, the trained manpower requirements, the often negative impact on regional inequities, and the absence
of a tax structure to siphon off a portion of the profits to establish similar
projects in other areas, it is difficult to imagine these development projects
either continuing as they are or expanding. The critical shortages of trained
manpower and financial resources alone indicate a very probable de-empha-
sis during the latter half of this decade.

Agrarian Reform in Pakistan

Introduction. The economy of Pakistan (formerly West Pakistan) is
overwhelmingly dependent upon agriculture: more than 45 percent of the
national income is derived from agriculture, which includes animal hus-
bandry, forestry, and fisheries; approximately 60 percent of the work force
is employed in agriculture; virtually all of Pakistan's exports are agriculturally related; most of the country's expanding industries are dependent
upon agriculture; and much of the government's revenue is derived from
taxes on land under cultivation and the products produced on that land.

Approximately one-fourth of Pakistan, or about forty-seven million
acres, is under cultivation. Much of this farm land is located in the Indus
Valley, and more than one-half of it is irrigated. The major crops grown
in Pakistan are wheat, cotton, rice, millet, sugarcane, and tobacco. From
75–80 percent of the land under cultivation is devoted to growing food
grains.

Despite the dominance of agriculture interests, the agricultural sector
is not without its problems. As Nyrop stated:

> Agricultural development lags behind the rest of the economy . . . and the
> yields per acre are among the lowest in the world. Quick profits to be made
> through commercial and industrial investmments have tended to attract
> capital away from agricultural development. Agricultural holdings are
> often fragmented into uneconomic plots, and many agricultural techniques
> remain primitive. Although improvements have been and are being made,
> plant and animal diseases are extensive, supply and marketing facilities are
> rudimentary, and credit facilities are inadequate. (Nyrop et al., 1971,
> p. 347)

Salinity and waterlogging, results of many years of flood irrigating,
are major, specific problems in many areas of Pakistan, as is an inadequate
supply of chemical fertilizers. It has been demonstrated that the proper
amount of chemical fertilizer, coupled with sufficient irrigation water, can
almost triple the yield per acre of many grain crops grown in Pakistan.
Farm mechanization has begun to add to the underemployment and unemployment problems in rural areas initiated by the small, uneconomic family
plots. Finally, perhaps the greatest problem is that the major technological
innovations implemented in the agricultural sector have not benefited the
majority of the farmers—the masses of peasant farmers living at the sub-

Years of irrigation are beginning to take their toll on the wheat fields in some parts of the Punjab. Photo by Edward C. Pytlik.

sistence level. Indeed, they are seemingly worse off now than they were prior to the influx of the technologies. Almost all the benefits seem to have been reaped by a very narrow segment of Pakistan's society—the bigger landowners, the money lenders, and the urban investors.

The agrarian reform of Pakistan included the formation of cooperatives as a means of ensuring the peasant farmer a share in the benefits received from the modernization of the agricultural sector. As already indicated, however, the masses of small farmers do not seem to have benefited from the new technologies; many are still living at the subsistence level.

Agrarian Reform and Planning. Pakistan became a nation on August 14, 1947. With independence from England and separation from India came a period of mass migration of Muslims from India into Pakistan and a reverse flow of Hindus from Pakistan into India. Despite the best efforts of government officials on both sides of the border, these mass migrations resulted in mass rioting and looting, mass panic, mass execution, and unimaginable bloodshed whenever waves of refugees met each other head on.

The country was in a state of mass confusion: Land with crops almost ready to harvest was abandoned; whole villages and even cities were found totally empty. Contrasting this abandonment and emptiness were the hordes of landless, possessionless immigrants with no place to go. It is somewhat of a miracle that a nation ever emerged from this confusion and panic.

Three years later, in 1950, when Karl Knaus became the first extension advisor from the Foreign Agricultural Service, U.S. Department of

Agriculture, to enter Pakistan, things were not much improved. The bloodshed had ended, at least for the time being, but the nation still was in the infant stage. Knaus described the situation in the following manner:

> Pakistan has no established national capitol; very little industry or raw materials for industry other than agricultural products; and few developed resources such as fuel, forests, and minerals. Abundant water power in the north was undeveloped. There was little organized international trade; inadequate marketing facilities . . . Irrigation is well developed, but there are tremendous problems of water supply, drainage, water logging and salt accumulation. Agriculture is the principal industry and engages over 85 percent of the people.
>
> Of the several agricultural colleges in old India, only one of recognized standing was within the borders of Pakistan. The Punjab Agricultural College at Lyallpur was well established and well managed. . . . A limited amount of agricultural training was offered at Islamia College in Peshawar, Northwest Frontier Province. Farmers and professionally trained people who work in rural areas have very low status. (Knaus, 1953, p. 1)

Knaus' job in Pakistan was to supervise the development of an agricultural extension service to "be made to reach the masses of the people with the known solutions to their problems of production, marketing and living standards and encourage efforts of self-help." There were several assumptions about this extension service: (1) That it would ultimately lead to the creation of an agricultural sector that would provide food and fiber to feed and clothe the nation's rapidly increasing population; (2) that it would provide a surplus of food and fiber for export to maintain a favorable balance of foreign exchange and revenue from export and import taxes; (3) that it would improve the natural soil and water resources; and (4) that it would develop a national awareness of the importance of agriculture.

To make the extension service an effective force in the agricultural sector of Pakistan, Knaus felt that an adequate base of scientific knowledge was required. He therefore recommended that priority be given to enlarging and improving the agricultural colleges. Knaus also realized that a method had to be found for acquiring the participation of the people, so he strongly urged that an effective, practical program be established; that it have a cooperative type organization; that it keep its administration close to the people; and that a committee of local volunteer leaders determine program priorities for their area. In addition, Knaus stated that adequate supplies of materials were required, as were a sufficient number of trained personnel knowledgeable in the new agricultural technologies.

The new agricultural extension service had barely begun, however, when Pakistan suffered from one of the lowest wheat harvests in the history of the Asian subcontinent. A severe drought, which resulted in extremely low river levels and a shortage of water in irrigation canals, a diversion of land and water to cash crops, insect attacks, and the uncertainties of still unsettled land reform all contributed to the 1952–1953 disaster. The wheat harvest for that period was 2,285,000 tons lower than the 1950–1951 harvest. This tremendous shortage of wheat necessitated importing 1,637,-300 tons of foodgrains, including almost 900,000 tons of wheat. The vast majority of these food grains came from Australia, Canada, and the United States.

This combined natural and man-made disaster resulted in one positive side effect, however. It stimulated a new effort at planned economic development in Pakistan. In 1953, Pakistani economists, aided by expertise from the United Nations Technical Assistance Program, the United Nations Economic Commission for Asia and the Far East, the Food and Agriculture Organization, the Agency for International Development, advisory groups from Harvard University, the International Bank for Reconstruction and Development, and the International Monetary Fund undertook to establish a new economic plan for Pakistan. The outcome was the first five-year plan (1955–1960), which was followed subsequently by the second, third, and fourth five-year plans covering the years 1960–1965, 1965–1970, and 1970–1975.

In the first five-year plan, industry received the largest percentage of the invested monies, 26.7 percent. It was followed by water and power, 21.3 percent; transport and communication, 16.7 percent; physical planning and housing, 13.1 percent; and agriculture, 9.5 percent. However, because much of the investment in the water and power area went for irrigation projects, agriculture's share was actually much greater than the 9.5 percent stated.

In the expenditures for the second five-year plan, industry's share of the total expenditures dropped to 22.3 percent, although it still retained the largest share. Agriculture jumped to 14.9 percent, still benefiting from much of the allocation to water and power, as before.

In the third five-year plan, industry's share remained at 22.3 percent, transport and communications rose to 20 percent, and agriculture increased slightly to 15.3 percent, while water and power's share declined to 16.4 percent.

The fourth five-year plan called for a total investment from the public and private sectors of Rs. 75 billion. Implementation of the fourth plan had barely begun when the country was wracked with internal political turmoil, which led eventually to revolution, civil war, and secession by the former provinces of East and West Pakistan, which became the independent nations of Bangladesh and Pakistan, respectively. It is therefore impossible to fairly evaluate the fourth plan at this time.

Cooperative Systems. There is one other institution to be considered when reviewing Pakistan's agrarian reform and planning, and that is the cooperative system. Pakistani cooperatives were originally organized under the Cooperative Credit Societies Act of 1904. Their major function until the 1950s was to supply credit to the agricultural sector of the country. However, in practice the cooperative societies "tended to be composed of

Construction of Mangla Dam, at the time the world's largest earth-filled dam, helped to provide more water for Pakistan's agriculture. Photo by Edward C. Pytlik.

reasonably well-to-do persons, many of them not farmers, and . . . loans were often spent for weddings or other ceremonies rather than for agricultural practices." (Nyrop et el. 1971, p. 376)

In the early 1950s when much of the country was still unsettled, with many refugees still homeless and landless, a large reclamation and colonization project was begun in the desert regions of western Punjab. One million two hundred thousand acres of land were to be reclaimed. Roads and irrigation canals were constructed, and villages were built. The purposes of the project were to resettle the refugees and make them not only self-sufficient, but actual contributors to the agricultural production of the country.

Each refugee family head was given twelve and one-half acres to cultivate, with the following restrictions:

1. He must become a member of the cooperative system.

2. He must live within the village confines.

3. He would pay for the land, house, and common village buildings by contributing a set portion of his crop to the cooperative each year for fifteen years.

4. He could not divide the land among his progeny; it must remain intact.

5. He could not sell the land since title remained with the Pakistan government.

The villages had provisions for a school, a health center, a mosque, a public assembly hall, grain storage, police station, bazaars, vegetable gardens, and a common pasture of forty acres. The cooperative system was also to provide the villager with seed, fertilizer, water, sprays, credit, and all the necessities for growing his crops. It was assumed that because these items could be purchased or provided on a large scale, the farmer would save money and be able to secure the necessary items when needed. It was also planned that the cooperative system would buy the farmer's products directly, store them in godowns, and then resell the grain, fiber, and so on sporadically over the entire year. Thus, through the law of supply and demand, the cooperative would create a stable market and a higher return for the individual farmer.

The cooperatives, managed by government civil servants, were also responsible for providing the refugees with new technological developments in agriculture. (The point caused considerable confusion and conflict with the extension service, whose responsibility was also to provide farmers with new developments.) In 1962, the cooperative society purchased one hundred farm tractors for its villages, followed by the purchase of another one hundred in 1964. All accompanying equipment—plows, harrows, wagons, and so on—were also purchased. Depending upon the number of farmers in the village, either one or two tractors were to be used cooperatively for cultivating the land and were to replace the water buffalo currently being used for that purpose. The farmers could then sell their buffalo and be able to plant an extra four acres of cash crops on land previously reserved for feeding the animals. It is this particular program that will be studied in depth.

During this same time period, Pakistan joined the green revolution by introducing the "package system" for improving crop production. The package consisted of new short varieties of miracle wheat developed in Mexico, proper cultivation practices, increased fertilizer, and sufficient irrigation water. This package, when applied correctly, would more than double the per acre production.

Receptivity to a Farm Mechanization Project. The government of Pakistan has been making a sustained effort to become self-sufficient in food production since the early 1950s. As a part of this overall, continuous plan, it was suggested by development planners in the early 1960s that the wheat production in the Punjab region could be significantly increased if the preparation and cultivation of the land were mechanized. The Punjab was the logical area for this emphasis because it is the breadbasket of Pakistan (see Table 7.2).

There were numerous reasons for supporting this suggestion. First, the farmers were leveling and cultivating their land by using primitive devices pulled by water buffalo or oxen. Since each farmer had his own animal, from one-third to one-half of the total land under cultivation had to be used for pasture and fodder crops for the animals. The introduction of tractors to prepare and cultivate the land would mean that the farmers

TABLE 7.2 Estimated Production of Major Crops in Pakistan and the Punjab (1973–1974)

Crop	Million Tons		Punjab's Percentage Share
	Pakistan	Punjab	
Wheat	7.32 [a]	5.60 [a]	76.5
Cotton (million bales)	3.70	2.53	68.4
Sugarcane	22.00	16.36	74.4
Rice			
fine (basmati)	0.47	0.47	100.0
medium and coarse	1.94	0.62	32.0
Maize	0.76	0.33	43.4
Gram	0.55	0.39	70.9
Rape and mustard	0.31	0.18	58.1

Source: Reprinted from *Punjab Development Review and Prospects* (3rd and 4th issues), published by Planning and Development Board, Government of the Punjab, June 1974.

[a] Actual for 1972–73.

would no longer need their buffalo, and therefore, significant amounts of land would be freed for the production of wheat.

Secondly, the primitive plow used by the farmers of the Punjab, literally a wooden stick, did little more than scratch the surface of the land. The soil in this part of Pakistan has a heavy clay base and, as a result, dries brick-hard in the sun. Even when plowed wet, the land is rarely penetrated more than a few inches. Consequently, when the crop was flood-irrigated, the majority of the water simply evaporated instead of soaking into the ground. It was reasoned that steel, tractor-drawn plows would be able to penetrate the soil deep enough to allow the soil to absorb a significantly larger amount of the scarce water.

Third, research being conducted in the reclamation of land lost to salinity seemed to indicate that the salts could be leached out through a combination of heavy irrigation and numerous deep plowings. Since soil salinity was becoming an increasingly important problem in the Punjab, it was anticipated that the tractors could be used in the off-season in land reclamation projects.

Four, high-yielding, short-stem varieties of wheat were being introduced into the Punjab. It was found that these new varieties were vulnerable to improperly prepared land. Fields that were shallow-plowed prior to seeding would yield harvests far below those that were deep-plowed prior to seeding. Therefore, tractors were needed.

For these reasons, then, the government of Pakistan purchased fifty John Deere Lantz diesel-engine farm tractors from Germany and fifty International Harvester diesel-engine farm tractors from England. The tractors and accompanying implements were distributed throughout the Punjab region under the auspices of the Colony Cooperative Farming Union, Khanewal (CCFU). Selected cooperative-member villages were sent one or two tractors, depending upon the size of the village, to replace the buffalo or oxen in cultivating and preparing the land. The villages differed in the number of farmers, but each farmer had only the twelve and one-half acres given to him by the government when he had migrated from India after the partition in 1947.

Theoretically, the project looked good. There were several substantial and documented reasons for introducing farm tractors to this particular part of the country. There was even an already well-established infrastructure—the cooperative union—to disperse the tractors and eventually to collect payments. In reality, however, the project proved to be less than perfect. The tractors were not well received by the villagers in the first place, and when the planning faults became evident, the project began to falter.

Flaws in the Project. The project was in trouble from the start because of a rather glaring oversight—the villagers were never involved in the planning. In fact, those who received the tractors had no recourse: They were not asked if they wanted them; they were told they had to take them. If the villagers had been consulted, the planners might have had second thoughts. They would have learned, for example, that the farmers had no intention of giving up their water buffalo, tractor or no tractor, because the buffalo performed many other services besides being a draft animal: The buffalo's milk was a substantial and important part of their diet; its dried dung served as fuel for cooking fires; it served as a pack animal and as a means of transportation when necessary; and even in death the buffalo provided the farmer with meat and a hide that he could either use or sell.

Had they taken the time to ask, the planners would also have discovered that the farmers were only a few years short of becoming free of their debt on the land. When the tractors and their payments were forced upon them, the villagers saw this as simply a way for the cooperative to extend its control for another extended period. Over the years, the villagers had become disillusioned with the CCFU. They saw it only as a political and financial burden that contributed little to their well-being, and they were looking forward to having at least financial freedom. The tractor scheme, of course, eliminated this possibility, and, as a result, the tractors were not welcome in most villages.

The farmers also saw the tractors as a weapon used by the cooperative union to accelerate the introduction of another technological innovation they were not particularly fond of—the short-stemmed varieties of wheat. Even though yields increased dramatically, the negative aspects of the new wheat varieties outweighed the increased yields in the minds of many farmers. For example, the wheat was much harder than the local varieties and therefore more difficult to grind; the resultant flour did not have the right consistency to form good chupattis, a wheat cake that is the major part of a rural Pakistani's diet; and even the color of the flour was not appealing. In addition, the new varieties required more fertilizers and irrigation water, increasing the investment in the crop to the point where the increased yield barely covered the added expense. The tractors added yet another unwanted and, in the farmers' opinion, unwarranted expense.

Finally, the farmers did not like the new wheat varieties because they were short stemmed. Local wheats had been specificially chosen because they were long stemmed. The farmers felt they were getting two crops for the price of one if they grew long-stemmed wheat—the grain, of course, they used themselves, and the stems they used for feeding their animals. With the length of the stem reduced to less than half the size of their local wheats, the farmers saw a drastic reduction in the size of their fodder crop. In the eyes of the farmer, then, the short-stemmed varieties of wheat were forcing them to: (1) take a great financial risk by increasing their initial investment, (2) produce a crop they did not like as well, and (3) actually reduced an important secondary crop. And the tractors were going to help them do it.

These initial objections to the introduction of the tractors, although formidable, were not unsolvable. Many of the objections could have been drastically reduced by informing the villagers of the positive potential of the tractors, and by attempting to educate them, at least to a basic understanding, of mechanical things. But no such project was undertaken. Thus, when the farmers did attempt to use the tractors (regardless of their opposition, they could not afford *not* to use them), their lack of technical knowledge became apparent and served as another deterrent to the success of the project.

The tractors were not in the fields long before the following flaws in the project were recognized:

1. The tractor drivers the CCFU assigned to each tractor were uniformly unskilled in proper cultivation and tractor maintenance procedures.

2. The implements accompanying the tractors were not suitable for working quarter-acre plots of land, the way the Punjabi farmers divided their land for irrigation purposes.

3. The closest fuel supply was from twenty to forty miles away.

4. There were no repair shops, trained mechanics, or tools and equipment to do major or even much minor repair work.

5. The farmers believed that the plowing had to be done during a specific period of time, which proved to be too short to plow every farmer's land.

The last flaw, quite naturally, caused a great deal of dissension among the farmers about who should get his land plowed first. The first four flaws, however, proved to be more critical to the project. One, or a combination of these flaws, resulted in nearly 90 percent of the tractors being in a state of disrepair within the first six months of operation. Some tractors were just out of fuel; others had minor mechanical problems such as dead batteries or flat tires; but some, perhaps 20 percent, already needed major mechanical repair, a condition caused by lack of maintenance, improper use, and the natural phenomena of intense heat and extremely dusty conditions.

The farmers were now faced with the choice of not repairing the tractors but still being forced to pay for them with absolutely no return, or taking on the added expense of having them repaired, meeting the further expense of keeping them properly maintained, and paying them off. The decision was not very difficult for many farmers. Why add more money to that already wasted, especially when they probably would not be able to receive any benefits anyway? Most farmers decided they wanted nothing further to do with the tractors and petitioned the CCFU to remove them from their village.

Instead, the cooperative union attempted to correct some of the flaws: They hired mechanics to begin repairing the tractors; they contracted for fueling dumps to be centrally located; they began to build several centrally located workshops; they recalled the drivers for a short, but intensive, training session in periodic maintenance procedures and proper cultivation practices; they set up a monthly maintenance check in which the driver would be fined if the vehicle was not properly cared for; and they modified the implements for use in small areas.

But all this took a great deal of time and money, and the villagers saw only an increasing financial burden with no real return. Their request to have the tractors withdrawn was ignored. Consequently, the tractors and everyone associated with them were met with increased hostility, and some farmers refused to use the tractors, while others continued to use them only under duress.

A demonstration and training session for tractor drivers also becomes an education session for the many observing farmers. Photo by Edward C. Pytlik.

Summary

Four assumptions can be made when dealing with the technology transfer process:

1. Regardless of the definition of technology, any technology can be transferred.

2. Regardless of the purpose of the transfer, it will always result in the introduction of technology that is different from the methods currently applied to the situation.

3. A transfer of technology will always introduce an element of change into a given situation.

4. An adoption–diffusion process must be an integral part of the transfer process in order to be successful.

The adoption–diffusion process is really a subprocess within the overall transfer of technology. Beal and Bohlen break down adoption and diffusion into five stages—awareness, interest, evaluation, trial, and adoption. The adoption stage, itself, was then broken down into five groups—innovators, early adopters, early majority, majority, and nonadopters.

If the technology transfer process itself seems complex, when placed in conjunction with the development of transitional societies or nations it becomes almost incomprehensible. There exists a preponderance of models, strategies, schemes, plans, and theories designed to promote the successful transfer of a technology and hence development in transitional nations. Many have been put into practice in development projects throughout the world. Most of these plans, however, have failed to produce anywhere near the success level predicted on paper. Even a plan that meets with success in one situation will usually fail miserably when duplication is attempted in another situation.

It is obvious that a universal development plan has not yet been devised. In fact, it is becoming increasingly evident that no such panacea is a realistic possibility. The best a development planner can hope for is that his unique plan will work in his particular situation at that particular point in time.

DISCUSSION QUESTIONS

1. Develop a scenario that will result in a successful conclusion to the second case study, regarding the introduction of farm tractors to the Punjab region of Pakistan.

2. At the conclusion of the first case study describing the three Ethiopian development projects, the following statement was made: "It is difficult to imagine these development projects continuing as they are or expanding." Do you agree or disagree with this statement? Defend your position.

3. In the summary of this chapter, the authors implied that a universal development model

would never be developed. Do you agree or disagree? Why?

4. Should developing nations concentrate on the urban–industrial sector, the rural–agricultural sector, a combination of the two, or neither? Explain your reasoning.

BIBLIOGRAPHY

Allen, F. R.; Hart, H.; Meller, D. C.; Obburn, W. F.; and Nimkoff, M. F. *Technology and Social Change.* New York: Appleton-Century-Crofts, 1957.

Azhar, B. A. "Land Revenue Assessment: A Case Study." *The Pakistan Development Review* 12 (1973): 232–46.

Aziz, Q. "Pakistan Opts for Higher Food Prices." *The Christian Science Monitor,* April 1975, p. 16.

Beal, G. M., and Bohlen, J. M. *The Diffusion Process* (Special Report no. 18) 6. Ames, Iowa: Cooperative Extension Service, Iowa State University, November 1962.

Beal, G. M.; Bohlen, J. M.; and Rogers, E. M. "Validity of the Concept of Stages in the Adoption Process." *Rural Sociology* 22, Doc. no. 2 (June 1957): 166–68.

Bohlen, J. M. "Needed Research on Adoption Models." *Sociologia Ruralis* 7, Doc. no. 2, (1967): 113–29.

Foster, G. M. *Traditional Societies and Technological Change.* 2d ed. New York: Harper and Row, 1973.

Gruber, W. H., and Marquis, D. H., eds. *Factors in the Transfer of Technology.* Cambridge, Mass.: M.I.T. Press, 1969.

Hawthorne, E. P. *The Transfer of Technology.* Paris: OECD, 1971.

It Came in a Torrent. Karachi, Pakistan: Ministry of Food and Agriculture, Government of Pakistan, 1955.

Kahnert, F.; Carmingnani, R.; Stier, H.; and Thomopoulos, P. *Agriculture and Related Industries in Pakistan.* Paris: Development Centre of the Organisation for Economic Cooperation and Development, 1970.

Knaus, K. *Beginning of Bilateral Technical Aid in Pakistan Agriculture.* Washington, D.C.: Foreign Agricultural Service, U.S. Department of Agriculture, 1953.

La Casa-Gomar, J. *The Sender-Linker-Receiver Communication Model.* Unpublished doctoral dissertation, Iowa State University, 1970.

Lesher, R. L., and Howick, G. J. *Assessing Technology Transfer.* Washington, D.C.: NASA, 1966.

Mason, R. H. "The Transfer of Technology and the Factor Properties Problem: The Philippines and Mexico." *UNITAR Research Reports,* Doc. no. 10. New York: U.N. Institute for Training and Research, 1972.

McClelland, D. C. *The Achieving Society.* Princeton, N.J.: Van Nostrand, 1961.

Moore, W. E. *The Impact of Industry.* Englewood Cliffs, N.J.: Prentice-Hall, 1965.

Murphy, J. J. "Retrospect and Prospect." In D. L. Spencer and A. Woroniak, eds. *The Transfer of Technology to Developing Countries.* New York: Praeger Publishers, 1967.

Naseem, S. M. "Mass Poverty in Pakistan: Some Preliminary Findings." *The Pakistan Development Review* 12 (1973): 317–60.

Niehoff, A. H., and Anderson, J. C. "Positive, Negative, and Neutral Factors—the Process of Cross-Cultural Innovations." *International Development Review* 6, Doc. no. 2 (June 1964): 5–11.

Nulty, L. *The Green revolution in West Pakistan.* New York: Praeger Publishers, 1972.

Nyrop, R. F.; Benderly, B. L.; Cort, A. S.; Parker, N. B.; Perlmutter, J. L.; Shinn, R. S.; and Shivanaudan, M. *Area Handbook for Pakistan.*

Washington, D.C.: U.S. Government Printing Office, 1971.

Office of U.S. Agricultural Attache, Islamabad. "Record 1974–1975 Pakistani Wheat and Rice Crops Could Alter Trade Patterns." *Foreign Agriculture* 12 (1974): 10–11.

Ogionwo, W. "Social Psychological Factors in Modernization: A Study of the Adoption of Technological Innovations in Nigeria." *International Review of Modern Sociology* 2, Doc. no. 1, (1972): 59–71.

Owens, E., and Shaw, R. *Development Reconsidered*. Lexington, Mass.: D. C. Heath & Co., 1972, 1974.

Ozawa, T. "Transfer of Technology from Japan to Developing Countries." *UNITAR Research Reports* Doc. no. 7, p. 50. New York: U.N. Institute for Training and Research, 1971.

Pearson, L. B. *Partners in Development*. New York: Praeger Publishers, 1969.

Punjab Development Review and Prospects (3d and 4th issues). Lahore, Pakistan: Planning and Development Board, Government of the Punjab, June 1974.

Qureshi, S. K. "Price Incentives for the Production of High-Yielding Mexican Varieties of Wheat: A Comment." *The Pakistan Development Review* 11 (1971): 54–61.

Rural Development: Sector Policy Paper. Washington, D.C.: World Bank, 1975.

Saleh, A. A. "Disincentives to Agricultural Production in Developing Countries: A policy Survey." *Foreign Agriculture,* (supplement), March 1975.

Schumacher, E. F. *Small Is Beautiful: Economics as if People Mattered*. New York: Harper & Row, 1973.

Spencer, D. L., and Woroniak, A. eds. *The Transfer of Technology to Developing Countries*. New York: Praeger Publishers, 1967.

Svennilson, I. "The Strategy of Transfer." In D. L. Spencer and A. Woroniak, eds. *The Transfer of Technology to Developing Countries*. New York: Praeger Publishers, 1967.

Tecle, T. "The Evolution of Alternative Rural Development Strategies in Ethiopia: Implications for Employment and Income Distribution. *African Rural Employment Research Network*. East Lansing, Mich.: Dept. of Agricultural Economics, Michigan State University, 1975.

Transfer of Technology for Small Industries. Paris: Organisation for Economic Cooperation and Development, 1974.

INTRODUCTION – PART II

We have attempted to define and characterize technology and to examine some of its applications on a global scale. Technology has permeated all segments of our society and holds the potential for solving many social ills. And because it is a human phenomenon, technology should be responsive to human control. Yet our generation still faces many problems of world-wide concern. Although this contradiction is sensed by all people, it is a difficult one to reconcile. In many instances, legislation has not solved social ills; indeed, many programs seem to add to the problems.

Some analysts of technological change state that technology feeds on itself, that it grows exponentially, and that it perhaps has grown beyond human control. Since technological growth requires human intervention in addition to vast amounts of energy and natural resources, this situation is ironic. By its nature, technology is neutral. Innovations and inventions are supported by people to meet needs. The technological fix, or ethic, that we seem to perpetuate provides technological growth without direction. This approach makes our societies crisis-oriented societies. Legislation after-the-fact or weak legislation often compounds the problem.

Unfortunately, conscious efforts to generate a new ethic have been prompted only by warnings of global collapse. Attempts are being made to: (1) identify specific problems, (2) anticipate problems before they mate-rialize, and (3) utilize a systems approach to handling actual and potential issues. Few of the world's problems are technological in nature. Rather, they are political, economic, sociological, and psychological. As all discussions about technology reveal, coping with innovation and invention is a matter of human values. If we want a clean environment; if we want to humanize work; if we want to eradicate disease; if we want alternate energy resources; if we want a viable future; human effort and technology can provide it.

Changes in society and the solutions to problems often begin with profound changes in science and technology. As these changes permeate our culture, they broaden into social processes that bring about even more profound changes. Ironically, we are very adept at predicting technical change, but we lack the imagination to predict social change. The conse-quence of this division is many of the social ills we face today.

What are today's crucial issues? Tomorrow's? What is harmful to health and well-being? What should our priorities be? Answers to these and many other questions are difficult to find. Most analysts of our technological culture agree that a number of critical issues must be solved in order to perpetuate human life. Part II of this text deals with some of these issues that threaten our very existence—namely, overpopulation, food, energy, ecology, work, health, and medicine. There are too many people making excessive demands on finite resources while productive systems continue to pollute our world. In many of these cases critical mass is close at hand. Therefore, solutions that control and provide for a humane existence are urgently needed.

New processes designed to concentrate on the development of materials and processes and on human aspirations, values, and motivations are already emerging to improve our future. Obviously, collective thought will be needed to determine which changes are possible, which are necessary, and which contribute to a rational social order. It will be tragic, indeed, if we have exceeded our ability to cope with growing complexity, density, and interdependence. Even more provocative is this possibility: Perhaps it is beyond our social capacity to maximize both technological growth and human potential. We do not subscribe to this conclusion. But as you progress through Part II, you must make up your own mind about our future.

PART II

Chapter 8
Population Growth and Its Demand on Global Resources

Introduction

Historically, as well as currently, few issues are as intricately interwoven into other worldwide issues and polarize the masses as does the issue of population growth. To be fair, we cannot even call the issue a problem because one faction contends that population growth is not a problem. This group emphatically states that the world's resources, combined with modern technology, could easily sustain a population ten to twenty times the current estimated world population of four billion. They insist that the real problem lies in the distribution of wealth, of resources, and of the population itself.

At the other end of the spectrum lie the Malthusians, who firmly believe that the world is doomed to a future of famine, pestilence, and war caused by overpopulation. They fear that it is already too late; even if worldwide measures were implemented immediately, the momentum already gathered by the population growth would carry us over the brink into catastrophe. They point out that, at the present rate of growth, world population will reach five billion by 1986 and six billion by 1995. In light of the current world situation, with the number of starving and malnourished people estimated to be more than one billion, or one out of every four persons in the world, the Malthusians conclude that the future can only bring total disaster.

In between these two poles are the hopefuls—those who believe that a population problem exists, but through worldwide planning and action programs the current exponential population growth can be altered in time to save us from total disaster. This group has concentrated mainly on reducing the birth rate, which is particularly high in most developing societies—those areas of the world that can least afford to feed more people.

Teitelbaum outlined the various positions of the group against population control programs and the group for population control programs.[1]

---

[1] Excerpted by permission from M. Teitelbaum, "Population and Development: Is a Consensus Possible?" *Foreign Affairs,* July 1974. Copyright 1974 by Council on Foreign Relations, Inc.

Positions Against the Need for Special Population Programs and Policies

1. The pronatalist position. Rapid population growth in a particular country or region is a positive force on grounds of: (a) economic development, in that a larger population provides necessary economies of scale and a sufficient labor supply; (b) protection of currently underpopulated areas from covetous neighbors; (c) differentials in fertility among ethnic, racial, religious, or political population segments; (d) military and political power and the vitality of a younger age structure.

2. The revolutionist position. Population programs are mere palliatives to fundamental social and political contradictions, which will inevitably lead to a just revolution and may therefore be viewed as inherently counterrevolutionary.

3. The anticolonial and genocide positions. The motives of rich countries that are pushing poor, developing countries to adopt aggressive population programs are open to suspicion. These rich countries went through a period of rapid population growth as a component of their own development processes, and their current efforts to restrain population growth in the developing countries are an attempt to maintain the status quo by retarding the development of these countries.

One can also see the undue emphasis on population as an attempt on the part of the rich, developed countries to "buy development cheaply."

Finally, a person who is very suspicious of the motives of the developed countries could see in their population efforts an attempt to limit or reduce the relative or absolute size of poor and largely nonwhite populations. Such a practice could be seen as a subtle form of genocide, deriving from racist or colonialist motives.

4. The overconsumption position. So-called population problems are actually problems of resource scarcity and environmental deterioration, which derive primarily from activities of the rich, developed countries and not from high fertility in the developing countries.

Even if fertility is too high in the developing countries, this is a consequence of their poverty, which, in turn, results from overconsumption of the world's scarce resources by rich countries.

5. The accommodationist position. As in the past, growing numbers can be readily accommodated by the improvements in agricultural and industrial technologies.

The world has already shown that Malthus' predictions were incorrect; the same is true of the neo-Malthusian predictions and solutions.

That which is termed "overpopulation" in a given situation is really a matter of underemployment. A humane and properly structured economy can provide employment and the means of subsistence for all people, no matter what the size of the population.

6. The problem-is-population-distribution position. It is not numbers per se that are causing population problems, but their distribution in space. Many areas of the world (or country) are underpopulated; others have too many people in too small an area.

Instead of efforts to moderate the rate of numbers growth, governments should undertake efforts to reduce rural–urban flows and bring about a more even distribution of population on the available land.

7. The mortality and social security position. High fertility is a response to high mortality and morbidity; if these levels were reduced, fertility would decline naturally.

Living children are the primary means by which poor people can achieve security in old age. Hence, a reduction in infant and child mortality levels or provision of alternative forms of social security would lead to a reduction in fertility.

8. The status and roles of women position. High fertility levels are perpetuated by norms and practices that define women primarily as procreative agents.

As long as women's economic and social status depends largely or solely upon the number of children they bear, there is little possibility that societal fertility will decline substantially.

9. The religious doctrinal position. In one form, this position holds that population is not a serious problem. Be fruitful and multiply, God will provide.

In another form, this position holds that while current rates of population growth are a serious problem, the primary instruments to deal with them are morally unacceptable—that is, modern contraception and surgical sterilization are "unnatural," abortion is "murder."

10. The medical risk position. The goal of fertility reduction is not worth the medical risks of the primary instruments of population programs. Oral contraceptives and intrauterine devices have measurable, if small, short-term risks, and some people fear their long-term effects. Sterilization and abortion are operative procedures, all of which have an element of risk, particularly when performed outside the hospital.

11. The holistic development position. Fertility decline is a natural concomitant of social and economic development, as proven by the European demographic transition.

Most of the fertility decline in developing countries with family planning programs therefore derives from the impact of social and economic development rather than from the programs themselves.

International assistance for development is too heavily concentrated upon population programs and is shortchanging general development programs.

12. The social justice position. Neither population programs nor economic development as presently pursued will bring about necessary fertility declines.

Fertility will not decline until the basic causes of high fertility—poverty, ignorance, fatalism —are eliminated through social policies that result in a redistribution of power and wealth among the rich and poor, both within and among nations.

Positions Supporting the Need for Special Population Programs and Policies

1. The population hawk position. Unrestrained population growth is the principal cause of poverty, malnutrition, environmental disruption, and other social problems. Indeed, we are faced with impending catastrophe on food supply and environmental fronts.

Such a desperate situation necessitates draconian action to restrain population growth, even if coercion is required. "Mutual coercion, mutually agreed upon."

Population programs are fine as far as they go, but they are wholly insufficient in scope and strength to meet the desperate situation.

2. The provision of services position. Surveys and common sense show that there is a great unmet demand for fertility control in all countries; hence, the main problem is to provide modern fertility control to already motivated people.

Some proponents also held that the failure of some service programs is due to inadequate fertility control technologies and that the need for technological improvements is urgent.

3. The human rights position. As recognized in the U.N. Tehran Convention in 1968, it is a fundamental human right for each person to be able to determine the size of his or her own family.

Furthermore, some argue that each woman has the fundamental right to the control of her own bodily processes. (This position usually leads to support for abortion as well as contraception.)

Health is also a basic human right, which population programs help to achieve through a variety of direct and indirect pathways, including the direct medical benefits of increased child spacing on maternal and child health, and the indirect effects of reducing the incidence of dangerous illegal abortions.

4. The population-programs-plus-development position. Social and economic development are necessary but not sufficient to bring about a new equilibrium of population at low mortality and fertility levels. Special population programs are also required.

Too-rapid population growth is a serious intensifier of other social and economic problems, and it is one, though only one, of a number of factors behind lagging social and economic progress in many countries.

Some countries might benefit from larger populations, but would be better served by moderate rates of growth over a longer period than by very rapid rates of growth over a shorter period.

An effective population program, therefore, is an essential component of any sensible development program. (Teitelbaum, 1974, pp. 750–53)

Teitelbaum proposes a compromise position which he calls the "consensus position." This position uses the population-programs-plus-development position as a base, but also assumes that: (1) population is not the only reason for the world's problems; (2) each country's population problem has its own unique characteristics; (3) population distribution and rural migration are equally as important as rates of population increase; (4) a dramatic increase in population is inevitable, barring some unforeseen worldwide calamity; and (5) most voluntary population control programs are in accord with the human right of individual determination of fertility.

All groups—optimists, pessimists, and hopefuls—agree that the world's population will continue to increase within the foreseeable future. Given this hypothesis, we can then determine what it will mean in demands on our global resources; how the population issue is interwoven with other major world issues; and what technological and social imperatives seem necessary in a world that might double its 1960 population of three billion by 1995, in just thirty-five years.

Population Trends

As stated earlier in the text, it is commonly accepted that the human race began about two million years ago, although discoveries in 1975 by Richard Leakey might eventually push the figure back another million years or so. In any case, it has been estimated that by the year 1 million B.C., the earth's population of humans had reached 125,000. Some 992,000 years later, or around 8000 B.C., the population had reached an estimated 5.3 million. Until this time, the human was probably still an endangered species, and only good fortune, increasing brain power, and a high fertility level kept our ancestors from going the way of the dinosaur.

But then the human species began to change from the precarious, nomadic hunting life to the more sedentary life of a food grower. Archeologists have found Iranian villages with an agricultural-based economy estimated to be about seven thousand years old—the dawn of the Neolithic period. This new, less dangerous way of life spread slowly throughout the world and, as it did, the first "population explosion" took place. Deevey estimated the population of 4000 B.C. to have been 86.5 million, more than sixteen times the population of only four thousand years earlier.

This rapid population explosion, however, did not last. For some unexplained reason, the rate of population growth dropped remarkably during the next four thousand years (see Table 8.1). There are varying estimates of the population at the time of the birth of Christ. Deevey, for example, claims it was about 133 million, while the United Nations' figure is between two hundred and three hundred million. If Deevey has the closer estimate, then the population in the year A.D. 1 was just a little more than one and one-half times the population level of 4000 B.C. If the United Nations' figures are more nearly correct, the increase in population would still have been only about three and one-half times the 4000 B.C. level.

TABLE 8.1 Historical World Population Trends

Approximate Year	Estimated Population	
1 million B.C.	125	thousand
8,000 B.C.	5.3	million
4,000 B.C.	86.5	million
1 A.D.	200	million
1000	275	million
1650	545	million
1750	728	million
1839	1.0	billion
1850	1.17	billion
1900	1.55	billion
1930	2.0	billion
1950	2.5	billion
1960	3.0	billion
1970	3.6	billion
1976	4.0	billion

The figure estimating the world's population during the A.D. 1000 reveals a continuing slow growth rate, but during the next six hundred fifty years the population almost doubled. It took only another one hundred ninety years, until 1840, for the world's population to double again; as it did, the human population passed the one billion mark around 1830. Much of this period's growth has been attributed to the improved standard of living caused by the Industrial Revolution, which began in England during the mid-eighteenth century and spread rapidly through Europe, the United States, and Canada. For the world's population to increase from one billion to two billion took only one hundred years, despite a bloody world war. In forty-six years the population doubled again; it took only thirty years for the human population to reach three billion, despite a second bloody world war; and only sixteen years for the human race to surpass four billion, despite large-scale famine and starvation in India, Bangladesh, and the African Sahel.

A Declining Birth Rate

One of the most amazing statistics related to world population growth is that, except for the decades 1915–1925 and 1945–1955, the world's birth

rate has been declining during the entire twentieth century (see Figure 8.1).
Seemingly, then, the birth rate is not the real problem; instead, the more
rapidly declining death rate is actually responsible for the increasing population growth rate. And that is the source of the dilemma. Those who are
concerned with the population issue certainly cannot call for an increase
in the death rate; such a move would be inhumane. (But, a visit to one of
the tragic slums of the world might make some persons wonder how con-
demning someone to such a life could be considered a humane act.) They
must, instead, promote programs that are designed to reduce the birth rate
further so that it is more nearly commensurate with the death rate.

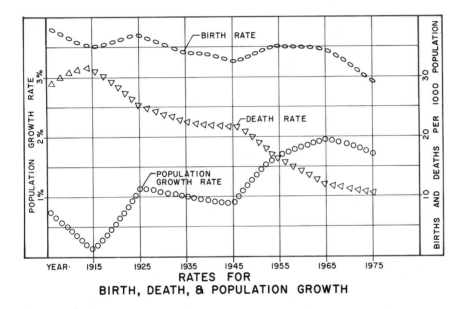

RATES FOR
BIRTH, DEATH, & POPULATION GROWTH

The declining birth rate allows the opponents of population control
programs to argue that such programs are not attacking the real problem.
They point out that the population growth rate is on the decline and has
been since 1965. What really needs to be attacked are the social, economic,
and distributive inequities that exist around the world. Those in favor of
population control programs counter with the claim that, although the
world's birth and population growth rates are declining, the figures are mis-
leadingly optimistic because those same rates are not declining in the transitional areas of the world (see Table 8.2). Consequently, their programs in
the transitional societies of the world at least are justifiable.

Table 8.2 reveals that during the first four years of the 1970s only
the North American and European regions had a lower average population
growth rate than the world average. Together, these regions contain the
majority of the world's highly developed societies. The European region has
by far the lowest average population growth rate—0.80. Twenty-four of
the thirty-two countries listed in the European regional table (see table 8.3)
had an annual growth rate of 1.0 or less, and four countries in the region

TABLE 8.2 Population Estimates (in millions)

Region	1970	1971	1972	1973	Percent of World Population	1970–73 Increase	Average Growth Rate [a]
World	3,632	3,706	3,782	3,860	—	228	2.35
Africa	344	354	364	374	.103	30	2.66
North America	321	327	332	339	.094	18	2.28
South America	190	195	201	206	.057	16	2.48
Asia	2,056	2,104	2,154	2,204	.610	148	2.63
Europe	462	466	469	472	.131	10	0.80
Oceania	19.4	19.8	20.2	20.6	.006	1.2	3.24

Source: United Nations Statistical Yearbook 1974, N.Y., 1975.
[a] Computed average population growth rates reflect only those countries in the regional tables having growth-rate statistics.

had a negative population growth rate. The countries that have a negative population growth rate were: Andorra (−5.9), the German Democratic Republic (−0.2), Malta (−0.4), and Portugal (−0.4). The only countries in the European region with population growth rates above the world average were the relatively small countries of the Isle of Man (4.1), Liechtenstein (3.1), Gibraltar (3.8), and Albania (3.2).

The Ratio of Births to Deaths

In the European region, Monaco, with the highest population density (16,107 per square kilometer) also has the lowest birth–death ratio of −4.7 per thousand. Four other countries also have negative birth–death ratios— German Democratic Republic (−3.1), Isle of Man (−2.1), Federal Republic of Germany (−1.6), and Luxembourg (−0.9). Albania has the highest birth–death ratio of 25.2 per thousand. The highest female life expectancy—77.4 years—is shared by Norway and Sweden. Sweden also has the highest male life expectancy of 72.0 years. Both of these figures are the highest in the world. Luxembourg has the European region's lowest life expectancies, 61.7 for males and 65.8 for females.

The North American region includes Canada, the United States, the Central American countries, and various Atlantic and Caribbean islands (see Table 8.4). The two most highly developed nations in this region, Canada and the United States, have a combined average population growth rate of only 1.05. When rates from these two countries are removed from the regional average, it jumps from 2.28 to 2.40, very close to the South American region's average population growth rate of 2.48.

TABLE 8.3 European Regional Population Statistics

Selected Countries	Population Estimate mid-1973 (in thousands)	Growth Rate	Population Density (per sq. km.)	No. More Births Than Deaths (per 1,000)	Life Expectancy Male	Female
Albania	2,347	3.2	82	25.2 [a]	64.9	67.0
Andorra	16 [b]	−5.9 [b]	35	12.1	—	—
Austria	7,529	0.6	90	0.7	67.4	74.7
Belgiun.	9,757	0.4	320	1.2	67.7	73.5
Bulgaria	8,490	0.5	78	6.9	68.8	72.7
Czechoslovakia	14,561	0.5	114	7.3	66.2	72.9
Denmark	5,022	0.6	117	4.2	70.7	75.9
Finland	4,656	0.4	14	2.9	65.9	73.6
France	52,134	0.9	95	5.8	68.5	76.1
German Dem. Rep.	16,980	−0.2	157	−3.1	68.9	74.2
Germany, Fed. Rep. of	61,967	0.7	249	−1.6	67.4	73.8
Gibraltar	30	3.8	4,932	11.7	—	—
Greece	8,972	0.7	68	6.6	67.5	70.7
Hungary	10,432	0.3	112	3.2	66.9	72.6
Iceland	212	1.3	2 [b]	14.5	70.7	76.3
Ireland	3,029	0.9	43	11.5	68.6	72.9
Isle of Man	56	4.1 [a]	95	−2.1	—	—
Italy	54,888	0.8	182	6.1	67.9	73.4
Liechtenstein	23	3.1	146	11.7	—	—
Luxembourg	351	1.2	136	−0.9	61.7 [b]	65.8 [b]
Malta	322	−0.4	1,018	7.8	68.6	73.1
Monaco	24	1.4	16,107 [a]	−4.7 [b]	—	—
Netherlands	13,438	1.0	329	6.3	70.8	76.8
Norway	3,961	0.7	12	5.4	71.2	77.4 [a]
Poland	33,361	0.9	107	9.4	66.8	73.8
Portugal	8,564	−0.4	93	9.0	65.3	71.0
Romania	20,828	0.9	88	8.3	66.2	70.9
Spain	34,858	0.6	309	10.7	69.7	75.0
Sweden	8,137	0.4	18	3.0	72.0 [a]	77.4 [a]
Switzerland	6,431	1.3	156	4.8	69.2	75.0
United Kingdom	55,933	0.3	229	1.8	67.8	73.8
U.S.S.R.	187,075 [a,c]	0.7 [c]	34 [c]	9.0	65.0	74.0
Yugoslavia	20,956	1.0	82	9.3	65.6	70.4

Source: United Nations, Statistical Yearbook 1974, N.Y. 1975.
[a] Highest figure.
[b] Lowest figure.
[c] European section of U.S.S.R. only.

In the North American region, the Bahamas have the highest population growth rate, 4.2, and Martinique has the lowest population growth rate, 0.05. Bermuda has the highest population density in the North American region, and although the country's birth–death ratio is not negative like that of Monaco, it does have the third lowest birth–death ratio in the region, 11.8 per thousand. The United States has the North American region's

TABLE 8.4 North American Regional Population Statistics

Selected Countries	Population Estimate mid-1973 (in thousands)	Growth Rate	Population Density (per sq. km.)	No. More Births Than Deaths (per 1,000)	Life Expectancy Male	Female
Antigua	74	1.9	167	22.0	60.5	64.3
Bahamas	193	4.2 a	14	18.1	64.0	67.3
Barbados	243	0.8	564	13.6	62.7	67.4
Belize	132	3.2	6	30.5	45.0	49.0
Bermuda	55	2.2	1,038 a	11.8	65.6	72.3
Canada	22,125	1.2	2	8.3	68.8	75.1
Costa Rica	1,872	2.7	37	25.3	61.9	64.8
Cuba	8,916	1.7	78	19.6	66.8	66.8
Dominica	73	0.6	97	26.3	57.0	59.2
Dominican Republic	4,432	3.0	91	33.8	57.2	58.6
El Salvador	3,864	3.0	184	32.1	56.7	60.4
Greenland	51 b	3.2	0 b	16.0	57.0	64.2
Guadeloupe	342	1.5	192	20.7	62.5	67.3
Guatemala	5,540	2.8	51	28.0	48.3	49.7
Haiti	4,440	1.6	160	24.2	44.5 b	44.5 b
Honduras	27,814	3.5	25	31.9	49.0	49.0
Jamaica	1,976	1.9	180	24.1	62.7	66.6
Martinique	343	0.5 b	311	15.6	63.3	67.4
Mexico	54,303	3.5	28	34.3 a	61.0	63.7
Netherlands Antilles	234	1.8	244	17.3	69.2 a	73.5
Nicaragua	2,015	3.2	16	29.5	49.9	49.9
Panama	1,570	3.1	20	32.3	57.6	60.9
Puerto Rico	2,951	2.8	332	16.8	68.9	76.0 a
St. Lucia	107	2.3	174	30.1	55.1	58.5
United States	210,404 a	0.9	22	5.6 b	67.4	75.1

Source: United Nations Statistical Yearbook 1974, N.Y., 1975.
a Highest figure.
b Lowest figure.

lowest birth–death ratio of 5.6 per thousand; Canada is next lowest with 8.3 more births than deaths per thousand. Mexico has the region's highest birth–death ratio, 34.3 per thousand. The lowest male and female life expectancies in the North American region are both found in Haiti, 44.5 years for each sex, while Puerto Rico has the highest female life expectancy, 76.0 years, and the Netherland Antilles has the highest male life expectancy of 69.2 years.

As noted earlier in this chapter, the South American region has an average population growth rate of 2.48, the third lowest of the six regions. The region population statistics table for South America (Table 8.5) shows that Paraguay has the region's highest population growth rate of 3.9, the lowest maximum population growth rate of any region. French Guiana, with the lowest population growth rate of 1.0, also has the lowest population density of the area, 1 per square kilometer. The population density figures are probably the most favorable statistic for the South American region because the highest density for the entire region is in Ecuador, which has an average of only twenty-four persons per square kilometer. The only other country with as many as twenty persons per square kilometer is Colombia. However, since much of the South American region is impenetrable jungle and uninhabitable mountain ranges and since these figures do not reflect such things as population distribution or standard of living, they can be somewhat misleading.

TABLE 8.5 South American Regional Population Statistics

Selected Countries	Population Estimate mid-1973 (in thousands)	Growth Rate	Population Density (per sq. km.)	No. More Births Than Deaths (per 1,000)	Life Expectancy Male	Female
Argentina	24,286	1.5	9	12.4	64.1	70.2
Bolivia	5,331	2.6	5	24.9	49.7	49.7
Brazil	101,433 [a]	2.8	12	28.3	60.7	60.7
Chile	10,229	1.7	14	19.1	60.5	66.0
Colombia	23,201	3.2	20	34.0 [a]	44.2 [b]	46.0 [b]
Ecuador	6,726	3.4	24 [a]	33.5	51.0	53.7
French Guiana	52 [b]	1.0 [b]	1 [b]	20.6	—	—
Guyana	758	1.8	4	28.7	59.0	63.0
Paraguay	2,674	3.9 [a]	7	33.8	59.4	59.4
Peru	14,912	3.2	12	30.7	52.6	55.5
Surinam	432	3.2	3	33.7	62.5	66.7
Uruguay	2,992	1.2	17	11.3 [b]	65.5 [a]	71.6 [a]
Venezuela	11,293	2.8	12	33.1	63.8	63.8

Source: United Nations Statistical Yearbook 1974, N.Y., 1975.
[a] Highest figure.
[b] Lowest figure.

In the South American region, Colombia has the highest birth-death ratio of 34 per thousand, while Uruguay has the lowest birth–death ratio of 11.3 per thousand. Uruguay also has the highest life expectancy for both sexes, 65.5 years for men and 71.6 years for women. Colombia has the lowest life expectancies for both sexes, 44.2 years for a male Colombian and 46.0 years for the female Colombian.

Demographic Transition

The South American regional statistics also reflect an important argument for the antipopulation control program group. As stated by Teitelbaum, the group claims that "high fertility is a response to high mortality and morbidity; bring these levels down and fertility will decline naturally." Colombia has both the lowest life expectancy and the highest birth–death ratio in the region. Conversely, Uruguay has both the highest life expectancy and the lowest birth–death ratio in the region. To those who would point out that this theory does not hold up in either the North American or European regions, the opponents of population control programs would argue that the major countries of those regions have already accomplished their natural changeover, or demographic transition. Teitelbaum defines demographic transition as "the process of change from high-mortality–high-fertility to low-mortality–high fertility, and finally to low-mortality–low-fertility." The current world situation seems to indicate that many countries are at the middle stage of low-mortality–high-fertility. How long they remain there could be crucial to the survival of the human race.

Asia, the most populated region, has an average population growth rate of 2.63, very close to the African region's 2.66, which is the highest of the five major regions. In fact, if Japan, the region's most highly developed country, is removed from the computation, the average population growth rate for the Asian region exactly equals the African region's 2.66. However, considering that the total population of the Asian region is almost six times that of the African region, it becomes obvious why the Asian region is so often alluded to when the population issue is discussed.

It is apparent that Japan has passed through its demographic transition (see Table 8.6). It has the region's lowest population growth rate (1.3), the lowest birth–death ratio (12.8), and the highest life expectancies, 70.1 for Japan's male population and 75.2 for Japan's female population. Also regarding the phases of demographic transition, apparently Kuwait is currently experiencing the second phase of its demographic transition. It has the region's highest population growth rate (5.8) as well as the highest birth–death ratio of 35.9 per thousand, indicating the low-mortality–high-fertility stage of the process. Afghanistan has the ill-fortune of having the Asian region's lowest life expectancies, 37.5 years for both males and females.

Life Expectancy

India and Pakistan, for some unexplained reason, are two of only four countries in the world to have a higher life expectancy for males than females. The other two countries are Liberia and Nigeria, in the African region. In India, the male life expectancy is 42.0 years, while the female is only 40.6 years. In Pakistan, the life expectancies are higher, but the gap between the two is much greater. The male life expectancy there is 53.7 years, while the female life expectancy is only 48.8 years, a gap of almost five years.

TABLE 8.6 Asian Regional Population Statistics

Selected Countries	Population Estimate mid-1973 (in thousands)	Growth Rate	Population Density (per sq. km.)	No. More Births Than Deaths (per 1,000)	Life Expectancy Male	Female
Afghanistan	18,294	2.3	28	24.0	37.5 b	37.5 b
Bahrain	227	1.8	365	—	—	—
Bangladesh	71,614	— c	497	—	—	—
Bhutan	894	2.3	19	—	—	—
Brunei	145	3.7	25	29.9	—	—
Burma	29,563	2.3	44	22.9	47.5	47.5
China	814,279 a	1.7	85	17.8	50.0	50.0
Cyprus	659	1.4	71	15.5	63.6	68.8
Hong Kong	4,160	1.7	398	14.2	66.7	73.3
India	574,216	2.1	175	26.1	42.0	40.6
Iran	31,298	3.0	19	28.8	50.0	50.0
Iraq	10,413	3.3	24	33.8	51.6	51.6
Israel	3,183	3.0	154	20.6	70.1	72.8
Japan	108,346	1.3 b	291	12.8 b	70.5 a	75.2 a
Jordan	2,537	3.3	26	33.1	52.6	52.0
Korea	47,992	2.0	218	26.1	58.7	60.9
Kuwait	883	5.8 a	50	35.9 a	66.1	71.8
Laos	3,181	2.4	13	24.9	47.5	47.5
Lebanon	3,055	3.1	294	20.2	—	—
Macao	262	1.6	16,375 a	—	—	—
Malaysia	11,609	3.7	35	29.4	58.0	59.0
Maldives	115	2.1	386	27.2	—	—
Mongolia	1,359	2.9	1 b	30.3	57.7	57.7
Nepal	12,020	—	85	21.7	40.6	40.6
Oman	722	3.2	3	—	—	—
Pakistan	66,749	3.6	83	24.0	53.7	48.8
Philippines	40,219	3.0	134	32.7	48.8	53.4
Qatar	86 b	2.9	8	—	—	—
Saudi Arabia	8,443	2.9	4	27.3	42.3	42.3
Sikkim	206	2.0	29	12.9	—	—
Singapore	2,185	1.7	3,761	16.6	65.1	70.0
Sri Lanka	13,249	1.9	202	21.8	64.8	66.9
Syrian Arab Rep.	6,890	3.3	37	32.2	52.8	52.8
Thailand	39,787	3.2	77	32.4	53.6	58.7
Turkey	37,933	2.5	49	25.0	53.7	53.7
United Arab Emirates	208	2.7	2	—	—	—
U.S.S.R.	62,674 d	1.6 d	4 d	9.0	65.0	74.0
Viet Nam	41,848	2.0	127	21.4	50.0	50.0
Yemen, Democratic	1,555	2.7	5	27.3	42.3	42.3

Source: United Nations Statistical Yearbook 1974, N.Y., 1975.

a Highest figure.

b Lowest figure.

c Rate not computed because of apparent lack of comparability between estimates shown for 1970 and 1973.

d Asian section of U.S.S.R. only.

Population Density

From the population statistics for the Asian region, it may be theorized that population density may play a role in natural population control. Macao, which has the world's highest population density of 16,375 persons per square kilometer, as well as Singapore with a population density of 3,761 persons per square kilometer, both have extremely low (for that region, at least) population growth rates, 1.6 and 1.7, respectively. The European countries of Monaco (population density of 16,107 persons per square kilometer and a population growth ratio of 1.4) and Malta (population density of 1,018 persons per square kilometer and a −0.4 population growth rate) also reflect this pattern. On the other hand, Gibraltar (4,932 persons per square kilometer and a 3.8 population growth rate) and Bermuda (1.038 persons per square kilometer and a 2.2 population growth rate) seem to refute the theory. There are no available United Nations satistics on the population growth rate of Johnston Island, the only other area of the world where the population density exceeds 1,000 persons per square kilometer.

The two most populated countries in the region and in the world, China (1973 estimated population of 814,279,000) and India (1973 estimated population of 574,216,000), do not seem to have very disproportionate population-related statistics, at least at first glance. Both countries have rather average growth rates, 1.7 for China and 2.1 for India; their population densities are reasonable, 85 and 175 persons per square kilometer, respectively; and their birth–death ratios are fairly average, 17.8 and 26.1 per thousand, respectively. However, when we read the life expectancy statistics, we find that India's life expectancies of 42.0 years for males and 40.6 for females are lower than the lowest figures of all the countries in the North American, South American, European, and Oceanic regions. Only the African and Asian regions have countries with lower life expectancies than India's. China's 50.0 years of life expectancy for each sex, although somewhat better than India's, is still not very high.

But the most frightening statistics to so many persons concerned with the population issue are the future population projections of these two countries. Even when we use their already relatively low population growth rate figures, we can project that China will pass the one billion population mark sometime in 1985; India's population will pass the three-quarter billion mark that same year (see Table 8.7).

The African region has the highest average population growth rate, with the exception of the Oceania region. However, Oceania has only about 0.006 percent of the world's population and therefore is not really a major population area. Africa, on the other hand, is the third largest region in total population. Statistically, the African region is the worst in the world in terms of the population issue: Excluding the Oceania region, the African region has the highest population growth rate. It contains the country with the world's highest population rate—Spanish Sahara at 8.9. It contains the

TABLE 8.7 Population Projections for India and China

Year	Estimated Population of China (1.7 Annual Growth Rate)	Estimated Population of India (2.1 Annual Growth Rate)
1974	828,121,740	586,274,530
1975	842,199,800	598,586,290
1976	856,517,190	611,156,600
1977	871,077,980	623,990,880
1978	885,886,300	637,094,680
1979	900,946,360	650,473,660
1980	916,262,440	664,133,600
1981	931,838,810	678,080,400
1982	947,680,160	692,320,080
1983	963,730,720	706,858,800
1984	980,114,140	721,702,830
1985	996,779,080	736,858,580
1986	1,031,724,300	752,332,610

countries with the world's lowest life expectancies for both males and females—Gabon with a male life expectancy of 25.0 years, and Guinea with
a female life expectancy of 28.0 years. It contains the country with the
highest life expectancy—the Sychelles Islands—with a male life expectancy
of 61.9 years and a female life expectancy of 68.0 years, which are lower
than similar countries of any other region (see Table 8.8).

The African region has the only countries in the world that have life
expectancies of less than 30 years. In addition to Gabon and Guinea, mentioned earlier, Chad has a male life expectancy of 29.0 years. Gabon has
the largest difference in male–female life expectancy. Although this country's male life expectancy is only 25.0 years, its female life expectancy is
45.0 years, a twenty-year difference.

Although the Oceania region is not of great importance to the population issue because it contains such a small percentage of the world's population, some rather interesting statistics are worth mentioning (see Table
8.9). For example, Norfolk Island has the world's highest population growth
rate of 13.2, but a population of only 2,000. It also has one of the lowest
birth–death ratios outside of the European region—7.1 per thousand. And
French Polynesia has the world's highest birth–death ratio of 36.6 per
thousand.

It must be remembered that all the figures in this chapter are estimates.
Figures from other sources may vary depending upon whose statistics they
are and what data were used in compiling the figures. In this case, all figures
were either extracted from the *United Nations Statistical Yearbook 1974,*
or figures from that reference were used to compile secondary data.

TABLE 8.8 African Regional Population Statistics

Selected Countries	Population Estimate mid-1973 (in thousands)	Growth Rate	Population Density (per sq. km.)	No. More Births Than Deaths (per 1,000)	Life Expectancy Male	Life Expectancy Female
Algeria	15,772	3.2	7	32.2	50.7	50.7
Botswana	646	3.7	1	21.6	41.0	41.0
Burundi	3,600	— [c]	129	22.9	35.0	38.5
Cape Verdi Islands	284	1.8	70	22.9	—	—
Chad	3,868	2.0	3	22.7	29.0	35.0
Comoro Islands	291	2.4	134	24.0	—	—
Congo	1,004	2.4	3	21.6	41.0	41.0
Dahomey	2,912	2.7	26	25.4	38.5	38.5
Egypt	35,619	2.2	36	21.7	51.6	53.8
Equatorial Guinea	298	1.5	11	12.9	41.0	41.0
Ethiopia	26,076	1.9	21	20.6	38.5	38.5
Gabon	515	1.1 [b]	2	7.5 [b]	25.0 [b]	45.0
Gambia	493	2.2	44	19.4	41.0	41.0
Ghana	9,355	2.7	39	28.8	46.0	46.0
Guinea	4,208	2.4	17	22.1	26.0	28.0 [b]
Ivory Coast	4,641	2.5	14	23.3	41.0	41.0
Kenya	12,482	3.6	21	30.3	46.9	51.2
Lesotho	994	2.2	33	17.8	43.5	43.5
Liberia	1,659	2.9	15	28.8	45.8	44.0
Libya	2,161	3.7	1	30.1	52.1	52.1
Malawi	4,791	2.6	40	24.0	38.5	38.5
Mali	5,376	2.1	4	23.2	37.2	37.2
Mauritania	1,257	2.7	1	21.7	41.0	41.0
Mauritius	868	1.3	424 [a]	14.9	58.7	61.9
Morocco	16,309	— [c]	37	33.0	50.5	50.5
Namibia	673	2.1	11	19.4	38.5	38.5
Niger	4,304	2.3	3	28.9	41.0	41.0
Nigeria	59,607 [a]	2.7	65	24.7	37.2	36.7
Réunion	474	2.1	189	20.9	55.8	62.4
Rhodesia	5,900	3.6	15	34.0 [a]	51.4	51.4
Rwanda	3,984	2.7	151	28.5	41.0	41.0
Senegal	4,227	2.5	22	23.5	41.0	41.0
Seychelles	56 [b]	2.6	149	21.8	61.9 [a]	68.0 [a]
Sierre Leone	2,667	1.5	37	22.1	41.0	41.0
Somalia	3,003	2.5	5	21.9	38.5	38.5
South Africa	23,724	2.8	19	23.7	49.0	49.0
Spanish Sahara	99	8.9 [a]	0 [b]	16.4	—	—
Sudan	16,901	2.5	7	30.5	47.6	47.6
Swaziland	463	4.3	27	28.8	41.0	41.0
Togo	2,117	2.4	38	25.4	31.6	38.5
Tunisia	5,509	2.4	34	30.3	51.7	51.7
Uganda	10,810	3.3	46	25.6	47.5	47.5

Source: United Nations Statistical Yearbook 1974, N.Y., 1975.

[a] Highest figure.

[b] Lowest figure.

[c] Rate not computed because of apparent lack of comparability between estimates shown for 1970 and 1973.

TABLE 8.8 African Regional Population Statistics (Cont.)

Selected Countries	Population Estimate mid-1973 (in thousands)	Growth Rate	Population Density (per sq. km.)	No. More Births Than Deaths (per 1,000)	Life Expectancy Male	Female
United Rep. of Cameroon	6,167	1.9	13	20.3	41.0	41.0
United Rep. of Tanzania	14,377	2.7	15	25.0	40.5	40.5
Upper Volta	5,737	2.1	21	20.3	32.1	31.1
Zaire	23,563	2.8	10	21.7	37.6	40.0
Zambia	4,635	3.5	6	29.1	43.5	43.5

Manipulating the Statistics

As with many other sets of statistics, if people look long enough and hard enough at the world's population statistics, they will be able to find figures that will support their particular point of view. For example, those who are against population control programs can look at the graph in Figure

TABLE 8.9 Oceania Regional Population Statistics

Selected Countries	Population Estimate mid-1973 (in thousands)	Growth Rate	Population Density (per sq. km.)	No. More Births Than Deaths (per 1,000)	Life Expectancy Male	Female
American Samoa	32	4.6	162	26.6	65.0	69.1
Australia	13,132 [a]	1.6	2 [b]	10.5	67.9	74.2
British Solomon Is.	179	3.2	6	23.1	—	—
Fiji	551	1.9	30	23.2	68.1	68.1
French Polynesia	120	3.4	30	36.6 [a]	—	—
Gilbert and Ellice Is.	63	3.8	71	15.0	56.9	59.0
Guam	93	1.9	169	30.6	—	—
Johnston Is.	1 [b]	—	1,000 [a]	—	—	—
New Caledonia	119	3.0	6	26.3	—	—
New Hebrides	90	3.0	6	25.0	—	—
New Zealand	2,963	1.8	11	12.0	68.2 [a]	74.3 [a]
Norfolk Is.	2	13.2 [a]	56	7.1 [b]	—	—
Pacific Is.	110	6.1	62	28.6	—	—
Papua New Guinea	2,563	1.0 [b]	6	23.8	46.8 [b]	46.8 [b]
Tonga	92	2.1	131	25.1	—	—
Western Samoa	152	2.1	53	31.8	60.8	65.2

Source: United Nations Statistical Yearbook 1974, N.Y., 1975.
[a] Highest figure.
[b] Lowest figure.

8.1, observe the almost steadily declining birth rate during this century, and the more recent, slowing and now-declining population growth rate, and declare that population control programs are unnecessary and unwarranted infringements on personal rights. They can scan the regional population tables and claim that very few countries of the world's total are really in serious trouble from overpopulation if population density is a yardstick. And further, they can argue that these populous areas are but microscopic dots in relation to the total world area. They can also contend that those countries that have extremely large populations or extremely high population growth rates appear to have ample space for many more people before overcrowding would become a problem. Consequently, many persons of this group favor greater emphasis on worldwide programs related to increasing the life expectancy and general welfare of the have-nots of the present world. Solutions to these problems, they predict, will allow all future human beings, regardless of the number, to live in a style currently reserved for only the elite.

On the other hand, the proponents of population control programs can point to the same statistics and observe that even though the birth rate has been declining for much of the twentieth century, the death rate has been declining even faster, and, therefore, the gap between births and deaths is steadily widening. They can point to rather conservative projections that have two countries reaching a combined population of over 1.75 billion during the mid-1980s—a figure that was reached by the total world's population only about seventy years before, around 1915. Those in favor of population control programs contend that the real issue is not whether or not there will be space available for the growing population, but whether or not our earth's resources can realistically support the numbers projected for the future (see Table 8.10). The remainder of this chapter is dedicated to the exploration of that issue.

TABLE 8.10   United Nations Alternative Projections of World Population (in billions)

	1970	2000	2050	2150
Low	3.6	6.0	9.2	9.8
Medium	3.6	6.5	11.2	12.3
High	3.6	7.1	13.8	16.0

Source: Reprinted by permission from In the Human Interest by Lester Brown, published by W. W. Norton and Co., New York, 1974.

Agricultural Demands on Global Resources

Increased Food Production

The most critical demand that the world's rapidly expanding population has created is the need for increased food production. World population is currently growing by an estimated 200,000 every day, a growth rate that food production—despite heroic efforts—has barely kept pace with. In 1975, for example, the world's farmers had record harvests in corn, wheat, oats, and rice, as well as in other cereal grains, to create a total world record grain harvest of 1.15 billion metric tons. Yet this harvest just barely met world demands. World grain reserves, which equalled more than one hundred days in 1961, were reduced to an estimated thirty-one days. Only three countries in the world exported more food than they imported—the United States, Canada, and Australia. The world's fish harvest, which peaked at over seventy million metric tons in 1970, continued to decline, partly because of overfishing—that is, of the dozen or so species that provide approximately three-fourths of the total catch, despite the availability of some twenty thousand other known species.

It has been estimated that the 1975 record grain harvest of 1.15 billion metric tons will have to be increased to 1.88 billion metric tons by the end of the century, just to keep up with population expansion. At the same time, similar increases in fruits, vegetables, and meat must be realized, not to mention a turn-around in the fish harvest, just to keep the status quo. And the status quo is far from a happy picture. A projection of the current situation would find 1.5 billion persons suffering from starvation and chronic malnutrition in 1995. It would find an additional 1.5 to 2 billion persons suffering from deficiencies of proteins, vitamins, and minerals, and from part-time hunger.

But there is also the nonquantitative side of the picture. In 1975, food was already being used as a political weapon, and some farmers were not producing at maximum levels in order to maintain scarcities and thus reap higher profits for their products. What, then, will 1995 bring? How long will the rest of the world condone the consumption of approximately 35 percent of the world's food production by one country (the United States) with about 6 percent of the world's population? Or will it still accept devoting so much farmland to growing nonfood items used to manufacture nonessential goods in highly developed societies? And what of today's malnourished children? Acute malnutrition in children stunts not only physical but also mental growth. While the stunted physical growth may be rectified by a balanced diet, permanent brain damage will occur if severe malnutrition occurs during the first five years of a child's life. Consequently, it is conceivable that one-quarter of the world's population in the year 1995 will be mentally retarded.

Scarcity of Farmland

Increasing the production of food to meet the current population growth rate will place an ever-growing demand on the world's finite resources. More land must be put under cultivation; but there is only so much prime farmland in the world, and each year more of it is lost to erosion. Natural causes, overcultivation, overgrazing, and ignorance are all responsible for this loss.

In the United States alone, it is estimated that almost five billion tons of topsoil is lost every year, or about ten pounds of soil is lost for every pound of grain produced.

Consequently, more and more marginal land must be put into production. Marginal land, however, requires additional inputs before a worthwhile crop can be grown. Fertilizers and irrigation water, which are themselves scarce commodities, are being required in increasingly greater quantities, not only for the marginal land, but also for increasing production levels from prime farmlands. Despite these added inputs, crop yields per acre on a worldwide basis are declining, primarily because of the large increase of marginal lands. It is estimated that some 14 percent of the world's crop-producing land is under irrigation. Even drifting desert sands are being made to produce. An oil-based mulch is mixed with the sand, stabilizing it and trapping moisture that would normally evaporate.

The Sudan is a pleasant exception to the rather negative statistics regarding world farmland. Several optimistic developments are anticipated: that this country will soon be able to begin farming two hundred million acres of virgin, rain-fed land in its central plains region; that future soil surveys will reveal another 100–200 million cultivable acres in the southern regions of Sudan; that much of this new farmland will be used to meet a projected Middle East grain shortage of twelve million tons by 1985.

Yield per Acre. The most critical aspect of the land resource in relation to food production, however, is yield per acre. Eight of the ten international agricultural centers sponsored by the Consultative Group on International Agricultural Research (CGIAR) devote at least part of their time to research on increasing the yields per acre of a variety of food crops. In addition to those centers described in Table 8.11, CGIAR also sponsors the International Plant Genetics Resources Board (GENES) and the International Center for Agricultural Research in Dry Areas (ICARDA), which were developed in 1976 to concentrate research on growing barley and lentils and sheep raising in the arid sections of the world. CGIAR, an international consortium organized in 1971, has as its primary goal the increase of food production in the developing world. It is cosponsored by the World Bank, the Food and Agricultural Organization (FAO), and the United Nations Development Programme.

Worldwide Research on Fertilizers

The research conducted at these institutes, at others like them around the world, and in private research by corporations and universities concentrate on such things as finding new seed and plant varieties that are more tolerant to temperature variations, that have a greater nutritional value, and that will produce higher yields per acre using less water and fertilizers. Recent shortages and the high cost have made reliance on chemical fertilizers a luxury only highly developed societies can now afford. The United

TABLE 8.11 Program Thrusts of International Agricultural Research and Training Centers

International Center[a]	Program Thrusts	First Year Funded	Location	Agro-climatic Area Served
IRRI	Rice, farming systems involving rice	1960	Philippines	Rainfed and irrigated areas—subtropical, tropical
CIMMYT	Wheat, maize, barley, triticale	1966	Mexico	Rainfed and irrigated—temperate/tropical
IITA	Alternatives to shifting cultivation. Cowpeas, cassava, yams, maize, rice	1968	Nigeria	Rainfed and irrigated—low tropics
CIAT	Beef/forage, cassava, field beans, maize, rice, swine	1969	Colombia	Rainfed and irrigated tropics—1,000 meters to sea level
CIP	Potatoes	1972	Peru	Rainfed and irrigated areas—temperate to tropical
ICRISAT	Sorghum, millets, chick peas, pigeon peas, farming systems	1972	India	Semiarid tropics
ILRAD	Blood diseases of cattle	1974	Kenya	Mainly semiarid tropics
ILCA	Cattle production	1974	Africa	Human to dry tropics

Source: Adapted from Ford Foundation Agricultural Programs: Observations and Issues, a Ford Foundation reprint.
[a] Sponsored by the Consultative Group for International Agricultural Research (CGIAR). The Asian Vegetable Research and Development Center (AVRDC) in Taiwan is an associated international institution but is not CGIAR-supported.

States, for example, used over twenty million tons of chemical fertilizers during the cropping year 1974–1975. India, on the other hand, which had about the same amount of land under cultivation, used only slightly more than three million tons of chemical fertilizer. However, it has been suggested by some that U.S. farmers are wasteful with fertilizers, applying them to their fields to the point of acutely diminishing returns, while at the same time, other farmers throughout the world must do without fertilizer.

Solid-Waste Experiments. Research aimed at reducing dependence upon expensive chemical fertilizers is currently being conducted in two areas that seem to have favorable futures. One area of research is in solid-waste fertilizer, both animal and human. Since 1926, Milwaukee, Wisconsin, has been recycling its solid wastes (80,000 tons per year) into a pelletized fertilizer. Unfortunately, the project has operated at a loss since its inception. Chicago has recently begun spreading its sewage sludge on downstate Illinois farmland, but local residents have complained about unpleasant odors resulting from the practice. In many developing countries, farmers' fields are also fertilized with human waste, but a negative side effect is the spread of numerous debilitating diseases. Animal waste, particularly from cattle feeder-lots and stockyards, has been used experimentally by American farmers with varying results. In many developing nations, particularly in areas of little vegetation, dung from buffalo, ox, and cow is used for fuel. Thus, if this fuel source were used to fertilize the fields, one problem would be solved by creating another.

Plant-Bacteria Symbiosis. The other area of fertilizer experimentation is related to the age-old custom of replenishing worn-out soil through crop rotation. The soil nutrient that is most often missing or used up most quickly is nitrogen. Farmers long ago learned that by rotating their corn or wheat crop with a legume crop, the following year's crop of corn or wheat would yield a harvest far greater than if they continued sowing the same crop year after year. This phenomenon is caused by the fact that a few plants, working in tandem with certain bacteria, can capture nitrogen from the air for the plants' benefit. It has been estimated that each year bacteria and blue-green algae alone fix some ninety million tons of nitrogen on agricultural fields around the world. Yet, because of the increasing pressure to produce more food per acre, another forty million tons of chemically produced nitrogen fertilizer is demanded by the world's farmers. Plant scientists are research-ing the symbiotic relationship between bacteria and legumes, hoping to transfer this relationship to a variety of cereal crops. This would allow the major world food crops to become self-sufficient in at least one critical nutrient—nitrogen.

Water Supply

Water is the decisive and in most instances the chief limiting factor in the growing of crops and raising of animals. Practically all life processes of the plant depend on water. This is pumped via the root hairs into the vas-cular strands of the roots; thence, through special mechanisms, it is carried further up into the stem and the leaves; finally it evaporates into the air. (Borgstrom, 1973, p. 61)

A lack of fresh water, then, rather than the availability of land or fertilizers may eventually be the most critical factor in determining the amount of food the world's farmers produce. Much of the world's prime agricultural lands are located in areas where natural soil moisture, in the form of rain and/or snow, is adequate. As noted earlier, only about 14 percent of the world's crop-producing land is irrigated, but this land pro-duces an estimated 25 percent of the world's food harvest. Obviously then, the availability of fresh irrigation water is critical to the world's food supply.

Irrigation. Irrigation farming is not a modern invention. Water from the Tigris, Euphrates, and Nile rivers was used to irrigate farmlands as far back as 3000 B.C., and perhaps even earlier. This irrigation process undoubt-edly was an important factor in the rise of ancient civilizations in those river valleys. Irrigation has continued as a significant factor in agricultural pro-duction throughout history, and today it is not only significant but critical to the well-being of many millions of people. China, for example, has an estimated one hundred million acres of farmland under irrigation. India, Pakistan, Egypt, Sudan, Spain, the Soviet Union, Mexico, and the United States have significant portions of their food grown under irrigation. In fact, few nations of the world are not at least partially dependent upon irrigation water to grow their food crops.

Although water is replenishable, like all of the world's resources, it is finite. There are elaborate schemes throughout the world to contain and store natural rainwater and melting snows behind a multitude of dams; to pump up subsurface ground water using thousands of tubewells; to redirect river flows; and to desalinize sea water. Despite these, the demands of irrigated agriculture, coupled with increasing demands from urban, industrial, and residential areas, are beginning to cause shortfalls of fresh water.

Long-term irrigation itself produces harmful side effects. Evaporation of irrigation water, particularly in flood irrigation systems, eventually builds up salts in the soil to levels at which the soil will sustain only the hardiest plants. Also, long-term irrigation will often raise the water table to the point where it begins to inhibit root growth, causing stunted plant growth, which, in turn, causes poor yields per acre. High water tables also create a health hazard because refuse water is not able to sanitize itself fully and naturally before it is reused.

A major loss of potential fresh water for irrigation occurs through evaporation. It has been estimated that an average of 4.3 trillion gallons of water falls on United States soil each day, but nearly three-fourths of this water transpires or evaporates. Some methods for reducing this loss, such as wind breaks and soil cover crops, have been used for many years, but they retain only a small portion of the moisture in the soil. No-till farming is being experimented with, as well as methods for slowing the evaporation process, such as covering reservoirs and storage ponds with plastic sheets. Irrigation methods that supply water directly to plant roots through an intricate piping system are also being used. Continuing research aimed at increasing the supply of fresh water for irrigation includes: more efficient methods for storing excess water to prevent its runoff to the oceans; harvesting more water through better watershed management; and recycling industrial and urban water.

Fossil Fuels for Mechanization

Another global resource that is increasingly in demand, at least by the modern agricultural sector, is the fossil fuels used to power mechanized equipment. Mechanization of agriculture in the United States has been largely responsible for having about 4.5 percent of the country's population devoted to producing all the food it needs, plus a surplus that helps sustain life in many other parts of the world. It allows each U.S. farmer to feed about fifty-two people. It has helped to make food prices in the United States the cheapest in the world in relation to income—in 1976 only 17 percent of an American's income was spent purchasing food. It allows one hour of farm labor to produce three times the amount it did only forty years ago.

However, the cost of this mechanization has been extremely high in terms of energy use. Although the energy value in terms of food produced might be as much as two and one-half times greater than the energy inputs of chemical fertilizers and fuels, the energy that goes into processing, transporting, and storing the food grown far exceeds the energy value produced. Lester Brown and Erik Eckholm described this phenomenon using the following statistics:

> In 1945 the production of an acre of corn in the United States required 925,000 kilocalories, of this total, well over half was in the form of gasoline used to operate farm equipment. By 1970 the total energy used to produce an acre of corn had increased to 2,896,800 kilocalories, of which 941,000 kilocalories were accounted for by the use of chemical nitrogen fertilizer, which is produced from fossil fuels. In other words, the energy required to provide the nitrogen applied to an acre of corn in 1970 exceeded the total energy inputs required to produce the acre of corn twenty-five years earlier.
>
> If the food producing system ended with on-farm corn production, it would remain on the plus side of the energy accounting ledger. Even at this level of the food producing system, however, the equivalent of eighty gallons of gasoline ... is used to produce an acre of corn. Much of the corn produced is fed to livestock, and the animal products in turn are then processed, packaged, and transported.
>
> However energy-intensive the on-farm production of food may be in the United States, it is the processing, transportation, and distribution of food that absorb most of the energy. Only 24 percent of the energy consumed by the U.S. food system in 1970 was used before the food products left the farm. (Brown and Eckholm, 1974, pp. 107–108)

Toleration of Pesticides

A final demand on our global resources related to food production, which, in turn, is directly related to population expansion, is toleration of our entire life-support system to an ever-increasing use of pesticides. Rachel Carson, in her book *Silent Spring,* was the first person to focus worldwide attention on the deadly potential of pesticides. A pesticide is a catch-all phrase that includes insecticides, herbicides, rodenticides, fungicides, miticides, and so on—most of which are deadly chemical poisons. Herbicides and insecticides have been singled out as the major threats to the environment's life-cycle because they are the two most prevalently used pesticides.

The two major complaints of herbicide misuse have been the indiscriminate "bombing" with herbicides in Vietnam by U.S. military personnel in the late 1960s and early 1970s in an attempt to defoliate enemy strongholds, and the overapplication of herbicides to farmers' fields. In Vietnam, no one knows for sure what the final outcome of the mass defoliation will bring, but thousands of acres of lush forest growth were destroyed, perhaps forever. What wrath the residual chemicals will wreak is still unknown, and may not become apparent for years to come. But the whole ecology of the herbicide "bombed" areas could have been permanently altered.

Scientists in the United States are becoming increasingly concerned about the vast amounts of herbicide and insecticide runoff from American fields that are turning up in the water, at the bottoms, and in the aquatic life of our rivers. Some scientists hypothesize that if the poisonous chemicals found in today's pesticides continue to be poured into our ecosystem at current rates, eventually the entire ecosystem could be destroyed. They feel that the pesticides are lethal time bombs set to go off and destroy the human food chain.

The three major chemical insecticide families used to protect farm crops are organochlorines, organophosphates, and carbamate compounds. The infamous DDT group is part of the organochlorine family. But all three of these insecticide families kill indiscriminately—the helpful as well as the harmful. They have the capability of upsetting the agricultural environment so drastically that formerly benign insects suddenly become threatening pests. When used heavily and frequently, they have the capability of becoming decreasingly useful in combating harmful insects because such applications aid the surviving insects in building up an immunity to the chemical poisons.

Research on Insecticides

The fact remains, however, that modern agriculture, with the single cropping of literally thousands of consecutive acres, cannot presently control insect pests without the use of poisonous chemicals. Thus, two areas of research on insecticides are concerned with biodegradable chemicals and biological control of insects through the use of hormones and pheromones. Hopefully, research in biodegradable insecticides will produce insecticides that will be deadly to the target insect but will not harm fish, birds, animals, or humans by accumulating in fatty body tissues, as do many of the insecticides currently used. Rather, the new chemicals will be attacked and broken down in the livers of the nontarget organisms. These biodegradable insecticides, however, would remain nonselective toward all insects, killing all they contacted.

The other area of insecticide research—biological control—would overcome this handicap. "Classical" biological insect control developed "a repertoire based on the three P's—predators, pathogens, and parasites." Modern, biological insect control has expanded its role to include research in a broad area of methods for the poisonless control of insects, including genetic engineering of pest-resistant plants, work in altering applications of irrigation and fertilizers, and different approaches to land cultivation practices.

Biological insecticides are third-generation insecticides. First-generation insecticides such as lead, nicotine, and kerosene, and second-generation

Indiscriminate spraying of insecticide is allowing some insect species to become immune to the chemical poisons. Photo Courtesy of Consulate General of Japan, Chicago.

insecticides such as DDT and dieldrin are all deadly chemical poisons. Third-generation insecticides are also chemicals, but they are not poisonous. Instead, they are hormones or pheromones or simulated hormones or pheromones of the target insect. When these chemicals contact the target insect in great quantities at the wrong stage of the insect's life, or are retained within the insect, they can disrupt the lifecycle so that the insect is unable to reproduce, or it begins changing stages prematurely, or it becomes unable to complete the stage-changing process.

All the biological insect control methods have one major advantage over the first- and second-generation insecticides. They do not kill indiscriminately; only the target insect is affected. However, biological pest control is still experimental, and, although numerous pilot projects have been successful, methods for applying these successes on a macroscale to aid farmers on a worldwide basis have not yet been discovered.

The need for the world's farmers to produce more food, caused by the increased world population, has in turn caused increasing demands on our global resources. Increased demand for land, fertilizer, water, energy, and a tolerance of pesticides have become critical issues that must be resolved in the present to prevent mass famine, starvation, and malnutrition in the future.

Case Studies

The following three case studies describe a small part of the work being conducted by two international agricultural centers as they attempt to help increase food production around the world. The first case study focuses on the International Rice Research Institute (IRRI) and a project designed to increase the rice production of Filipino farmers. The second case focuses on the International Maize and Wheat Improvement Center (CIMMYT) and a project aimed at increasing the corn production of Mexican farmers. The third study describes the CIMMYT's involvement with improving the nutritional value of the food produced, in this case, high-lysine corn.

Increasing the Rice Production of Filipino Farmers

In 1973–1974, the Philippines achieved the highest annual rice production in their history—a 28-percent increase over 1972.[2] A substantial contributing factor is a national rice production program called Masagana 99, which brings modern rice technology to small farmers and helps them apply it. Last year the government invested nearly $72 million in the drive, more than two-thirds of it in loans to farmers; the production technology and extension methods were developed by the International Rice Research Institute (IRRI), which also helped with the training of technicians.

These days, a Filipino farmer may go out to his rice field and find a flag waving from a tall wand—a signal that his crop is in trouble and that instructions on how to save it are taped to the shaft. Before long, the extension man should pull up on a new motorbike to make sure that the message got across and the rice is being properly treated.

The farmer is apt to pay attention because he, himself, has seen thriving rice plots on a demonstration farm, or perhaps has been to a film or slide demonstration showing the differences in yields between the old ways and the new. Or he may have a bank loan that requires him to follow the technician's instructions. Posters, banners, broadcasts, and other media persuaders urge him on.

As early as 1965, IRRI demonstrated that seven to eight tons of rice per hectare could be obtained on irrigated land by using newly developed,

[2] Based on data from Irene Uribe, "Rice: Larger Yields for Smaller Farmers." *RF Illustrated* 2 (March 1975): 1. Published by The Rockefeller Foundation. Reprinted by permission.

high-yielding varieties and by giving them proper care. Further research turned out rices that can yield up to eleven tons under ideal conditions and at least four to five in farmers' fields. These gains are phenomenal, but they depend on irrigation, which reaches only one-quarter of the farms in the Philippines and possibly one-third of all rice-growing Asia. This fraction cannot produce enough of a surplus every year to supply all of Asia's people, especially with populations doubling in the space of one generation.

Masagana 99 was aimed primarily at the millions of farmers whose fields are unirrigated and who missed the first rice boom. "Masagana" means "bountiful harvest," and 99 cavans is the yield target—an equivalent of 4.3 tons per hectare. (A cavan is a sack of rice weighing about 100 pounds.) A goal of 99 cavans per hectare must have sounded like pie in the sky to farmers whose best efforts were bringing them one-quarter as much.

Early results encouraged the scientists to go ahead with the training of extension specialists who could supervise on-farm demonstrations of the new techniques. Eleven men were selected from the Philippine government extension service for special courses in rice production under upland and rainfed conditions. They spent three weeks at IRRI, in seminars and out on the experimental plots around the countryside, learning what could go wrong with rice and what should be done about it. When the course was over, they took possession of their new motorbikes and dispersed to the barrios assigned to them, to organize Masagana 99 field trials and keep an eye on their progress.

Harder to convince than the farmers were the rural banks. In 1972, rice was grown on 2,600 hectares with supervised credit, and on another 3,000 hectares using the IRRI practices but with financial backing from other sources. The results made the bankers revise their policy: Many farmers using Masagana 99 technology topped 99 cavans per hectare; some harvested 145. Their neighbors who stuck to the old varieties and practices averaged 40 to 65 cavans.

The barrios that had cooperative bankers were easy to spot. Where credit policies were liberal, 85 percent of the farmers were using the new technology, and those districts became favorite showplaces. High officials were impressed with the pilot project, and in 1973 the massive government-backed program was launched. IRRI trained 680 technicians and the University of the Philippines another 214; in addition, some 1,200 took a three-day crash course. The government bought over a thousand motorcycles and put $200,000 into a promotion effort. The payoff was record rice production.

The program was intended to reach 1.2 million hectares; it already has reached more than 900,000 hectares. The program initially aimed to enroll 500,000 farmers; more than 650,000 have signed up so far. Average production on the targeted hectarage was about 60 cavans before the program began; it is now 78 cavans, according to the government. Six hundred million pesos were lent to small farmers during fiscal 1974, and the repayment rate is nearly 85 percent.

Increasing the Corn Production of Mexican Farmers

By 1967, the scientists at the International Center for the Improvement of Maize and Wheat (CIMMYT) were facing a frustrating fact of life.[3] Their improved seeds and farming methods were delivering dramatically increased maize yields in CIMMYT's research fields. But beyond the fences, despite this example, most of the Mexican campesinos who were the intended beneficiaries of their success, continued to farm in traditional, less productive ways. The average yields of small farms in Mexico remained low, and the small farmers remained poor.

Although the postrevolutionary reforms of the 1920s had greatly altered the political and social organization of the Puebla villages, many government promises had remained unfilled, and many subsequent efforts at reform were frustrated. Bitter disappointment had produced cynicism. The farmers were incapable of wide-scale cooperation, were suspicious of outsiders, and were especially distrustful of government programs. Fertilizer, seed, and pesticides, when they were made available in local markets at all, often arrived late and were frequently ill-suited to the area's ecological conditions. Credit, too, was poorly timed, if available at all, so that loans were sometimes dissipated on nonagricultural needs and became difficult to repay.

The success of the Puebla Project depended on changing farmer attitudes, so that a small group of trained personnel could reach a large number of the area's 43,000 families. The infrastructure for providing agricultural services was already in place. Good roads connected the state of Puebla with outside markets. Agencies existed to provide credit, fertilizer, crop insurance, and price supports. But the quintessential input for the small farmer was not seed or fertilizer, but credit, without which he could not finance his next harvest. The four major credit institutions in the area were reluctant to make loans to individual, small farmers.

Under a new arrangement worked out by the united campesinos with the Agricultural Bank, one of the largest credit institutions in the area, only one member of a campesino group is required to show clear title to his land to qualify the whole group for credit. In return, the group generally guarantees the loans, assessing its members when one defaults. Under the new system, the amount of agricultural credit extended to the Puebla campesinos increased from 1.3 million pesos in 1968 to more than 12.5 million pesos in 1972. In the same period, there was a marked improvement in the loan-repayment rate, which rose to average well over 90 percent at the three largest credit institutions.

The distribution of fertilizer was also reformed. Formerly, local dealers supplied fertilizer to the highest bidder in each village, so the poorer farmers

[3] Based on data from Anthony Wolff, "Who's Got What? The Puebla Project." *RF Illustrated* 2 (August 1975): 10. Published by The Rockefeller Foundation. Reprinted by permission.

were shut out. The new system established central fertilizer markets in Puebla and two other regional centers, where the farmers buy directly from the producers at a single, official price.

At the government price-control agency, which purchases maize at fixed prices at fourteen warehouses throughout the area, unwieldy procedures have been simplified. Crop insurance, which is a requirement for government credit, is still little understood among the farmers, but the system has been adjusted to improve protection against small-scale losses.

The first year of field tests demonstrated that the best results were achieved with local strains already familiar to some Puebla farmers. Thereafter, the researchers focused on defining recommended production practices for these varieties, taking into account variations in soil morphology, planting dates, elevation above sea level, and moisture availability. In all, packages of recommended practices were developed for sixteen different production conditions. The most significant changes were made in plant density and rate of nitrogen fertilization.

In the very first year of the project, the yields of the 103 participating farmers averaged a bumper 4.0 tons per hectare, compared with the 2.1 ton average for the entire project area. The number of farmers on the official credit roll (a conservative indicator of actual participation in the project) swelled from 103 in 1968—a mere 0.2 percent of the Puebla farmers, tilling just 0.1 percent of the land—to 2,561 farmers the next year, representing almost 6 percent of the total and 7.3 percent of the acreage (see Table 8.12).

TABLE 8.12 Participants in the Puebla Project

	1968	1969	1970	1971	1972	1973
Number of cooperators	103	2,561	4,833	5,240	6,202	7,194
Percent of total	0.2	5.9	11.1	12.1	14.3	16.6
Hectares in plan	76	5,838	12,601	14,438	17,533	20,604
Percent of total	0.1	7.3	15.8	18.0	21.9	25.8

Note: The "official" definition of a participant in the Plan Puebla program is any farmer who is on a credit list. Based on this very restrictive definition, the table shows the growth in direct Plan Puebla coverage during the first six years.

For the area as a whole, average yields increased by approximately 30 percent during the first four years of the project. Forty-four percent of the farmers increased production between 1967 and 1970, and 80 percent of these attributed their success either directly or indirectly to the project (see Table 8.13).

Although the lessons learned during the first years at Puebla cannot be prescribed universally, the program's graduates are now using their Puebla experience at regional programs in three other countries: Colombia, Peru,

TABLE 8.13 Increased Crop Yields

Note: The main purpose of the project was to increase maize yields. Maize yields in Puebla (over the whole area) are estimated to have risen as follows:

Year	General Average kg/ha
1967	1,330
1968	2,140
1969	1,832
1970	1,962
1971	1,927
1972	2,499

and Honduras, as well as other Mexican states, including Mexico and Tlaxcala.

Improving the Nutritional Value of High-Lysine Corn

Improved corn varieties equal or exceed many of the world's existing strains in yield, disease resistance, and taste.[4] But even more important, while ordinary corn is notably poor in vital protein, the newest CIMMYT varieties are as rich in balanced protein as skimmed milk.

It has taken ten years of sophisticated science and patient field labor at CIMMYT and elsewhere to translate a Purdue University laboratory breakthrough into a plant adapted to the tropical agriculture and consumer preferences of the world's hunger belt. The final step is to get the new seed out of the test fields at CIMMYT and into farmers' fields and local markets around the world, and finally into the stomachs of protein-starved people.

It has been known for at least sixty years that corn, the world's third most important food after rice and wheat, is nutritionally inadequate. In 1914, researchers at the Connecticut Agricultural Research Station induced starvation in laboratory rats by feeding them generous helpings of corn. The specific deficiency of the corn diet was identified when the rats were restored to health with small supplements of two protein fractions, the amino acids lysine and tryptophane. There were, it seemed two ways to starve: One was lack of food; the other was lack of balanced protein.

The problem with corn is that while the normal kernel is about 10 percent protein, half of it is locked up in the fraction zein, which is useful

---

[4] Based on data from Anthony Wolff, "Corn as Rich in Protein as Milk." *RF Illustrated* 2 (March 1975): 6–7. Published by The Rockefeller Foundation. Reprinted by permission.

in the manufacture of textiles, plastics, and other things, but is totally indigestible by single-stomached creatures. Moreover, the normal corn kernel is especially poor in lysine and tryptophane—essential amino acids that the human body cannot synthesize and must get from food.

This nutritional deficiency of corn does not show up only in laboratory rats. It can be recognized in people wherever corn is a major source of protein—perhaps the only regular source—in the daily diet. Protein starvation is often called by an exotic name—"kwashiorkor"—but its symptoms are familiar: stunted growth, bellies bloated by edema, diarrhea, and brittle hair with an abnormal reddish color. Kwashiorkor is the leading cause of mortality among infants and children in many parts of the world, and the proximate cause of many more deaths ascribed to other illnesses. In Latin America, where protein-poor cereal grains are the imperfect staff of life, eighty-two of every one thousand children die before their first birthday, another twelve before they reach the age of four. Even many of those who survive half-starved do not escape: Often brain-damaged, they become the adults who are most in need of help and least able to help themselves.

It was not until 1963 that a Purdue University team headed by biochemist Edwin T. Mertz applied newly developed methods of protein analysis to an odd group of mutant corns characterized by soft, floury endosperm inside an opaque, chalk-white kernel. The Purdue tests showed that the opaque characteristic, which had been noted as early as 1915 without exciting much scientific interest, is associated with a recessive gene that replaces some of the kernel's useless zein with valuable lysine and tryptophane. The second of the mutants to be tested—routinely tagged opaque-2, or O_2 for short—revealed a lysine content of 3.4 percent, a vital increase of the 2.0 percent lysine in normal corn. In addition, opaque-2 corn showed elevated levels of tryptophane and other amino acids.

Translating the laboratory discovery in Indiana into a corn crop in Columbia took almost two years. From Purdue's small experimental seed supply Dr. Harpstead was able to get only twenty-five kernels early in 1965. After increasing the seed, crossing it with varieties adapted to local conditions, and testing the results in the laboratory, it was not until the January 1967 harvest that Dr. Harpstead had enough high-lysine corn to begin the first nutritional tests on animals.

After one hundred thirty days, a control group of twenty-pound weanling pigs on a diet of unsupplemented ordinary corn had an average weight gain of only 6.6 pounds and exhibited the stunted skeletal development, cell damage, and liver degeneration associated with protein starvation. In startling contrast, the pigs fed straight O_2 corn had gained a respectable 73.2 pounds each and showed no ill effects from their monotonous menu.

But the millenium that seemed so near in 1967 has remained frustratingly out of reach. Corn breeders at CIMMYT and elsewhere have had to work for six more years to transform high-lysine corn into a potential staple for tens of millions with incomes of perhaps $100 per year. The major obstacle, ironically, has been the O_2 gene itself. Although it has superior nutritional value, the mutant gene is linked to the O_2 corn's soft, floury kernel, which is both light in weight and vulnerable to pest attacks, producing lower yields for farmers. By the same token, opaque corn is unattractive to the majority of consumers, who are accustomed to the harder "flint" or "dent" kernels with a deeper, translucent color. In the marketplace, the "super grain" cannot compete with less nutritious varieties; and what the consumer will not buy, the farmer will not grow. For CIMMYT's plant breeders, then, the problem was to marry the opaque-2 gene to corn varieties better adapted to the demands of local farmers and consumers.

On May 10, 1972—nine years after the discovery of high-lysine corn at Purdue, more than four years after the demonstration of its food value for starving people in Colombia—CIMMYT harvested the first crop of improved tropical corn that included both high lysine content and a hard kerneled, flinty textured kernel. The total harvest was just four bushels of seed. By the end of the year, that seed had been increased to twenty tons for trials around the world. Beginning in 1974, the opaque-2 gene, with modifier genes to correct color and texture, has been bred into every strain in CIMMYT's growing catalog of improved tropical corn plants.

The "super grains" must still be tested and fine-tuned under local conditions around the world; adopted and distributed by the agricultural agencies of dozens of national governments; properly grown in tens of thousands, even millions, of individual farmer's fields; and ultimately accepted by hundreds of millions of consumers. Only in the United States, Brazil, and Colombia (where the development of opaque-2 corn began), has the new seed been released to farmers on even a limited basis. Most of this improved corn is for livestock rather than for people, although in Colombia a commercial food has been produced from earlier high-lysine varieties by grinding the kernels into a form in which its floury texture is acceptable to consumers.

Moreover, the high-lysine seeds releasd so far are hybrids, which require a highly developed system of seed distribution. CIMMYT is collaborating with national programs in seven other countries to develop well-adapted, high-lysine varieties that are open-pollinated—capable of reproducing from their own seed—for use in the small-farm agriculture typical of poor countries. "None of these national efforts has reached the point where the government can promote opaque-2 as a change of crop and food," reports CIMMYT, "but that time is rapidly approaching, perhaps within the next two or three years."

Nonagricultural Demands on Global Resources

Two of the nonagricultural demands on our global resources that are partially caused by the rapidly expanding population, are two of the same resources demanded by the need to increase food production—land and water. Urban sprawl, the name given to the increased need of land for living space around our larger cities, has manifested itself in elite, suburban development for persons desiring to leave the inner city and in indescribable slums for landless, unemployed peasants.

Urban Sprawl Usurps Farmland

Earlier in this chapter we noted that population density has reached the critical stage in only a comparatively few isolated areas of the world. When urban sprawl consumes agriculturally unuseable land, the resource consumption is not critical. However, the situation becomes critical when expansion uses land that is valuable for food production. For example, in Great Britain an estimated 50,000 acres of farmland is lost each year to the expansion of cities and towns, the creation of new water reservoirs, and the building of new roads. In the United States, an estimated one-half million acres of farmland are lost each year to similar expanding cities and towns, airports, shopping centers, and rural housing developments (as illustrated by the Northeast corridor from Boston to Washington, D.C.).

Some people believe that if they own the land, they have the right to do with it as they please. They contend that if a greater profit can be made by converting productive farmland to a suburban home development or an industrial park, the landowner should be allowed to convert the land if he so chooses. Dissenters, however, claim that the ever-increasing loss of productive or potentially productive farmland, coupled with the population expansion, will result in a shortfall of food-producing land. The dissenters charge that if urban sprawl is a necessary fact of our times, it should be directed vertically, not horizontally.

Land Reclamation. On the plus side of the land ledger is the formerly unusable land that has been reclaimed by human ingenuity. Former swamps, jungle, desert, and even one-time sea bottoms have been converted to useable land. Parts of the infamous New Jersey swamps and Hackensack River meadowlands, for example, once made a large part of northeastern New Jersey a smelly eyesore. They have been drained and filled to provide land for industrial sites, recreational parks, a sports complex, interstate highways, and housing developments. Deserts in the southwestern United States have been irrigated with subsurface water and made to bloom. In the wake of this literal flowering have sprung hundreds of resort areas, retirement villages, recreational facilities, and productive farmland. Other deserts of the world have also been reclaimed for growing agricultural products, but unfortunately, in still other areas hundreds of acres of productive farmland are being lost each year to the invasion of desert sands.

Human ingenuity has terraced formerly unuseable mountainsides, where homes have sprung up like weeds, clinging tenaciously to the almost vertical land. Some of these developments have spawned luxurious living quarters like those in the canyons of southern California. Other developments, however, have spawned festering slum shacks like those on the hillsides surrounding Hong Kong, Rio de Janeiro, and countless other cities throughout the world. Jungles such as those in Brazil are being transformed, for better or worse, into more useable land, and perhaps someday even the ocean floor will be permanently inhabited by humans. Many believe this will happen out of necessity rather than as a novelty. And once the ocean floors are conquered, can the habitation of the moon and even other planets of our solar system be far behind?

Water—A Vital Resource

Fresh water and food are the two most basic necessities of human life. Without water or food, of course, the human being and nearly all other living things known to us will die. Yet mankind has been so negligent with the vital resource of water that shortages exist when the supply should be adequate for a hundred times the inhabitants of the earth. Pollution, misuse, and poor watershed management are responsible for wasting billions of gallons of water each day.

Conservation Needed. The human need for water is directly related to the level of technological society achieved. Members of a low-level technological society require only about one gallon of water each day. A highly developed technological society, however, will require between fifty and sixty gallons of water each day for each of its members, including about thirty-five gallons for domestic use. The remaining water is used in the production of consumer goods used daily by each member. For example, each gallon of gasoline refined takes a gallon of water; each ton of steel manufactured takes two hundred tons of water; to make a ton of potatoes into potato chips takes four thousand gallons of water; and each paper mill and chemical factory may use as much as fifteen million gallons of water each day.

But how much of this water could have been recycled and used again? How much is wasted on producing mindless, nonessential consumer goods? How much is just simply wasted? How much refuse water is expelled into clean water, thus contaminating it too? The combined answer to these questions probably amounts to millions of gallons of needlessly used and misused water each day. Of course, water is always purifying and replenishing itself. It is one of the few global resources that revives itself from the ravages performed on it by humans. But water is still a finite item, and purification and replenishment take time. Consequently, if nature becomes recalcitrant for even a short period of time, sudden acute shortages of useable water for domestic, industrial, and/or agricultural use quite likely will occur.

Research on Desalinization Methods. In addition to the conservation techniques being implemented in highly developed technological societies, untapped sources of water are also being researched. One exotic idea is to capture huge icebergs from the polar regions and tow them south by a fleet of oceangoing tugs to add to the water supplies of the larger coastal cities.

But the major research concerned with increasing the water supply is devoted to desalinizing ocean water. With 72 percent of the earth's surface covered with salty ocean water, a major breakthrough in this area could almost permanently solve the world's water problems.

Several methods for desalinization, such as freezing, electrodialysis, reverse osmosis, and distillation, have proved successful and are currently being used throughout the world to produce fresh water. So far, they are used only on a very limited scale because of the high cost of these processes. Still, more than eight hundred desalinization plants produce over one hundred million gallons of fresh water each day.

When salt water freezes, the ice crystals that form are almost pure water. Drawing off these crystals separates the fresh water from the salt and from other impurities. The electrodialysis process for desalinizing sea water involves passing an electrical current through the water to produce an electrical charge in the water's impurities. These electrically charged particles, called ions, are then attracted by oppositely charged electrodes, purifying the water. This method has been especially successful in small-scale production situations. Reverse osmosis forces the water through a series of membranes, allowing only the water, but not the impurities, to pass.

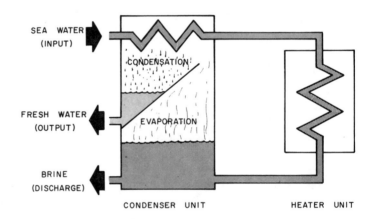

MULTI-STAGE FLASH DISTILLATION PROCESS

The method most commonly used to desalinize ocean water is the distillation method. David Hamilton describes the process:

> In commercial plants the distillation process is mostly carried out under reduced pressure to lower the boiling point, and in as many as thirty to forty stages, in what is called multiflash distillation. Some of the heated water "flashes" into steam as it is injected into a chamber in which the pressure has been reduced, and pure vapour is collected on the condenser tubes. Each chamber is at a slightly lower temperature and pressure, and the water is passed through them all. Sea water is recirculated through the condenser tubes so that it picks up heat from the hot condensing vapour,

and is then fed into the first chamber of the series once more. This means that it needs little heating before its temperature is high enough for it to be injected at the start of the cycle again. (Hamilton, 1973, p. 216)

Scarcity of Mineral Resources

Another of the major nonagricultural demands on our global resources caused in part by the rapidly growing population is the demand for mineral resources. Increased demand, which has raised the price of many of these minerals, and new refining processes, have made it profitable for many mining companies to begin reprocessing their waste piles as well as mining areas that were once considered too poor in mineral content. Greater demands and higher prices have also made the recycling of metals a profitable enterprise, for which the environmentalists are extremely thankful.

Shortages of some minerals have begun to affect world political decisions. Many of the minerals required for manufacturing processes in highly developed countries are found almost exclusively in developing countries, many of which are politically unstable. Political wheeling and dealing to acquire rights to those scarce minerals has resulted in political upheavals, revolutions, and military confrontations in several developing countries. The acquisition of mineral rights has also been a deciding factor in determining whether or not a developing nation receives food and/or economic assistance from a highly developed country.

The acute shortage of minerals critical to the survival of the industrial sectors of highly developed nations is illustrated in Table 8.14, which depicts past, present, and anticipated future import requirements of the thirteen basic minerals required by industries in the United States. In virtually every highly developed country, demand for the majority of essential minerals necessary in industry exceeds the amount that country is capable of producing itself. Hence, the dependence on imported minerals and their increasing importance to the economies of both developed and developing nations.

The Ocean Floor. Strange as it may seem, the most promising source of a new supply of minerals is the same source that shows the most promise for creating a new supply of fresh water—the oceans. About one hundred years have passed since the crew of the British oceanographic ship, H.M.S. *Challenger,* first discovered strange looking formations lying on the ocean bottom. These formations, called nodules, were comprised primarily of manganese and iron. Although it was later discovered that concentrations of these nodules were relatively common on the ocean floor, interest remained low because the nodules were from three to five miles deep, and iron and manganese were readily available on land.

But in the 1950s, John Mero discovered that the nodules dredged from the Pacific Ocean floor contained significant amounts of copper, nickel, cobalt, molybdenum, vanadium, and zinc. These nodules could be profitably

TABLE 8.14 U.S. Dependence on Imports of Principal Industrial Raw
Materials with Projections to 2000

Raw Material	1950	1970	1985	2000
			(percent imported)	
Aluminum	64	85	96	98
Chromium	n.a.	100	100	100
Copper	31	0	34	56
Iron	8	30	55	67
Lead	39	31	62	67
Manganese	88	95	100	100
Nickel	94	90	88	89
Phosphorus	8	0	0	2
Potassium	14	42	47	61
Sulfur	2	0	28	52
Tin	77	n.a.	100	100
Tungsten	n.a.	50	87	97
Zinc	38	59	72	84

Source: Reprinted by permission from *In the Human Interest* by Lester Brown,
published by W. W. Norton and Co., New York, 1974.

refined if methods for getting them off the ocean bottom could be devised.
Presently, several dozen companies from several highly developed countries
are attempting to solve this technological problem. One promising solution
for getting the nodules from the ocean depths of three to five miles involves
a hydraulic lifting system, which operates like a vacuum cleaner. A dredge,
connected to the mother ship by about three miles of piping, moves along
the ocean bottom; pressure induced by pumping air into the pipe pumps the
nodules, along with a large amount of water, up to the ship on the surface.
Another method involves a continuous-line-bucket system, consisting of a
continuous loop of nearly ten miles of heavy polypropylene cable. Attached
to the cable every eighty feet are dredge buckets, capable of handling between one and five tons of nodules each. The cable is strung between two
ships, cruising slowly, a half mile apart. The cable is lowered to the ocean
bottom, and a rotary action is begun, using huge drums on board the ships.
Both of these techniques have been tested at the prototype stage, with sufficient success to make their developers optimistic.

Hydrothermal Deposits. A second potentially rich source of minerals is
in hydrothermal deposits. Some half-dozen hydrothermal deposits have been
located in ocean bottom trenches, probably caused by continental drift.
Portions of these trenches contain scalding hot water that contains dissolved
copper, gold, silver, iron, manganese, nickel, zinc, and cadmium, as much
as ten times richer than the water above it. Although these hydrothermal
deposits are much more difficult to mine, they are at the same time much
more valuable than the nodules. A hydrothermal deposit in a trench in the

Red Sea, for example, is estimated to contain about $6 billion worth of copper and zinc in the uppermost thirty feet of sediment alone.

Summary

The population of the world is growing at an unprecedented rate. Even if worldwide, heroic birth control measures were implemented, the impetus of this population expansion will undoubtedly double the 1960 population figure of three billion by the year 2000. However, the implementation of heroic birth control methods in the immediate future is a very slim possibility since there is much sentiment against such programs. Many persons believe that numbers is not the critical issue. Rather, it is the distributon of economic opportunities that is more responsible for the world's problems.

Shortages of food (both bulk and nutritional), land, water, fertilizer, energy, and minerals have all become world issues in recent years. Solutions to the demands on our global resources seem to be divided into two categories—technological imperatives and social imperatives. On the technological side, the sheer number of births requires new and improved birth control methods and programs, at least for those who do not want more children but do not know how or cannot afford to prevent them. New technological solutions must be found for problems that permeate all phases of food production: for raising average yields per acre even higher than they currently are; for supplying arid areas with plenty of water; for providing a cheap and sufficient supply of fertilizer to all farmers regardless of economic level; and for creating pesticides that are nonpoisonous to all living things whether plant, animal, or insect, except the target pest.

At the same time, there are social imperatives: Dissemination of the problem-solving technologies through formal and informal education processes to all persons, not just a select few, must be undertaken. Values that are no longer compatible with a changing society must be left behind, while realizing that to change values without a solid foundation of reason will surely result in disaster. Technologies must be found that produce employment and economic growth, not the reverse. The nutritional value of the foods most often consumed by the world's poor must be increased to prevent chronic malnutrition and its consequences. The inequities of life must be eliminated that make one country's life expectancy twenty-five years while that of another is seventy-eight years.

DISCUSSION QUESTIONS

1. Teitelbaum outlined twelve positions against the need for supporting population programs and four positions supporting such projects. Discuss the strengths and weaknesses of each position.

2. Food and minerals, two global resources becoming increasingly scarce, are being distributed or denied because of political affiliations and beliefs. Do you agree or disagree with this tactic? Defend your position.

3. Farmers throughout the world defend the use of poisonous pesticides by claiming: (1) that they must produce the vast amount of food needed to feed the world; (2) that the ecolog-ical damage is really minimal compared to the result; and (3) that a reduction of pesticide use will result in widespread famine. Do you agree or disagree? Defend your position.

BIBLIOGRAPHY

A Richer Harvest. New York: Ford Foundation, October 1967.

Alexander, T. "Mining Bonanza at Sea: Geologists' Theory Points to Lodes on Ocean Floor." *Nature/Science Annual, 1975,* New York: Time-Life Books, 1974.

Becker, T. "To Feed the Swelling Multitude." *The Christian Science Monitor,* October 22, 1975, pp. 14–15.

Borgstrom, G. *Harvesting the Earth.* New York: Abelard-Schuman, 1973.

Borrie, W. D. *Population, Environment, and Society.* Auckland, New Zealand: Auckland University Press, 1973.

Bourne, E. "Poverty Persists in India: Population Growth, Drought Add to Problem." *The Christian Science Monitor,* April 23, 1975, p. 26.

Brown, H. *The Challenge of Man's Future.* New York: Viking Press, 1954.

Brown, L. R. *In the Human Interest: A Strategy to Stabilize World Population.* New York: W. W. Norton & Co., 1974.

————. *Seeds of Change.* New York: Praeger Publishers, 1970.

Brown, L. R., and Eckholm, E. P. *By Bread Alone.* New York: Praeger Publishers, 1974.

Carson, R. *Silent Spring.* Boston: Houghton Mifflin Co., 1962.

Childe, V. G. *Man Makes Himself.* New York: New American Library, 1951.

Cowen, R. C. "Is Growth Good for Us?" *The Christian Science Monitor,* November 3, 1975, pp. 16–17.

Deevey, E. S., Jr. "The Human Population." *Scientific American* 203 (September 1960): 195–204.

Eberstadt, N. "Program in Context: Population." *RF Illustrated* 2 (March 1975): 10–11.

Frejka, T. *The Future of Population Growth: Alternative Paths to Equilibrium.* New York: John Wiley & Sons, 1973.

Graham, F., Jr. *Since Silent Spring.* Boston: Houghton Mifflin Co., 1970.

Gwatkin, D. R. "Policies Affecting Population in West Africa." *Studies in Family Planning* 3 (September 1972).

Hamilton, D. *Technology, Man and the Environment.* London: Faber & Faber, Ltd., 1973.

Hardin, L. S. *Ford Foundation Agricultural Programs: Observations and Issues.* New York: Ford Foundation, 1974.

Harkavy, O. "The Rationale for International Assistance to Population Programs in the Developing World." *International Journal of Health Services* 4 (1973).

Heer, D. M. *Society and Population.* 2d ed. Englewood Cliffs, N.J.: Prentice-Hall, 1975.

International Research in Agriculture. New York: Consultative Group on International Agricultural Research, 1974.

NASA, Technology Utilization Office. *Space Benefits—The Secondary Application of Aerospace Technology in Other Sectors of the Economy.* Washington, D.C.: U.S. Government Printing Office, 1975.

Nature/Science Annual, 1975. New York: Time-Life Books, 1974.

"New Donors Support Agricultural Centers." *RF Illustrated* 2 (March 1976): 12.

Oka, T. "Managing Our Planet: Pattern for Survival." *The Christian Science Monitor,* February 10–14, 1975.

Rural Development: Sector Policy Paper. Washington, D.C.: World Bank, 1975.

Shaplen, R. *Toward the Well-Being of Mankind: Fifty Years of the Rockefeller Foundation.* Garden City, N.Y.: Doubleday & Co., 1964.

Sowing the Green Revolution: International Institute of Tropical Agriculture, Ibadan, Nigeria. New York: Ford Foundation, April 1970.

Teitelbaum, M. "Population and Development: Is a Consensus Possible?" *Foreign Affairs* (July 1974): 742–60.

Tonge, P. "Farming: The Challenge Ahead" (a 4-part series). *The Christian Science Monitor,* March 9–12, 1976.

United Nations Statistical Yearbook, 1974. New York: United Nations, 1975.

Uribe, I. "Rice: Larger Yields for Smaller Farmers." *RF Illustrated* 2 (March 1975): 1.

Willman, F. "Biodegradable Pesticides: The Congenial Environment." *RF Illustrated* 2 (March 1975): 5.

Wolff, A. "Corn as Rich in Protein as Milk." *RF Illustrated* 2 (March 1975): 6–7.

———. "Hormones and Pheromones: The Congenial Environment." *RF Illustrated* 2 (August 1975): 5.

———. "Who Got What? The Puebla Project." *RF Illustrated* 2 (August 1975): 10.

Chapter 9
The Energy Issue

Introduction

Since the dawn of the Industrial Revolution and the introduction of prime movers to the mass production of goods, energy and its sources have become an increasingly important issue for many of the world's inhabitants. As far back as the early 1900s, scientists were predicting that the world's supply of coal, then the major source of energy, would be totally consumed within twenty years. Fortunately, those scientists have been proven wrong in their assessment of coal reserves in the world; so have their contemporary counterparts who, only a few short years ago, were predicting the depletion of the world's crude oil reserves, the current major energy source. Despite increased energy use, new reserves of coal and oil have been found in recent years.

However, to expect that this good fortune will continue indefinitely is foolish. Fossil fuels are finite items requiring millions of years for nature to create. Continuing to find new reserves to keep pace with fuel consumption is unlikely; add to that problem the prediction that consumption will increase in the future. The fact that energy consumption and, therefore, fossil fuel consumption will increase in the future must be accepted as true. Energy consumption is directly related to the development of a society, particularly its industrial development. Therefore, if future energy consumption does not increase, then world development must come to a standstill and even regress in some areas, which is a highly unlikely possibility. Obviously then, new energy sources must be discovered and/or created to replace the fossil fuels just as oil replaced coal during the twentieth century.

And therein lies the crux of the energy issue: Which energy or energy source should replace the fossil fuels? Should we continue to rely on one major energy supply? Or should we develop multiple major energy sources? Is the continued search for and discovery of new reserves of fossil fuels only compounding the problem by not forcing the issue to an immediate solution, or are these new discoveries actually saving us from a technological disaster? Or, should the major focus of the issue be on reducing the amount of energy wasted and on conserving current energy supplies, rather than on finding new supplies? What shall we do about the vast differences in energy consumption between the have and have-not societies? How will converting new energies and/or a new energy source(s) affect the world's economy? These questions and others like them are the reasons why energy is currently one of the major world issues.

The answers to these questions—when they are found, if they are found—will affect the lives of everyone in the world. In this chapter we shall discuss current and future energy uses from three perspectives: in terms of the amount of use; who is or will be using the energy; and for what purpose. The major portion of the chapter, however, will explore the major potential energies or energy sources of the future.

Worldwide Energy Use

The amount of energy consumed by each individual in the world is determined, not only by the society's technological level, but also by the individual's age and marital status. A person living in a highly developed technological society obviously consumes much more energy than someone living in a transitional or tribal society. In fact, energy consumption is sometimes used as one indicator to determine the technological level of a society—the more energy consumed, the higher the technological level is hypothesized to be. Also an individual's energy consumption increases significantly whenever an independent household is initiated. Therefore, it is conceivable that a man and woman in a transitional society, living in a newly established household, might be consuming more energy than two single individuals in a highly developed society who have not yet established an independent household.

If we discuss energy usage at this microlevel, the disparities seem only minor. However, when use is discussed at the macrolevel, the disparities become major in comparing highly developed nations to developing nations. The United States has always been a glutton in the use of energy. Some comparative data stress this fact dramatically: The energy consumed in the United States in 1976 is about equal to all the energy consumed by the whole human race prior to 1900; U.S. energy consumption provides each American with the equivalent of two hundred servants; all of Asia, containing more than 60 percent of the world's population, consumes only one-third of the energy used by Americans; per capita energy consumption in China is one twenty-fifth that of U.S. use; Western Europe's population consumes only one-third of the per capita energy consumption in the United States; and per capita energy consumption in the U.S.S.R. is about one-half that of the United States. Of the total energy consumed worldwide annually, the United States consumes about 35 percent.

United States Consumption

This edge in energy consumption has helped to give the United States the highest standard of living in the world. It has also helped provide food

New York City consumes as much energy as some entire countries. Photo by Edward C. Pytlik.

for those nations that are not self-sufficient in food production since America's highly mechanized agricultural system can produce huge surplus harvests. However, growing food uses only about 2 percent of the total energy consumed in the United States. Industrial concerns use about 42 percent of America's energy, with the six major areas of primary metals, chemicals and allied products, petroleum refining, the concrete-glass-clay-stone industries, paper, and food industries consuming over two-thirds of the total industrial figure.

Transportation, America's second major energy consumer, uses over 25 percent of the total. If the manufacturing of transportation vehicles were included in this figure, however, the energy consumption for transportation would rise to almost 35 percent of the nation's total energy consumption. The automobile is by far the greatest consumer of transportation's share of energy. In fact, the automobile is the single, greatest subcategory consumer, using approximately 13 percent of all the energy consumed in the United States. Total residential usage is less than 20 percent, and total commercial usage is less than 15 percent of the U.S. energy consumption.

The greatest criticism against the large amount of energy consumed in the United States is that so much of it is wasted. Studies have shown that as much as 40 percent of the energy used in residential and commercial buildings could be conserved, and even more could be conserved in the transportation area. Studies conducted in industry have shown that energy savings totaling 25 percent could be realized from that area. "In 1972 about 25 percent of the total raw fuel consumed in the United States was used for the production of electric power. Yet because of wasteful methods of production, electricity accounted for only about 8 percent of the total energy delivered to consumers." (Freeman, 1974, p. 28)

In 1975, Worldwatch Institute conducted a study that revealed, among other things, that in the United States trucks transport less than 20 percent of all the freight moved within the country, yet they consume almost half of all the fuel used for that purpose. The study also revealed that heating and cooling losses in buildings increase electricity consumption from 35–50 percent more than necessary. The study also reported that lighting standards in a large percentage of new buildings are about twice as powerful as needed, which is another large waste of electricity. Finally, the Institute study reported that the food industry overrefines, overprocesses, and overpackages their products.

Self-Perpetuating Dilemma

A growing concern about energy consumption is the amount of energy that is required to produce new energy sources. When fossil fuels, for example, were easily accessible and lying close to the earth's surface, the costs of energy required to extract them were minimal. But now that many oil wells must be drilled deeper than one mile, with increasing numbers of them located offshore, a great deal of this new oil is needed just to pay back the invested energy. The Alaskan Pipeline and the British North Sea oil drilling are two contemporary projects that required substantial investments of energy. How many weeks, months, or years of operation will be required before these projects begin to produce a net energy gain?

As we shall see later, many of the techniques being researched to produce new energy supplies are, themselves, large consumers of energy. Processing shale oil, for example, will take huge amounts of energy, as will nuclear fission, initially, if it can ever be contained. So, too, will methods to capture and store solar energy. New processes, new materials, new technologies will be required before the energy problem can be solved.

But many experts believe that we are seeing only the beginning of the energy problem. They cite as examples for their pessimism: the expanding population and its predicted energy demands; the continued development of the world's transitional societies and their predicted demands; the previously mentioned demands by the energy industry itself; and the seemingly inherent waste of energy in the United States. It has been estimated that if the worldwide rate of energy consumption in 1968 were the same as the U.S. rate, then more than six times the energy produced would have been required. And right or wrong, this is what the majority of the world is striving for—to be able to have the same standard of living as citizens of the United States. The pessimistic energy experts doubt, however, that such amounts of energy will ever be produced, at least not in a manner that would be beneficial to our environment.

Alternative Solutions

Two alternative solutions to this distributive problem exist. One way is for the people of the United States to regress, to use less energy, and to moderate their lifestyle. It is a noble and moral alternative, but one that has little chance of occurring. Americans are proud of their lifestyle and probably would return to a lower lifestyle only under duress or direct confrontation. The other alternative would be to find a cheap, replenishable, storable, and plentiful supply of energy that would be available to everyone. Unfortunately, such a major breakthrough does not appear to be probable in the near future. The pessimists seemingly have won the day.

On the other hand, optimists in the energy field believe that things are not nearly as bad as they seem. They contend that a super energy, or energies, or energy technologies will be developed in the future that will allow the rest of the world to share the Americans' luxurious lifestyle. In the meantime, innovations in contemporary energy and energy source utilization will enable the world to at least hold its own. And if strict conservation techniques are implemented, perhaps world development may even continue to advance. The rest of this chapter discusses the states of the various contemporary energies and energy sources, in an attempt to determine which of the energy experts are more nearly correct—the pessimists or the optimists.

Existing Fossil Fuel Energy Sources

Coal

Coal is by far the most abundant of the world's fossil fuels. The known world coal resources total more than 8,600 billion tons, of which the U.S.S.R. has about 5,900 billion tons and the United States just over 1,400 billion tons. Asia has about 450 billion tons of coal, which leaves the rest of the world less than 850 billion tons. This energy resource is nearly sixty times greater than the combined oil and gas reserves.

The U.S.S.R. is the world leader in coal consumption, using roughly 700 million tons a year. The United States consumes about 600 million tons of coal annually; China, about 400 million tons; and Great Britain, approximately 115 million tons a year. Most of this coal is burned to produce electrical energy or is used by large industry, particularly the iron and steel industry. In the United States, the 600 million tons of coal consumed represent approximately 17 percent of the total annual energy consumption.

Coal was the first of the world's nonrenewable resources to be exploited intensively. From the late nineteenth century through the middle of the twentieth century, coal was the energy king. By 1910, the United States alone was producing some 500 million tons of coal annually, and Great Britain's production was close to 300 million tons, of which almost 100 million tons were exported. Almost all industrial and transportation facilities were run on coal during that period, and homes and commercial buildings were heated by burning coal. In the United States, coal was responsible for producing 90 percent of the energy consumed that year. It also changed America's lifestyle.

> Coal ushered in a new era in American civilization and radically changed people's lifestyles. People moved into urban America to be near the factories that offered jobs. The coal-fired steam engine made possible large-scale operations that were much more economical than small plants, and big plants steadily replaced the small-scale, decentralized and subdivided manufacturing process. The steam engine not only brought economies of scale, it also became the epitome of progress. (Freeman, 1974, p. 17)

But coal had its drawbacks. It was dirty; it was difficult and dangerous to mine; it was costly to ship; when burned, it produced an ash that had to be removed and discarded; it required large storage facilities and complicated equipment to move it; and its burning produced an acrid and, at times deadly, smoke. Consequently, when large quantities of oil became available and consumers realized that oil eliminated many of the negative aspects of coal, they quickly shifted to the new energy source. Coal became an old-fashioned energy source that had seen its day and that was no longer required by the modern world. Thousands of mines all over the world closed, with only the most economic surviving, putting millions of persons out of work. Oil and natural gas became the new kings and reigned supreme from the early 1950s to the present, despite the energy crunch of the 1970s. It is ironic that when the oil and gas shortages became apparent in the early 1970s, many energy experts began to call for a return to coal consumption. Obviously, coal is not yet ready for the retirement some people had willed.

Major Drawbacks. However, the drawbacks to coal use have not yet been resolved in many cases although work is being done in some areas. The two methods of coal mining, for example, strip mining and deep-shaft mining, still have many unresolved drawbacks. In strip mining operations, which is used in areas where the coal lies close to the surface, the earth, or overburden, lying above the coal was literally stripped off with huge earth-moving machines to expose the vein of coal. Until very recently, no attempt was made to separate the top soil from the subsoil or to separate the various layers of subsoil; it was all scraped into one big pile. Also, until very recently, once the coal vein was exhausted, the miners moved on to another area, rarely even taking the time to fill in the hole they had created. The deserted land in many cases resembled a moonscape.

For years, environmentalists have been pleading with the federal government to force the coal mining companies to repair their damage to the environment. In recent times, their efforts have met with some success. Strip miners are now required to salvage as much top soil as possible when removing the earth cover and to relandscape the area with growth indigenous to the area. Whether or not these actions are being taken depends upon the point of view. The environmentalists maintain that the coal companies are still not meeting specified requirements, while the coal companies claim they are doing the maximum amount of restoration they can economically afford.

A similar debate continues about shaft mining. However, the argument is not about the environment, but rather mine safety. Deep-shaft mining has always been a hazardous occupation, and despite modern mining techniques, safety features, safety equipment, and safety inspections by federal mine inspectors, hundreds of coal miners continue to die each year in coal mining disasters. A less sudden, but no less fatal, hazard related to deep-shaft coal mining is the crippling black lung disease—a condition caused by the inhalation of coal dust over a long period of time. Over the years, the number of coal miners forced into early retirement and/or early graves from this debilitating disease probably numbers into the millions.

New Technologies. But again, new technologies are beginning to brighten the lives of the deep-shaft coal miner. In 1945, for example, 95 percent of the coal mined underground was cut by hand. Today, 95 percent is cut by machine. In 1945, three shifts of coal miners were lucky to move more than a few feet every twenty-four hours. The modern coal cutting machines, traveling up and down steel belts along a two-hundred-yard coal face and shearing off the coal like a gigantic razor, progress along the vein at better than twelve feet in a twenty-four-hour period. But the mining method of the future premiered at Beverscotes in Nottinghamshire, England, in 1966. There, one man in a movable cabin in front of a complex of dials, controls the cutting, loading, and advance of the conveyor belt and the hydraulic props. Periodic maintenance patrols are the only persons required to ever approach the coal face. In addition, the per-hour production at the mine is about four and one-half times greater than the production in conventional mines.

Another problem inherent in the use of coal as an energy source is that much of it is dirty— that is, it contains noncombustible materials and sulfur. The sulfur is particularly harmful because the sulfur dioxide produced when coal is burned pollutes the surrounding environment. The Environmental Protection Agency (EPA) has set standards that require that all coal burned should contain less than 2 percent sulfur. Unfortunately, much of the world's coal reserves contain sulfur contents much higher than 2 percent. Research is currently being conducted on methods for cleaning or washing out the impurities in the coal, thus making it suitable for use.

It is highly unlikely that coal will ever regain dominance in the energy field. But it certainly can play an important role as a supporting, if not a major, energy source in the future, assuming, of course, that its major drawbacks can be eliminated.

Oil and Gas

Oil and natural gas are currently the world's major sources of energy. In the United States, oil and gas fill nearly 75 percent of the energy require-

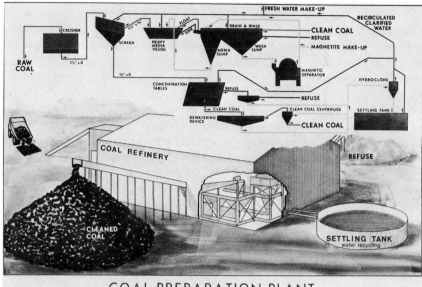

COAL PREPARATION PLANT

ments. In Western Europe and Japan, oil alone satisfies over 50 percent of those countries' energy needs. The highly developed nations of the world have become extremely dependent upon having a constant, cheap supply of oil to run their manufacturing industries, heat their homes and buildings, and run their transportation systems. Consequently, when the Organization of Petroleum Exporting Countries (OPEC) was formed in the early 1970s, it more than doubled the cost per barrel and restricted shipments of crude oil to highly developed nations. These actions threw the highly developed nations into a state of panic. The inflation rate rose sharply; prices of petroleum products more than doubled; cutbacks in processing and rationing were implemented in some cases; and even hints were heard of invasion of some oil-producing nations by some oil-consuming nations.

Vulnerability. The actions by the OPEC countries, all of which are in a transitional stage of development, made the highly developed nations realize just how vulnerable they were to actions of persons outside of their direct control. The highly developed nations had built up their own countries using someone else's resources. The highly developed nations, like the United States and Great Britain that were fortunate enough to have reserves of their own, quickly increased their levels of exploration and production in an attempt to reduce their dependence on OPEC oil. In 1971, the United States produced a little over four billion barrels of oil, but consumed almost three times that amount. The present goal for the United States is to become self-sufficient in energy, which is a highly unlikely situation until a major breakthrough in energy sources occur.

Fluctuating World Reserves. In 1971, the known world reserves of oil were nearly 633 billion barrels (see Table 9.1). During that same year, just over eighteen billion barrels of oil were consumed, which means that if consumption remained the same and no new oil reserves were found, the world would run out of oil in thirty-five years, or around the year 2006. But consumption is not remaining at eighteen billion barrels a year; it is increasing steadily. In the United States alone, consumption of crude oil is expanding at a rate of about five hundred million barrels each year. However, new reserves are also being found each year, so that the actual amount of known reserves has been growing despite the increased level of consumption. This apparent good fortune is not appreciated by some energy experts, who complain that such discoveries only tend to encourage complacency among energy users, who will then continue to waste energy. They further complain that the new discoveries will also discourage the search for new sources of energy, which they consider to be a necessary activity if the world is to continue to develop.

The world reserve of natural gas is a little more difficult to predict. Most estimates are based on the amount of known oil reserves, using a

TABLE 9.1 World Petroleum Proven Reserves (1971)

By Region	Billions of Barrels	Percentage of Total
Africa	59.3	0.093
Asia	467.6	0.737
Europe	16.4	0.025
North America	60.2	0.094
Oceania	3.1	0.004
South America	27.0	0.042
Total	633.6	
By Major Country		
Algeria	12.3	0.0194
Canada	10.2	0.0161
China	20.0	0.0316
Indonesia	10.4	0.0164
Iran	55.5	0.0876
Iraq	36.0	0.0568
Libya	25.0	0.0395
Nigeria	11.7	0.0185
Saudia Arabia	157.5	0.2486
United Arab Emirates	20.5	0.0324
U.S.S.R.	75.0	0.1184
United States	45.4	0.0717
Venezuela	13.9	0.0219

Source: U.S. Geological Survey Professional Paper 817, Washington, D.C., 1973.

ratio of between 6,000 to 7,500 cubic feet of gas available for every barrel of oil. This means, then, that there are approximately 8,000 to 12,000 trillion cubic feet of natural gas reserves—a reserve equivalent to as much as 2,000 billion barrels of oil. The saddest thing about this energy source is that so much of it is wasted. Natural gas is often found in the same formations as crude oil, but until recently it was considered by everyone to be useless, and was flashed, or burned off at the well head.

Modern technology, however, soon found ways to transport the gas overland through pipelines and later found ways to transport it over the oceans by liquifying the gas and pumping it into tanker ships. This liquifying process, unfortunately, requires expensive processing plants at both ends of the trip, as well as specially prepared ships. These added expenses increase the cost of imported natural gas to the point that only a relatively few countries can afford to purchase it. For example, the wellhead price for about two hundred fifty cubic feet of natural gas in the Middle East is about one cent. But, by the time it is ready for use in an American city, the cost for that same amount is nearly thirty cents to the wholesaler. Consequently, the burnoff of thousands of cubic feet of natural gas is continuing today because it is still uneconomic to produce.

New Technologies. Technology is also beginning to make inroads in the petroleum industry. Contrary to a common belief, neither oil nor natural gas is found in underground pools. Rather, they permeate the earth and rock in certain areas so that they can literally be sucked or pumped out of the earth. Unfortunately, conventional pumping removes only about 30 percent of the oil out of the ground; the rest is too expensive to salvage. Recent price increases and oil shortages, however, have now made it economical for oil companies to drill adjacent to the wells and pump water down into the ground, which, in turn, forces out much of the remaining oil. Some oil is too viscous or heavy to be pumped out of the ground in the conventional manner. In this case, adjacent wells are drilled, and steam is forced into the earth, heating up the oil and making its consistency light enough to be pumped out in the conventional manner. When they become perfected, these two methods, alone, can add hundreds of billions of barrels of oil to the world's oil reserve.

The Promise of Shale Oil. The most promising area for new reserves of oil, however, is shale oil. An estimated 600 billion barrels of economically recoverable oil is located in the United States alone, an amount that will almost double the known world oil reserves if and when the technical and environmental problems can be eliminated. Most of the technical problems connected with the production of shale oil on a large scale have already been solved or are close to solution. Small-scale oil shale producers had actually been operating in the early 1900s, but the discovery of large deposits of oil in Texas and Oklahoma in the 1930s drove the price of oil per barrel so low that shale oil production became uneconomical.

One of the major problems associated with the production of shale oil is its environmental impact. Virtually all the shale oil found in the United States is located in the three western states of Wyoming, Colorado, and Utah, whose residents are fiercely proud of the beauty of their land and the absence of a large population. Shale oil production on a large scale would change all that. Mountains of shale oil could be hollowed out, leaving the original landscape intact; but processing of the rock would result in a mass roughly 12 percent greater than the original mass. Instead of leveling mountains as in strip mining, shale oil production would fill valleys with sterile waste on which few things could grow for many years. In addition to the environmental problems related to the actual processing of shale oil, large-scale production would also bring thousands of new people to the area. What permanent effect they would have on the environment can only be conjectured, but they would certainly need homes, schools, roads, entertainment centers, and so on. The strain they would create on the area's existing water, sewer, and power systems must also be considered.

It is apparent that the major problems regarding any of the fossil fuels —coal, oil, or natural gas—lie not in the supply, but rather in the methods that will be economical in extracting these fuels and, at the same time, will leave the environment intact. Historically, environmental concerns are heeded only when surpluses abound. Whenever an energy shortfall is predicted, environmental concerns are given a back seat, and energy production receives priority. Hopefully, future technological breakthroughs will introduce methods either to remove fossil fuels from the environment harmlessly or to make another source the major energy producer.

Nuclear Energy Sources

Nuclear Fission

One of the most controversial contemporary issues has been whether or not to make nuclear fission a major energy source. Advocates for assigning it this role claim that quite likely the increased use of nuclear fission energy will be the only way to prevent economic and environmental disasters in the future. They argue that large-scale use of this energy will prevent the raping of the world's environment to reach fossil fuels, which would play only a minor role in a nuclear energized world. They also argue that nuclear fission research has had such a headstart over research of other energies that only it will be in a position to supply the huge amounts of energy the developing world will demand in the future. Nuclear fission, they contend, is as safe as any other energy. Advocates of nuclear fission support this claim by stating that there has not been a single death or significant property damage as a result of an accident at a nuclear power plant. Further, they claim that no such occurrence could ever take place because of extremely stringent safety measures that are common to all such plants. They believe that the storage of radioactive wastes from the active power plants is and will continue to be safely stored until technologies are developed to deactivate the wastes permanently.

Potential Hazards. Opponents of the large-scale use of nuclear fission energy contend that the potential hazards related to this energy make it unacceptable as a major energy source. They believe that even now millions of persons could die from a nuclear catastrophe. Their major fears are radiation contamination that could result from either a nuclear reactor meltdown or by leakage from a nuclear waste storage unit, and the potential theft of nuclear waste by a reactionary group for use in a bomb.

The foes of nuclear fission point to the poor safety record at nuclear power plants (some 1,400 "abnormal occurrences" in 1974) noting the several major tragedies that came within a hair of occurring, and argue that it is only a matter of time before a major meltdown will result in massive radioactive particles being windblown over thousands of square miles of inhabited land. Compounding the safety problem inherent in nuclear reactors are the safety factors inherent in storing the toxic wastes from large-scale use of nuclear fission. The more potent of these wastes will remain radioactively lethal for 500,000 years. Opponents of large-scale nuclear fission use have serious doubts about the likelihood of a fail-safe storage system being devised that will protect these deadly wastes from social and natural instabilities—that is, revolution and earthquakes.

In 1976, thirty of the fifty states had bills pending in state legislatures and/or court cases on the state docket aimed at restricting, refusing, or setting guidelines for the use of nuclear fission energy. Similar legal action was also pending at various levels of the federal legislative and judicial systems. One of the key debates at the federal level is concerned with the proposed building of a liquid metal fast breeder reactor (LMFBR), or simply breeder reactor for short.

Breeder Reactors. The breeder reactor derives its name from the fact that it creates more fuel than it uses, which is a critical feature if nuclear fission is to become as great an energy source as its advocates predict. In 1975, fifty-three fission reactors operating in the United States produced 7 percent of the nation's electrical energy. But federal government goals anticipate expanding this number to two hundred active fission reactors operating by 1985—a number, they say, that will barely keep up with increased energy demands. The greatest obstacle to this expansion is an inadequate domestic supply of uranium, a fission reactor's fuel.

Less than 1 percent of the uranium found in its natural state is fissionable—the splitting of uranium nuclei with neutrons to create two or more light elements, new free neutrons, and energy. In a nuclear chain reaction, the new free neutrons collide with other uranium nuclei, splitting them, and thus creating still more free neutrons, as well as two or more lighter elements and energy, and so on. The process continues until no more fissionable uranium nuclei are available. In a fission reactor, this chain reaction is controlled by a series of control rods interspersed among the fuel rods, which "catch" many of the freed neutrons, thus slowing the process. The released energy heats up the water in which the fuel and control rods are immersed, which, in turn, passes the water through heat exchangers to a second water system. It is this second, outer (or noncontaminated) water system that is converted to steam to turn the turbine and generators to create electricity.

Proving that Matter is Converted into Energy During Nuclear Fission

$$\text{Formula:}\quad {}_{0}^{1}n + {}_{92}^{235}U \rightarrow {}_{56}^{139}Ba + {}_{36}^{94}Kr + {}_{0}^{1}n$$
$$\text{(reactants)}\qquad\qquad\text{(products)}$$

Mass of Reactants:
(in AMU's—atomic mass units)

$${}_{0}^{1}n = 1.0087$$

$${}_{92}^{235}U = \dfrac{232.12}{236.13} = \text{total mass of reactants}$$

Mass of Products:
(in AMU's—atomic mass units)

$${}_{56}^{139}Ba = 138.95$$

$${}_{36}^{94}Kr = 93.96$$

$$3\,{}_{0}^{1}n = \dfrac{3.0261}{235.94} = \text{total mass of products}$$

Mass Defect: $236.13 - 235.94 = 0.19$
(in AMU's—atomic mass units)

n = neutron
u = uranium
Ba = Barium
Kr = Krypton

As noted earlier, the breeder reactor will eliminate the need for finding new uranium deposits (no new major deposits have been found in the United States since the 1950s) since it will create more fissionable material than it will use. This fuel is so powerful that fuel pellets the size of a pencil eraser will produce heat energy equivalent to over five hundred pounds of coal. This created fissionable material, however, is plutonium; it is extremely radioactive and has a half-life of 24,360 years; but it is also highly flammable, a lethal poison, and the material from which nuclear bombs are made. It is this material that the critics of large-scale nuclear fission fear the most. On the other hand, supporters of nuclear breeder reactors insist that the risks must be accepted; that such risks have been blown out of proportion by their opponents; and that the risks, such as they are, will be substantially reduced in the coming years.

Which side is right? Can the world risk the chance of a wrong decision? Are the risks worth the anticipated positive returns? Will the energy demands be as great as predicted? Is a fail-safe system for protecting nuclear fuels and nuclear wastes technologically possible? These and other questions are the heart of the nuclear fission energy issue. The final decisions, right or wrong, will undoubtedly affect the world's civilizations for centuries to come.

Nuclear Fusion

While nuclear fission is by far the most controversial of the potential major energy sources for the future, nuclear fusion is probably the least controversial. All who have studied this potential energy source regard it as the potential solution to the world's needs for a cheap, safe, and abundant energy supply. However, the only nuclear fusion created by human beings to date has taken place during the explosion of hydrogen bombs. Scientists have yet to control nuclear fusion; its control is regarded by the contemporary scientific world as the most difficult, as well as the most sophisticated, problem ever undertaken by human civilizations.

Nuclear fusion, in one sense, is just the opposite of nuclear fission. It does not split nuclei, but, instead, fuses them together. And the nuclei are not from highly radioactive uranium or plutonium; rather, two hydrogen nuclei combine to form a single helium nucleus plus one neutron. As in the case of nuclear fission, the process also causes a loss of mass, or mass defect, which is converted to energy.

The fuels for nuclear fusion will be deuterium and tritium—two forms of hydrogen known as "heavy hydrogen." In the common variety of hydrogen there is a single particle in the nucleus—a proton—around which a single electron orbits. In deuterium, however, the nucleus contains a neutron as well as a proton, and tritium nuclei have two neutrons accompanying the proton. Deuterium is a natural form of hydrogen. One out of every 6,700 hydrogen atoms is an atom of heavy hydrogen, and since there are two hydrogen atoms in every molecule of water, literally oceans of nuclear energy fuel exist on the earth, a virtually inexhaustible supply. Tritium, on the other hand, is a mostly synthetic, radioactive hydrogen isotope, only small quantities of which are found in nature. Tritium, with a radioactive half-life of twelve and one-half years, is formed by bombarding lithium with neutrons.

Naturally occurring nuclear fusion is a common process in our universe. It is the action taking place in our sun and in the countless stars. Obviously, to make two hydrogen protons overcome their natural resistance to repel each other and fuse together to form an atom of helium requires a tremendous amount of force and a tremendous amount of heat. Creating vast amounts of force and heat, and then containing them together so that introducing deuterium or tritium fuel will result in a controlled nuclear fusion, the energy from which could then be purposefully used, have been the major obstacles confronting the scientists to date. The temperature required for deuterium or tritium protons to overcome their natural repellency and fuse is about fifty million degrees centigrade. And the amount of accompanying pressure required can be illustrated by the fact that to trigger the nuclear fusion of a hydrogen bomb requires a nuclear fission bomb. Controlled nuclear fusion, however, will obviously require a triggering device somewhat less destructive.

The first step in a controlled nuclear fusion is to turn hydrogen gas into a plasma. Plasma is the fourth state of matter—solid, liquid, gas, plasma. To make a plasma from hydrogen gas is a relatively simple process: It requires injecting the gas into a vacuum chamber and heating it to ten thousand degrees. This procedure will cause the electrons to separate from the nuclei, ionizing the gas. Plasma is ionized gas. The next step, however, is more difficult: The plasma must be confined within its chamber without the ions ever touching the sides of the container. Since plasma is a conductor of electricity, it is affected by magnetic fields; and therefore magnetic fields are used to contain the plasma. In a tokamak (a Russian invention that was a major breakthrough toward the control of nuclear fusion), the shape of the container that holds the plasma is like a large hollow doughnut, called a "torus." The magnetic lines of force spiral around the container in helical paths like the stripes on a barber pole. The ions travel along these paths in an endless sequence, never touching the sides of the chamber.

Another innovation of the tokamak was the method it used for heating the plasma. Until its creation, heat was introduced into the plasma by either squeezing it or injecting hot particles. The Russians, however, induced an electrical current into the plasma which generated heat when the current met with resistance. Electrical current meeting resistance along its path will always create heat. Another method for heating the plasma that is currently in the experimental stage involves imploding frozen hydrogen pellets with a laser beam to produce an instantaneous, hot, and dense plasma.

Widespread Research. Research aimed at finding a method for controlling nuclear fusion began in the United States in the early 1950s. Other countries conducting research on nuclear fusion, in addition to the United States and the U.S.S.R., are Japan, Great Britain, and, under the auspices of Euratom, West Germany, Italy, Belgium, Netherlands, Luxembourg, and France. To date, scientists have succeeded in reaching required temperatures, confinement time, and plasma densities necessary for nuclear fusion, but only in separate incidents. Nor has tritium yet been burned in any of the experimental models. The next step on the road to controlled nuclear fusion, obviously, will be to combine two or more of these elements and study the results. Each step, however, will require new, bigger, and more expensive machinery.

In the United States, researchers successfully test-fired the Princeton Large Torus (PLT) in December 1975. The PLT is a tokamak-like machine designed to produce plasma that has characteristics similar to a tritium plasma, and to perform confinement and heat tests on this plasma. The cost of this machine was about $14 million. If American plans go according to schedule, a Doublet III tokamak, costing nearly $26 million, will become operative in San Diego in 1978. Its purpose is to create plasma conditions conducive to nuclear fusion, but only regular hydrogen, which will not fuse, will be used in the testing. The first American machine to attempt actual fusion of deuterium and tritium will be the Tokomak Fusion Test Reactor (TFTR), scheduled for completion in Princeton, New Jersey, in 1981. While the TFTR will produce pulsed fusion energy, the major purposes of this machine will be to study the physics of plasmas in the nuclear fusion process and to study the engineering aspects of actual energy-producing tokamaks.

By the mid-1980s, the United States project is expected to be able to have the Experimental Power Reactor (EPR-1) operating. Utilizing the results from the previous experimental projects, the EPR-1 is expected to be able to generate between ten and one hundred megawatts of electricity from pulsed fusion. The first continuously operating nuclear fusion reactor is projected to be the EPR-II, whose anticipated operation date is around 1990. This machine will be designed to produce one hundred megawatts of electricity. Finally, large, commercial, nuclear fusion, power generating reactors are anticipated to be in operation by the mid to late 1990s.

Will nuclear fusion supply the answer to the world's energy problem? It is still too early to tell. Many technical problems need to be resolved before a definite answer can be given. But considering the previous records compiled by scientists, researchers, and technicians, the chances seem quite good that nuclear fusion will at least be one of the major world energy sources in the near future.

Other Important Energy Sources

Solar Energy

Approximately every forty minutes, the earth absorbs enough solar energy to satisfy a full year of the world's energy requirements. And the figure represents less than half of the possible solar energy available since nearly 60 percent of the energy radiated to earth by the sun is either reflected back into space or absorbed by the atmosphere. It is ironic that the major drawback for using this free and abundant energy is cost—the cost of the hardware required to convert this raw energy into useful energy and the cost of the research and development required to solve the technological problems inherent in this new, potential energy industry.

Lack of Adequate Research. To date, business has been reluctant to invest much of its time or money in solar energy research because it could never recoup its investment since it will never be able to control the energy source. In all other major energy sources or potential energy sources, the energy must be created, converted, or manufactured in a concentrated place and transmitted to the areas of use. By monitoring and/or regulating this transmission, corporate investors are able to charge their customers according to use and thus have a constant return on their investment. When dealing with solar energy, however, the energy is everywhere, at least when the sun is shining, and all that a customer needs to use this energy is an initial investment in the conversion hardware.

The burden for developing this energy source has fallen on the research and development teams sponsored by and answerable to federal governments. But the United States, with the largest federal investment in research and development in the world, has only lately taken a leading role in solar energy research. In fact, prior to 1970, practically no solar energy research was being directly sponsored by the U.S. government. It has been rumored that quiet, behind-the-scenes lobbying by the energy corporations who were concentrating on nuclear energy was responsible for this neglect.

Even if this charge were true, however, undoubtedly the major reason for the lack of interest in developing solar energy is the complacent attitude held by most Americans, both private citizens and government officials, toward the energy issue. Most felt that the supply of fossil fuels that was cheap and abundant then would be available until the technological problems related to nuclear energy were solved. Few foresaw either the formation of OPEC and the resultant rise in fossil fuel costs, or the growing resistance to building large numbers of nuclear fission reactors before the potential dangers surrounding such reactors and their radioactive wastes were satisfactorily solved.

Other countries have not been quite so complacent. For example, large numbers of domestic hot water heaters warmed by solar energy are being used in Japan and in Israel, with over two and one-half million currently in use in Japan alone. France, Switzerland, West Germany, India, Russia, and Australia, in addition to those countries already mentioned, have begun to make large investments in solar energy research. The United States, jarred out of its lethargy, increased its solar energy research budget by more than 250 percent in fiscal 1975 to nearly $50 million. For the 1976 fiscal year, various government agencies received over $100 million to subsidize and support solar energy research, particularly research aimed at reducing the costs of the hardware and the installation of the hardware required to heat and/or cool residential and commercial buildings.

Current Uses. Solar heating or cooling of a building requires a large area of solar collectors covered by glass or transparent plastic. Usually mounted on the south side of the building's roof and set at a 40 to 60-degree angle, the collectors contain two flat pieces of thin metal, between which water, a liquid chemical, or air passes. The liquid or air is heated by the sun's rays to temperatures exceeding 130 degrees Fahrenheit, and the heated medium circulates throughout the system for immediate use; or it may be stored in a space heater, as a hot water supply, in a bed of rocks, or in some other heat-retaining material. The heat may also be used to operate an air conditioner.

In 1974, a survey of the average climatic conditions in a number of U.S. cities revealed that much of their heating and cooling requirements could be accommodated by solar energy. The survey projected that all of Los Angeles' heating and 98 percent of its cooling requirements could be met by solar energy; for New York City, the figures projected 84 percent of the heating needs and 77 percent of the cooling needs.

But solar energy can be used for other purposes besides heating and cooling buildings. It can be directly converted to electrical energy in solar cells or used to produce the more conventionally made turbine generator electricity. In the latter process, parabolic mirrors concentrate the solar energy on an enclosed supply of water. The concentrated heat turns the water into extremely hot steam, which is fed across the blades of a steam turbine, causing the turbine to spin. The spinning turbine is mechanically attached to an electrical generator, which would spin with the turbine, producing electricity.

Parabolic mirrors are also used to concentrate solar energy in solar furnaces. Concentration of solar energy in solar furnaces, such as the one the French built in the Pyrenees Mountains, can create temperatures that exceed 5,400 degrees Fahrenheit. Such temperatures are not obtainable in the more conventional blast, open hearth, or electrical furnaces. In the French-built solar furnace, each of the two, large, parabolic mirrors is comprised of several hundred, small, flexible pieces. Each individual piece may be independently focused and curved to achieve the desired maximum concentration of the sun's rays.

The parabolic shape is also used in the solar cooker—a device similar to the solar furnace, but one that does not require such intense temperatures. Solar energy is also used in distilling fresh water from sea water. To date, however, only small amounts of fresh water can be distilled in this manner—quantities large enough to suffice as a source of drinking water but insufficient for irrigation. Ten square feet of collection area are required to produce about a gallon of distilled water in one day.

Future Prospects. The major drawback to many solar energy devices that are presently being experimented with is that they are much more expensive and less efficient than methods currently producing similar results. The technical know-how for heating homes and commercial buildings with solar energy has been available for over thirty years. But until recently, solar energy could not compete with the cost of heating these buildings with oil or gas or electricity. However, thanks to OPEC, inflation, increasing energy demands, and an enlightened world population, the future for solar energy looks bright. Planned projects, such as the one that will use satellites to collect solar energy and beam it to earth in microwaves of varying lengths, will become economically feasible. End-of-the-century projections call for a $1 billion-a-year market for solar heating and cooling units in the United States alone. And some futurists predict that by the year 2025, some 35 percent of all the world's energy needs will be met by solar energy.

Solar energy, like nuclear fusion, has the potential for becoming a major source of cheap, safe, and inexhaustible energy. Unlike nuclear fusion, however, whether or not solar energy fulfills its potential is not dependent upon one technological breakthrough, but rather on a series of breakthroughs, and perhaps also on when and in what manner the nuclear fusion problems are solved. Conceivably, there might not ever be a need for the further development of solar energy. It seems unlikely that the world will ever require so much energy that the full development of both solar energy and nuclear fusion energy will be required.

Geothermal Energy

It is doubtful that geothermal energy will ever become a major world energy resource, but it does have the potential for becoming a strong secondary source. What makes geothermal energy attractive to many scientists and researchers is its economy and, at least at great depths, its inexhaustible supply. An example of the first benefit can be seen at Niland, California. There, the only electricity-producing geothermal power plant in the United States, which began permanent operations in the early 1960s, produces electricity at about half the cost of nuclear reactor generated electricity. It is the cheapest electricity produced in the country.

The second attraction of geothermal energy—its inexhaustible supply —stems from the well-known fact that the rock and minerals below the earth's crust are molten. One scientific explanation of this phenomenon is that the earth was formed entirely of molten material. The exterior of this once-fiery mass has cooled into the earth's crust, but the interior still remains in its original state, cooling and solidifying very slowly. A second scientific hypothesis states that the molten condition of the earth's center is caused by a combination of radioactive decay and friction. Whatever the cause, this vast, virtually untapped, energy source should play a strong role in alleviating the energy shortages of the future.

Early Experimentation. Why has this vast and cheap energy source not been developed? The answer is in two parts. First, geothermal energy development is not a recent advent. It is theorized that even before prehistoric peoples learned to control fire, they were using fumaroles (holes in the earth from which scalding hot steam escapes) to cook their food. Humans have long believed that naturally heated mineral springs are healthfully beneficial. The first known industrial use of geothermal energy occurred at Larderello, Italy, in 1827. As a means to extract boric acid from the local hot springs, the Italians used fumarolic steam to boil the hot spring water away. The first geothermal electrical generating plant, located at Larderello, began operating in 1913. In 1924, the Japanese began operating an experimental one-kilowatt, geothermal-powered electrical generator at Beppu.

In the 1920s, the United States also began experimenting with geothermal energy in Niland, California, where the country's only geothermal power plant is currently operating. Although the results of the test-borings were positive then, the experimentation was discontinued because there were no local markets for the potential electricity. Iceland began experimenting with geothermal energy in the 1920s also, but for a different reason. By drilling into the earth's crust at Reykjavik in 1928 and at Reykir in 1933, Icelandic scientists produced enough hot water to serve as the major means for heating the homes in those cities. Ninety percent of the homes in Reykjavik are now geothermally heated. Prior to 1940, similar hot water wells were heating homes in Rotorua, New Zealand.

Following World War II, Italy, Japan, and New Zealand all resumed geothermal energy research, not only as a means for producing electricity and heating homes, but also as a source of heat energy for industrial enterprises like paper mills, desalinization of sea water, agriculturally related projects, and mineral extraction from the mineral enriched hot water. Russia, Mexico, China, Zaire, Nicaragua, El Salvador, Chile, Kenya, Ethiopia, France, and Turkey have all either begun to develop or are expected shortly to begin developing geothermal fields. In the United States, geothermal experimentation is being conducted in the states west of the Rocky Mountains.

Unsolved Problems. There are two types of geothermal fields—dry steam and hot water—with hot water fields much more common than the dry steam fields. Unfortunately, dry steam geothermal fields are best suited for conversion to electrical energy. The hot water or combination of hot water and steam fields may have as much as a 30 percent mineral content, which creates many unsolved technological problems. That is the major reason why geothermal energy development has not proceeded more rapidly. The minerals, some of which are deadly poisons, such as arsenic and mercury, can pollute the surrounding area. Near a geothermal power plant in New Zealand, for example, one farmer reported he had lost fifty head of cattle when he fed them fodder made from plants harvested from the river in which the power plant ejects its waste water. Also, rainbow trout from the same river were found to have excessive amounts of mercury in their bodies.

In an attempt to overcome this surface pollution, many geothermal projects are reinjecting the refuse water into the ground. This not only saves surface land from pollution, but also lessens the chances of earthquakes and land sinking. However, this reinjection often causes the wells to become clogged with particulate matter and lose their porosity, requiring redrilling of the supply well in another area. The minerals contained in the water are also responsible for rapid corrosion of the turbine blades they contact as well as corrosion and blocking of the pipes through which the water and steam flow. The release of hydrogen sulfide into the atmosphere can also be a serious problem. Of comparatively lesser importance are problems related to noise pollution, concentrations of water vapor, and heat pollution.

Contemporary Uses. Geothermal energy is commonly used to produce electrical energy in one of three ways. In the flashed steam system, the geothermal energy beneath the ground is under pressure in the form of hot water. As the water approaches the surface, the pressure lessens, and the water changes to steam, or flashes to steam. The steam is then directed to a centrifugal separator where the majority of the minerals and corrosive materials are removed. From the separator, the steam proceeds to the turbine where it is directed against the turbine blades, causing the turbine to spin. After it has passed through the turbine, the steam is cooled and condensed back into water; it is remixed with the minerals from the separator and disposed of by either releasing it into the environment or by reinjecting it into the ground.

In the binary fluid system for converting geothermal energy to electrical energy, the hot water pumped from the ground is kept under pressure and not allowed to flash. Through a heat exchanger, the heat energy in the hot water is transferred to another fluid—isobutane or freon. This fluid, uncontaminated with minerals, passes across the turbine blades after absorbing the heat energy, thus eliminating one of the major problems associated with geothermal energy. The fluid, now cooled, is returned to the heat exchanger to be once again recharged with energy, completing its journey within its enclosed loop. The hot water, in the meantime, having given up some of its heat energy, is reinjected into the ground.

The third system for converting geothermal energy to electrical energy is the total flow system. In this system, everything that is pumped out of the ground—water, steam, and minerals—is fed directly to the turbine blades. Once it has passed through the turbine blades, the material is sent to a condenser, and from there to a storage pond before being reinjected into the ground. An obvious problem with this method is the corrosive action that the geothermal fluid and minerals have on the turbine blades. However, the total flow system is by far the most efficient system for converting geothermal energy to electrical energy, and it is expected that special noncorrosive metal alloys, although they will be an extremely expensive initial investment, will prove to withstand the corrosion satisfactorily.

An Uncertain Future. The future of geothermal energy at this time is very tenuous: If the technological problems can be solved; if no major breakthrough in one of the "miracle" energy resources occurs; if federal governments around the world continue, at the least, to finance geothermal research at its present rate or even increase its financial backing; if the world's energy requirements in the future are as great as they are predicted to be; then geothermal energy could make a significant contribution to the world energy picture in the future. If, on the other hand, the majority of those propositions go against geothermal energy, then its future could be bleak. Energy experts' predictions of the amount of the world's energy that will be produced through geothermal energy by the end of the century range from as little as 1 percent to as much as 30 percent. With such a wide variation predicted among the experts, the rest of us can do little but watch and wait.

Wind Energy

The energy issue has rekindled scientific interest in one of the oldest forms of energy exploited by humankind—the wind. The two most common uses of wind energy are sailing ships and windmills. The earliest documentation of a windmill's existence appears in a Persian chronicle relating the capture of a murderer. In A.D. 644, it was recorded that Abu Lu'lu'a, the builder of windmills and the assassin of the Caliph Umar ibn al-Khatab, had been captured. It is believed that the windmills of this era were similar to those constructed about two hundred years later, near what is now the border between Iran and Afghanistan. It has been theorized that both of these sets of windmills were derived from waterwheel designs common in Asia Minor by the first century B.C. The design of these early windmills incorporated sails that rotated in a horizontal plane and were mounted on a vertical shaft.

By the time the windmill design had reached Europe, around 1180 in France and by 1191 in England, the windmill's sails were rotating in the more familiar vertical plane on a horizontal shaft. Since this arrangement made it necessary for the sails to always face the direction from which the wind is coming, these windmills had to be directionally adjustable. To accomplish this, the entire windmill body, the stone, and the gearing were mounted on a center support post to allow the entire assembly to pivot around the center post by pulling on a long tailpole that extended from the back of the windmill. By 1300, windmills of this design, commonly called post mills, had been modified into a tower mill, in which the stone and gearing were contained in a stationary mill body and only the top or cap of the structure, containing the sails, was rotated.

Windmills continued to provide a source of local energy for many rural dwellers, especially throughout Europe and America until the early 1950s, when extremely cheap electrical energy became available. From then until the mid-1970s, the windmill's popularity, which peaked at more than six million in the United States, dwindled steadily. The turnaround in popularity began in 1973, when the United States provided scientists with $200,000 for research in wind energy. By fiscal year 1977, that figure had jumped to over $16 million. Current U.S. research concentrates on building giant windmills with two-hundred-foot sails resembling huge airplane propellers that will be able to create enough energy to meet the requirements of an entire small town. Although long-range plans by the Energy Research and Development Administration (ERDA) call for more than one hundred prototype windmills to be erected eventually, it is expected that only four will be operable by 1978. The Dutch, world famous for their use of windpower, currently intend to convert the infamous North Sea winds into electrical energy. The proposal calls for building a long chain of wind-powered turbines stretching along the coast or on artificial islands at sea. About a half-mile apart and constructed on platforms resembling offshore oil rigs, each unit would contain three turbines driven by three rotor blades approximately 165 feet long. It is anticipated that this project, with a projected starting date in the early 1980s, will produce about 450–500 megawatts of electricity.

Technical Problems. Two of the major technical problems related to wind energy are similar to those related to solar energy—storage and the inconsistency of supply. In large-scale conversion of wind energy to electrical energy, the storage problem is no different from any other large-scale conversion process, but in small-scale conversion enterprises, the electrical energy is usually stored in batteries. Storage batteries, however, emit noxious fumes, take up a lot of space, and are expensive. Therefore, contemporary research concentrates on finding alternative means for storing electrical energy created by small-scale methods. The major technical problem with wind energy conversion, however, is variability. Wind velocity can vary from zero miles per hour (absolute calm) to well over one hundred miles per hour in a severe storm. Thanks to research in airplane propellors and helicopter blades, too much wind can be counteracted in the design of the sail and by allowing the sail to "feather," or turn its face partially away from the wind's force. Too little wind, on the other hand, cannot be technically overcome, and areas having less than an average wind speed of twelve miles per hour are unsuitable for operating an economical wind energy conversion apparatus.

Theoretically, a windmill can extract 16/27 of the wind's energy, or roughly 60 percent, as it acts upon the sails. Realistically, however, an efficient windmill will be able to extract only about 75–85 percent of the theoretical maximum. Windmill efficiency can be measured in terms of power developed, which is dependent upon such things as air density, wind velocity, and length of the blades or sails. The formula for computing windmill power is $16/27 \times (1/8\ \pi\ p\ D^2 V^3)$. The 16/27 and 1/8 are constants; π is, of course, 3.1416; p represents wind density; D^2 is the diameter squared of the area swept by the blades or sails; and V^3 equals the cubed velocity of the wind.

A final problem related to converting wind energy to energies for large-scale consumer use is economic. It is anticipated that each of the four giant U.S. windmills to be erected by 1978 will cost between $1 million and $3 million. The Dutch anticipate that their future wind energy project will result in electrical energy that is fifty percent more expensive than the amount it costs to produce electrical energy in a more conventional manner. Scientists and researchers conducting these and other experiments with wind energy are quick to point out that all other energy research is equally as expensive and that these initial prototype costs can be substantially reduced if the experimentation proves successful and if large-scale manufacture of the equipment is implemented.

Hardly anyone is predicting that wind energy will be one of the major energy sources of the future. But at the same time, wind energy is natural, pollution-free and limitless in supply (particularly when considering the jet stream)—all these are attributes many scientists and researchers consider critical for a major energy source of the future. Consequently, wind energy could be the sleeper or the dark horse to become the unexpected hero of the future energy picture. Undoubtedly, it will at least become a strong secondary source of energy in those parts of the world where the average wind velocity is sufficiently high.

Energy From the Oceans

Nearly three-fourths of the world is covered by ocean water. As an energy source, the ocean water has limitless potential. Unlike the other energy sources, which have only one or two ways of producing potentially useful energy, the oceans offer a wide variety of methods. Ocean water movement, tides, waves, and currents, can be harnessed to provide useful energy, as can the potential energy contained in water temperature variation at different ocean depths. The minerals from the ocean water can be used to nurture plant life, which, in turn, can be converted to methane gas and used to produce electrical energy or heat energy for residential and commercial buildings. Finally, the ocean water, itself, can be broken down into its simple elements—hydrogen, oxygen, and numerous minerals—and the two gases used individually to create useful energy.

Of all these methods for creating useful energy, however, only tidal power has progressed beyond the theoretical and experimental stages, and it has only one major success story—the power plant located on the Rance estuary between St. Malo and Dinard, France. Completed in 1966, this combination dam, tunnel, lock, and series of turbines annually produces about 500,000 megawatts. The difference between high and low tides at Rance can be as much as forty-four feet and the maximum flow of water is close to one-half million cubic feet per second. The turbines operate on both the incoming and outgoing tides, and during the periods of low energy demands, the generators double as motors to pump water into the tidal dam where it is stored until periods of high energy demand. Although great differences are required between high and low tides, in addition to other physical requirements, over one hundred potential sites for erecting tidal dams in over a dozen countries have been identified to date. But it is doubtful that any country in the near future will expend the time, effort, money, and technical expertise necessary to build another tidal-powered, electrical generating plant.

Current Research. There are two general experimentation areas seeking ways to convert wave energy into useful energy. One concerns itself with the up and down movement of waves, while the other area of experimentation concentrates on harnessing the rolling motion of waves. Because of physical laws related to frequency and resonance, the water that will fill a hollow tube when it is immersed in the ocean will oscillate differently and will seek a higher level than the water surrounding the tube. In addition, the water in the tube reacts more slowly than the surrounding wave motion. Consequently, if a float is attached to the tube, the water in the tube will remain high as the tube falls into a wave trough, and each wave will create a higher water level in the tube if a one-way valve is inserted in the tube. The valve can open and let in water as the tube falls with the wave motion and close to trap the water when the tube begins to rise again. The pumping action of the water accumulating in this method in a tube has the potential for operating a fifty-kilowatt electric generator.

Regarding the experimentation for capturing the energy contained in a wave's rolling motion, the University of Edinburgh, Scotland, has developed a plan that would incorporate vanes turning on horizontal axes. Planners envision building ten almost completely submerged concrete and steel structures off the Hebrides. Each would be one kilometer long and contain from twenty to forty vanes. The power acquired from this system would be used to extract hydrogen gas from the ocean water. This gas would then be converted to useful energy on shore. The major concern so far is whether or not the structures will be able to withstand the severe pounding they will receive when a major storm builds up the wave force beyond the normal level. Devices similar to those proposed by the University of Edinburgh, containing a series of vanes and looking very similar to paddle wheels, have been proposed to capture the slow, but constantly moving, ocean currents. Research aimed at harnessing the ocean currents, however, has not yet gone beyond the thinking stage.

Nor has the research in converting the differences in water temperature at different ocean levels progressed beyond the early stages. In tropical climates, especially, the water temperature on the ocean surface may be as much as forty degrees warmer than the water at the ocean bottom. It has been theorized that low-pressure steam turbines could very effectively utilize this temperature variation to produce electrical energy or to process hydrogen gas or deuterium from the ocean water.

A potential energy source of a different type, yet connected to the oceans, is the energy contained in giant kelp. Kelp, a variety of seaweed that can grow as much as two feet a day, is already being processed into an emulsifier for salad oil and a binder of paints. If the theorists are correct, in the future, huge commercial kelp farms perhaps as large as 100,000 acres would produce kelp that could be used for animal and fish food, fertilizer, plastics, synthetic gas, and other fuels. On the energy production side, it is anticipated that the kelp will be converted to methane gas by the action of bacteria. In 1975, an experimental, seven-acre plot of kelp was "planted" off the coast of California on a nylon rope bed anchored forty feet below the surface. Scientists will study whether or not the ocean water at that depth contains sufficient nutrients for maximum growth or if it will be necessary to pump nitrogen- and phosphorous-rich water from the ocean floor a thousand feet below. They will also study the effects of wave action, winds, and varying temperature ranges on the kelp bed. Successful experimentation should result in huge commercial beds off the California coast by the mid 1980s.

As noted earlier, the oceans of the world offer a variety of potential ways for supplying unlimited amounts of energy. However, only one of these ways—tidal power—is presently producing useful energy, and even it has been used very little and has produced little useful energy. None of the other potential ways for producing energy from the ocean have been developed very far yet. Perhaps the greatest energy derived from the oceans will not be the forces built up in waves or currents or temperature variation or what grows in it, but rather from the water itself. Perhaps the deuterium contained in the ocean water, used to fire nuclear fusion reactors, will be the ocean's greatest contribution to solving our energy problem.

Summary

Fossil fuels have been supplying the world with the major portion of its energy for nearly two hundred years. Despite dire predictions to the contrary, the known reserves of these fuels have continued to increase, even though their consumption has increased a thousandfold or more in the past one hundred years. However, because it takes fossil fuels millions of years to reach the state in which they are useful as fuels, it can only be a matter of time before they are exhausted. The many unanswered questions about the steps to be taken and the methods for taking them in order to replace fossil fuels with another energy source affect the lives of everyone on earth.

Energy consumption is directly related to the level of technological development attained by an individual society or country. The United States is the world's largest consumer of energy. Asia and all of Western Europe each consumes only one-third as much energy as the United States; Russia consumes about one-half as much; and China only about one twenty-fifth as much. This large energy gap is primarily responsible for the almost equally large gap in the average standard of living between Americans and the rest of the world.

Approximately 42 percent of the energy consumed in the United States is consumed by the industrial sector, about 25 percent by the transportation sector, and less than 20 percent and 15 percent by the residential and commercial sectors, respectively. The major criticism leveled against disproportionate energy consumption in the United States is that so much of it is wasted.

The rest of the world seems eager to narrow the energy gap between themselves and the United States. The problem is that few energy experts feel the world will even be able to sustain such a high energy output without total destruction of the environment. The optimists, on the other hand, believe that a major breakthrough in available energy is imminent, and also that this energy breakthrough will produce a cheap, replenishable, and plentiful supply of energy that will satisfy all the world's energy needs for all time.

And what will this super energy be? That is still one of the unanswered questions. Contemporary research however, indicates that the energies that will at least share a major portion of the future energy picture are nuclear fission, nuclear fusion, and solar energy, with fossil fuels, geothermal energy, wind energy, and ocean energy supplying strong supporting roles.

DISCUSSION QUESTIONS

1. Half of today's world population seems to believe that energy supplies must be increased regardless of cost, while the other half seems to think that the energy seekers are permanently destroying the environment. Defend one of these opinions against the opposing opinion of classmates.

2. That the United States wastes a huge portion of the energy it consumes each year is a well-established fact. Discuss methods that can be implemented to reduce waste. (Go beyond the trite energy saving tips advocated by the oil companies since the mid-1970s.)

3. Which of the potential major energy sources of the future would you most like to see become the major source? Defend your choice.

4. The summary suggested that three energies discussed in this chapter have excellent chances for becoming major energy sources in the future. Do you agree or disagree with the choices? Why?

5. Four energies were nominated for supporting roles in the future. Do you agree or disagree with these selections? Why?

BIBLIOGRAPHY

Alpern, D. M.; Bishop, J., Jr.; and Cook, W. J. "Pulling the Plug on A-Power." *Newsweek,* February 24, 1975, pp. 23–24.

Aronstead, C. H., ed. *Geothermal Energy: Review of Research and Development.* Paris: UNESCO, 1973.

Bowin, R. G. "Energy Technology to the Year 2000." *Technology Review,* October/November, 1971.

Cook, E. "Energy Sources of the Future." *The Futurist* 4 (1972).

"Energy: Half Goes to Waste." *The Christian Science Monitor,* February 6, 1976, p. 36.

Fisher, L., and Biere, A., eds. "Energy and Agriculture: Research Implications." *North Central Regional Strategy Committee on Natural Resource Development,* no. 2 (October 25, 1973): 98.

Ford Foundation Energy Policy Project. *Exploring Energy Choices: A Preliminary Report.* New York: Ford Foundation, 1974.

Foreign Policy Implications of the Energy Crisis: Hearings Before the Subcommittee on Foreign Economic Policy of the Committee on Foreign Affairs, House of Representatives

92nd Congress, 2nd Session. Washington, D.C.: U.S. Government Printing Office, 1972.

Freeman, S. D. *Energy in the World of the Future.* New York: M. Evans and Co., 1973.

————. *Energy: The New Era.* New York: Vintage Books, 1974.

"Fusion Power Comes Closer to Reality." *The Futurist* 10 (February 1976): 45–46.

Ganiow, G. *Cosmology, Fusion, and Other Matters.* Boulder, Colo.: Colorado Associated University Press, 1972.

Gannon, R. "Shale Oil . . . How Soon?" *Popular Science* 205 (September 1974): 80–83.

Goodwin, I., ed. *Energy and Environment: A Collision of Crises.* Acton, Mass: Publishing Sciences Group, 1974.

Gough, W. C. "The Promise of Fusion Power." *The Futurist* (October 1973): 211–15.

Halacy, D. S. *The Coming Age of Solar Energy.* New York: Harper and Row, 1973.

Hellman, H. *Energy in the World of the Future.* New York: McEvans & Co., 1973.

Hottel, H. C. "Cloudy Forecast." *Skeptic* 18 (March/April 1977): 47–48.

Kruger, P., and Otte, C. *Geothermal Energy: Resources Production, Stimulation.* Stanford: Stanford University Press, 1973.

Loth, D., and Ernst, M. L. *The Taming of Technology.* New York: Simon and Schuster, 1972.

NASA, Technology Utilization Office. *Space Benefits—The Secondary Application of Aerospace Technology in Other Sectors of the Economy.* (Report to Congress, April 16, 1975). Washington, D.C.: U.S. Government Printing Office, 1975.

Oka, T. "Britain's New Coal Revolution." *The Christian Science Monitor,* March 10, 1975, p. 5.

Quigg, P. W. "World Environment Newsletter: The Useful Concept of Net Energy." *Saturday Review,* April 5, 1975, p. 57.

Rhodes, R. "God's Big Fix." *Playboy* 19 (November 1974): 137.

Salisbury, D. F. "The Breeder Reactor: Is America Ready for It Now?" *The Christian Science Monitor,* June 23, 1975, pp. 16–17.

————. "Fusion Energy on Verge of Proof." *The Christian Science Monitor,* October 22, 1974, p. 12.

Smith, F. "Power from the Ocean." *Sea Frontiers* 20 (March 1974).

Sobin, D. P. *The Future of the American Suburbs: Survival or Extinction.* Port Washington, N.Y.: Kennibat Press, 1971.

Spanides, A. G., and Hatzikakides, A. A. *Solar and Aeolian Energy: Proceedings.* New York: Plenum Press, 1974.

Strout, R. L. "All in the Name of Energy." *The Christian Science Monitor,* February 6, 1976, p. 35.

Taylor, T. "The Ultimate Source." *Skeptic* 18 (March/April 1977): 42–45.

Wheelock, T. D. "Advanced Coal Cleaning Methods." *Changing Scene* 2 (February 1976): 2.

Chapter 10
The Ecological Question

Humans have relentlessly manipulated and attempted to master the natural environment in the twentieth century. This process has produced countless effects that make life more enjoyable. We have controlled the atom, conquered space, redirected rivers, and developed synthetics; and the future of science and technology promises even greater exploits. Unfortunately, exploits can turn into exploitations, and our efforts to control our natural environment have brought mixed blessings.

To control and utilize our environment requires human intervention. We have always had to work with nature in order to perpetuate life, a process that initially had little effect on our environment. In 1798, planet Earth had a population approaching one billion, it had limited industrial production, and it was able to cope with human life. However, with a population of over four billion today and rising global economic standards, our finite resources and our environment are being exploited relentlessly. As population and consumption increase, our environment must be altered even more. We will continue, therefore, to intervene in the ecosystem in order to survive.

Ecology, the study of the "oikos,"—the dwelling place, one's habitat—is the study of the fragile interrelationship between living organisms and their environment. Such study is not a recent innovation; it has been with us ever since we began to seek ways to control the natural environment. Only in the past twenty-five years, however, have serious and conscious efforts been made to limit the misuse of our total system. In 1962, as mentioned earlier, Rachel Carson wrote *Silent Spring,* which was one of these early efforts. Her book exposed the misuse of pesticides, and met with violent opposition. Alarmed manufacturers of pesticides tried to prevent the book's publication. However, today it stands vindcated and is heralded as a landmark in ecological awareness. Today, the dangers that Rachel Carson predicted are being confirmed, and many of the questions she raised still await answers.

In April 1970, a rediscovery of environmental issues was launched

Note: We acknowledge, with appreciation, the contributions made to this chapter by Dr. Ray Loyd, Iowa State University.

during Earth Week. Environmental sit-ins, demonstrations, teach-ins, and the mass media, among other techniques, called to the public's attention the need for public understanding of environmental crises as well as their potential cures. Since that time, countless pieces of legislation have been passed to limit the blatant misuse of our environment. Other social controls have also been instigated to help solve the problems (polluted streams and air, noise pollution, vanishing species) evident around us.

The primary social controls needed to solve ecological ills are human attitudes and rational priorities. Evidence suggests that these efforts are beginning to solve many ecological issues. Today's schools provide instruction in environmental education; the media generate awareness and action by highlighting ecological blunders; organizations have been designed to study ecological problems. The Office of Technology Assessment (see Chapter 13), for example, gives top priority to the study of our natural environment. Awareness and action are now global efforts. The International Institute of Applied Systems Analysis, a research center staffed jointly by Russian and U.S. investigators, directs its attention to global ecological issues. This total effort is our hope for survival.

The effort to provide future generations with a self-sustaining environment is a complicated one. Research is needed to identify irreversible elements that erode the total ecological system. Alternatives to current social systems are vitally necessary. If there is to be a future, political and economic decisions must be made with finite resources in mind. Just as we have indicators of economic development, our society needs indicators of ecological stability. Economic answers by themselves will no longer suffice. What is needed is a psychology and a philosophy that consider the sustaining of life as a harmonious venture between living organisms and their environment.

The Environment as a System

Almost daily, we read about environmental crises such as diminishing resources, vanishing species, and other events that are harmful to our habitat. Since earth has survived for millions of years, why does it appear to be heading toward collapse during our generation? A response to this question must be based upon an analysis of the fragile system we call environment, which consists of three elements: lithosphere, hydrosphere, and atmosphere. We all use these terms every day although we may use them in various contexts. The lithosphere—the solid portion of the earth—contains the soil basic for all kinds of life. The hydrosphere is the aqueous portion of the biosphere and appears as a solid, a liquid, or a vapor. Water in liquid form covers more than 70 percent of the earth's surface. Unfortunately, this resource is not distributed equitably throughout the world. The atmosphere is a gas that envelops the earth and contains the oxygen necessary to sustain life.

In the search for life on Mars, experiments were designed to search

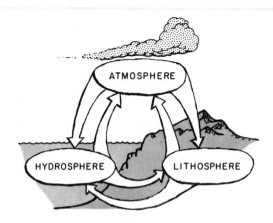

THE BIOSPHERE

for the proper combinations of soil, water, and atmosphere to sustain and
perpetuate life. To destroy one, eliminates the potential of the other two.
Without human influence, this interrelationship is very efficient and self-
sustaining on planet earth. These elements can cleanse and renew themselves and are an intricate part of the process we call life. In spite of this
phenomenal capability, we have discovered that it is a finite system—a
system with parameters. We have learned that earth has many nonrenewable
resources that must be utilized wisely, and that alternatives to those resources must be found eventually. We have learned that the system can
accommodate just so much input from human life. Rivers can die from an
overload of waste just as living organisms can. If this line of thinking is
pushed to its ultimate threat, we can see the possibility for extinction.

Working like a cybernetic system, nature utilizes cycles of events for
maintaining ecological order. A commonly referred to cycle is the fresh-
water ecological cycle made up of fish, organic waste, bacteria, inorganic
products, and algae. If the temperature of the water is raised by unusually
warm weather, a rapid growth of algae can occur, which depletes the supply
of inorganic nutrients. However, the ecological cycle begins to work. The
excess algae provide easier feeding for the fish, thereby increasing fish waste
production, decreasing the algae and increasing the levels of nutrients when
the waste decays. Consequently, the algae and nutrients return to their
original balance.

In ecosystems everything is connected to everything else and is stabil-
ized by self-compensating elements. Yet, there is always danger of total
collapse if any one element is overtaxed. Since we arrived on the ecological
scene, too many parts of the system have been overstressed. Nature was not
designed to accommodate large deposits of industrial wastes, of pesticides,
of nonbiodegradable materials—the residue of human innovation and invention—that unbalance the ecology.

The Human Influence

When examining the environment as a system, we must include human habitation as part of that system. This raises many concepts that must be dealt with if we intend to make intelligent decisions about the future. Since World War II, our ecological problems have intensified dramatically. An increase of two hundred to two thousand percent in pollution levels must be blamed on humans and their propensity for technological growth. In his Book, *The Closing Circle,* Barry Commoner stated:

> The over-all evidence seems clear. The chief reason for the environmental crisis that has engulfed the United States in recent years is the sweeping transformation of productive technology since World War II. The economy has grown enough to give the United States population about the same amount of basic goods, per capita, as it did in 1946. However, productive technologies with intense impacts on the environment have displaced less destructive ones. The environmental crisis is the inevitable result of the counterecological pattern of growth. [Commoner, 1972, p. 177]

Many leading scholars believe that population growth may be one of the most important trends affecting the future of our environment. For example, Lester Brown of the Worldwatch Institute argues for reducing population growth in order to cleanse our environment. Each additional person, especially in the affluent areas, increases the burden on our environment. At the same time, the world demand for goods and services continues to expand at 4 percent per year, nearly tripling between 1950 and 1975. Approximately one-half of all production gains were absorbed by population growth and the other half in per capita consumption.

People require food, water, energy, heat, and countless natural resources for survival. Simple mathematics tells us that to sustain more lives our system must be taxed proportionately. Increased population taxes finite resources: It requires the production of more food leading to overgrazing of land, the use of more pesticides, deforestation, and so on; crowding; starvation; and the loss of individual freedom and the right to the elements nature provides.

Studying ecology is not done solely for survival; of equal importance is the quest for a humane existence on earth. There is no reason for living organisms to suffer the consequences of degradation of our environment. To survive physically while tolerating sacrifices caused by mishandling resources is inexcusable. To solve these problems, we need not only technological innovation and invention, but also human commitment.

Major Forms of Pollution

Water Pollution

Any phase of the hydrosphere can accumulate foreign matter. If this foreign matter deteriorates the quality of the water, the material is termed a "pollutant." There are many different kinds of water pollutants: Synthetic chemicals like phosphate detergents, pesticides, phenols, and some coal products are one variety. They are persistent pollutants because they are not easily degradable and can be transferred from one form of life to another.

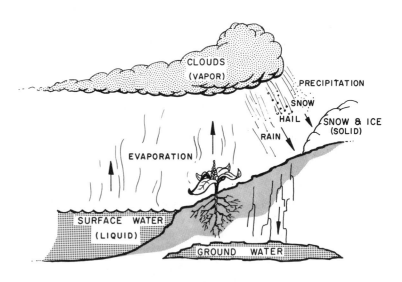

HYDROLOGICAL   CYCLE

Nondegradable Pollutants. Pollutants that will not change significantly or degrade in the water system are called "nondegradable pollutants." Inorganic colloidal matter consisting of the ordinary variety of salts as well as heavy metallic salts, can be toxic and can ruin plumbing, boilers, and other home and industrial water equipment through corrosion, flaking, pitting, and scaling of metals.

The nondegradable pollutants that create the greatest problems are lead, mercury, and cadmium. During a rain storm, lead deposited on highways from automotive exhausts can enter waterways with relative ease. If lead is ingested by humans or animals, they may die. Mercury in water contaminates fish; those who eat contaminated fish ingest the mercury with the fish. A recent commercial ban on the sale of fish from Lake Erie occurred because fish there contained twice the amount of mercury judged to be safe. Japan has had several human deaths from cadmium-contaminated rice.

Degradable Pollutants. Pollutants from organic wastes, on the other hand, are degraded by bacterial action. Excessive organic wastes can create an overabundance of plant nutrients, which, in turn, causes algae blooms or excessive algae growth. Algae in itself is not harmful to natural water systems, but if growth remains unchecked, algae can become toxic, produce odors, reduce aesthetic appeal, and increase the treatment problems of a water system.

Another degradable pollutant is bacteria itself. Although bacteria was once the major problem in sewage water treatment, contemporary treatment systems have eliminated it as a hazard, at least in most developed nations. Diseases like typhoid, paratyphoid, dysentery, and gastroenteritis have been controlled by efficient sewage treatment methods. However, not all countries have modern, sophisticated technologies of sewage treatment; therefore, outbreaks of these and other pollution-related diseases occur periodically in some countries.

Viruses present an even greater problem to sewage treatment because they are not easily destroyed. This is a major concern to health officials because viruses are associated with some of the most deadly diseases. However, the prospect for virus control in water is promising. Processes such as radiation can now be used to destroy viruses in emergency situations, and research in this area receives priority treatment around the world.

Other Pollutants. With increased power consumption and the advent of the steam electric power plants, a new form of pollution threatens the earth's water system: thermal pollution, which is simply a change of water temperature. The ramifications of raising the natural temperature of a water ecosystem are still not fully understood, but many experts agree that since temperature adaptations of animals result from a long evolutionary history, a major change in environmental conditions associated with water could affect the balance of nature.

Water is also easily contaminated by radioactive material. Once radioactive material is in water, it becomes concentrated in whatever forms of life exist in that body of water. Unfortunately, fresh water is very susceptible to contamination from underground leaks of radioactive wastes from underground storage areas.

Another pollutant related to human activity is silt—surface soil eroded by wind and rain and washed into water systems. The quantity of eroded soil in a water system determines the definition of silt as a pollutant. The pollution itself begins, however, when aquatic animal life on the bottom of waterways are smothered or when light cannot penetrate the water to support plant life. Sediment from silt can eventually fill or can greatly change a waterway, a lake, or even an ocean. Geologists estimate that the oceans of the world receive about four billion tons of dissolved matter annually.

Principal Sources. The principal sources of water pollution are industry, agriculture, and domestic discharges. Industrial processes require over 50 percent of the volume of water used in the United States; and organic, inorganic, synthetic, radioactive, or thermal pollution may come from chemical, paper, food, metal, electrical, nuclear, and other types of industry.

Agricultural pollution occurs in two major ways: The first by runoff of irrigation waters when pesticides, fertilizers, salt, silts, and other pollutants are picked up by the irrigation water and carried into the waterways, lakes, and oceans; the second form of agricultural pollution occurs because of the tons of sewage produced each year by animals domesticated for farm use or raised for slaughter.

Domestic sewage is the third major source of water pollution. Besides human excreta, other chemicals and solids, are discharged into water systems through sewer systems. Food wastes, paper, soap, detergents, dirt, cloth, microorganisms, and other miscellaneous material are regularly discarded via the domestic sewer.

Solutions and Social Values. The problem of water pollution requires major technological solutions and some change in social values. Some technological solutions already exist. Safe pesticides and safe fertilizers are being developed. Animal wastes can be contained or treated for fertilizers. Municipal sewage treatment has been a developing technology since the late 1800s. Today, a three-phase process of treatment effectively removes solids, biologically degrades organic matter, and filters out inorganic materials.

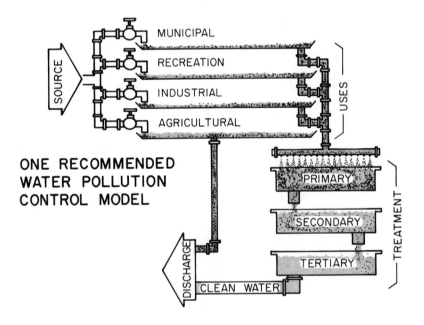

The social value aspect of the problem remains, however. Since water is one of the "commons,"—one of those attributes of the earth that humans use jointly and over which no one possesses exclusive ownership rights—it is difficult to force proper or respectful use of it. An individual's share of the cost of discharging personal waste into the commons is less than the cost of the waste before discharging it. That, of course, is why the individual discards the material. Thus, the rational individual will conclude that it is personally cheaper to continue to discard things into a water system that moves the waste out of sight. The collective cost, however, is considerable; humanity fouls its own nest. Yet, changing the way we live is probably costlier for the individual than letting things remain the same. The interests of the individual and the interests of society are not necessarily the same. Thus, a new way of thinking and legislating about the commons must emerge in social contexts where sophisticated technology dominates and where many people congregate.

Air Pollution

Air pollution associated with technological development severely affects the well-being of the human race. Death caused by polluted air is the most obvious, severe consequence of air pollution; in a surprising number of instances air pollution caused by industry has killed many people.

Effects on Humans. In the 1930s, the Meuse Valley of Belgium had a temperature inversion that immediately caused about sixty deaths and probably later contributed to the premature deaths of hundreds of others. In addition to the deaths, thousands of respiratory problems were noted. The industrialized region had a heavy concentration of sulfur dioxide and sulfur trioxide that the inversion retained for a week.

Donora, Pennsylvania, suffered a similar occurrence in 1948, when a temperature inversion caused air pollutants to concentrate in the area for four days. The effluents came primarily from the sulfur-rich ores used for home and industrial heating systems. Coal burning with its waste of sulfur dioxide, nitrogen dioxide, hydrocarbon, and other effluents, together with a temperature inversion, caused twenty deaths. Before the weather changed sufficiently to break the inversion, 5,910 of the 12,000 inhabitants of the region complained of illness.

The extensive use of coal in London, England, has produced three deadly smogs. In 1952, over four thousand deaths occurred during one temperature inversion. More than a thousand died in London during a heavy smog that was held static by another temperature inversion in 1956. And as recently as 1962, several hundred deaths were reported in London during a third bout with the deadly smog. Many factors contributed to the problems in London, but sulfur dioxide from the burning coal was the irritant mainly responsible for illnesses and deaths. Three hundred deaths resulted from a three-week temperature inversion which held a heavy smog over the Los Angeles area in the late 1960s

Although pollutants in the air are as varied as their sources, the five most common are carbon monoxide, sulfur dioxides, hydrocarbons, nitrogen oxides, and particulate matter. Sulfur dioxide is produced when coal or fuel oil is burned. Internal combustion engines that burn gasoline with additives produce carbon monoxide, nitrogen dioxide, lead oxides, and other contaminants. Mining operations, industrial processing, manufacturing, and agricultural activities contribute much of the aerosols or particulate matter that also form air pollution.

Some pollutants are formed only when combined with other chemicals in the air. Some threatening aerosols, for example, come from the agricultural spraying of pesticides, herbicides, and liquid fertilizers. Sulfur dioxide develops into sulfuric acid by the simple addition of moisture. Other types of pollutants such as arolein, formaldehyde, and peroxyacetylinitrate can result from nitrogen dioxide and nitric oxide interactions.

Plant Life Threatened. Human life is not the only form of life threatened by air pollution. One example of air pollution's effect upon plant life was dramatically demonstrated when a copper smelter in one area of Tennessee discharged up to forty tons of sulfur dioxide per day into the atmosphere. Almost all the vegetation on over twenty thousand acres downwind from the smelter was destroyed. Citrus fruit crops in southern California have been damaged because of ozone and peroxyacetylinitrate. Plant damage around the world will likely increase as air pollution gets worse.

Domestic animals and wildlife have also been exposed to air pollution. Very little research has been conducted to substantiate the suspected harm air pollution has on these animals. Laboratory animals used in experiments with air pollution have indeed suffered and many have died. The dangers are there although documentation is scarce. However, after the 1952 smog in London, cattle that had been on exhibit there during the time later had to be destroyed because they became afflicted with heart and respiratory diseases. An animal health problem that has recently been noted is a direct result of air pollution. Fluorosis—the abnormal calcification of bones and teeth—results from animals eating the fallout of various fluorine compounds on trees, plants, and grass.

Property damage from contaminants in the air probably exceeds $15 billion per year in the United States. The corrosive action of some pollutants can deteriorate the surfaces of metals and masonry. Other materials become discolored or brittle and crack or peel. Particles of matter in the air form an abrasive dust that can damage furniture finishes, drapery material, upholstery material, carpeting, clothing, painted walls, and automobile finishes.

Transportation vehicles contribute more to urban air pollution than any other sources. Most of these vehicles are powered by gasoline-fueled internal combustion engines. In the United States alone, more than one million automobiles, small vans, light trucks, and pickups serve a variety of uses, including nothing more than transporting one person a very short distance on a nice day.

Many of the problems associated with personal use of the private automobile have been debated repeatedly. Attempts to control the use of the private automobile are usually resisted, however. Some cities have legislated to encourage commuters to form car pools. One example is the diamond lane on the Los Angeles freeway system that allows speedier travel for autos with two or more passengers.

New Technologies. Other approaches to control the effluence of automobiles are the aim of various technologies. New automobiles are being designed to run on gasoline without tetraethyl lead or other antiknock additives. Liquified petroleum gas, compressed natural gas, liquified natural gas, and methanol are all cleaner-burning fuels than gasoline and they reduce emissions significantly. Yet, special consideration has to be given these fuels because of the unique problems involved in their storage and shipment. Control devices, such as the catalytic converter, thermal reactor, vapor liquid separator, carbon canister, exhaust gas recirculation system, and others offer some promise in controlling emissions beside the new fuels.

Still another area of research devoted to curbing auto emissions is the designing of new engines and motors such as the rotary engine, the gas turbine, the steam engine, and the electric motor—all of which are alternatives to the gasoline engine. The stratified-charge engine, one of the candidates that shows promise, is designed to burn fuel more completely and to reduce emissions significantly. It also has the advantage of being similar to conventional, internal combustion engines and, therefore, would not require complete alteration of auto design or servicing systems.

Transportation vehicles are an especially perplexing source of air pollution because of their size, quantity, and mobility. It is difficult to make all of them less polluting or to discard them for a new mode of transportation. Their size prevents mobility, and it would be virtually impossible to restrict their movement to certain areas only. These unique attributes of modern transportation make it difficult to control or eliminate them as sources of contaminants.

Although industrial controls are less complex, these contaminants are often more damaging because of the volume of discharge from a single source. Most of the industrial contaminants are particulate matter, and control methods are directed primarily toward eliminating these. A settling chamber can be used to remove large particles from the polluted discharges. The suspended particulate matter is gradually pulled by gravity to the bottom of the chamber, after which they are collected by a hopper while the cleaned air is discharged into a second cleaning system. The illustration on page 220 (top) is a sectional view of a settling chamber.

Another air cleaning system, called a cyclone or centrifugal collector, relies on centrifugal force. The air containing the contaminants is discharged on a tangent at the top of a large, cylindrical container with a conical bottom. The air spirals to the conical bottom, and at the same time particulate matter drops to the hopper opening below. The cleaner air spirals up the center of the cylinder and exits at the top. The cross-sectional view of a cyclone collector is shown on page 220 (bottom).

Bag filtering systems, or baghouses, clean particulate matter suspended in industrial air effluents. Although this method is expensive, it is very efficient. The process is diagrammed on page 221.

Other contaminants such such as oxides of sulfur and nitrogen must be controlled by other means. Scrubbers or spray collectors use a fine spray

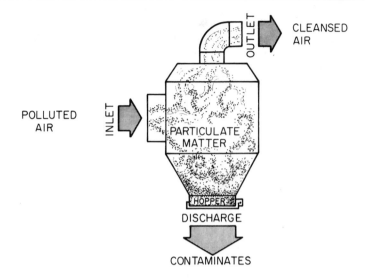

SETTLING CHAMBER SECTION

of water to collect gaseous pollutants. Solid particles can also be removed in these systems. The discharge of dirty air is usually near the bottom of the scrubber. Several nozzles distributed in the upper half of the scrubber spray water continuously in the system. The collected material is funneled out at the bottom. A scrubbing system is illustrated at the bottom of the following page.

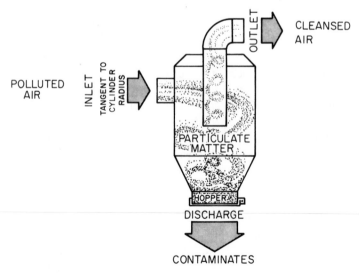

CYCLONE COLLECTOR SECTION

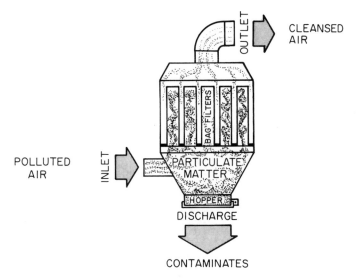

BAGHOUSE FILTER SECTION

The electrical principle that opposite charges attract each other is employed in electrostatic precipitators. The particulate matter is negatively charged with a high voltage of electricity, and the collecting surface is grounded, thus attracting the particles. Precipitators are commonly used where large quantities of small particles are discharged. Although they are used to collect particles of all sizes, the major advantage of precipitators (as shown at the top of page 222) is their efficiency for collecting minute particles.

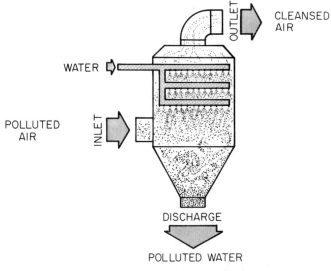

SCRUBBER SECTION

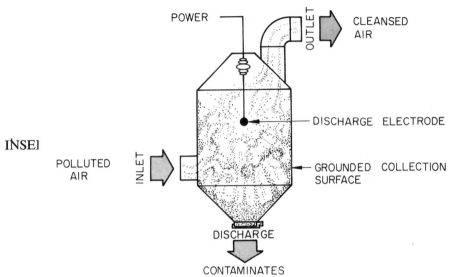

ELECTROSTATIC PRECIPITATOR SECTION

One other system that is efficient in removing gaseous pollutants is the adsorber collection system. Activated carbon is used to collect the gas molecules. This system is effective because of the large amount of surface area in a small amount of activated carbon. The surface area is an important factor because the gas molecules stick to these surfaces or are adsorbed by them. A typical adsorbing system is shown here.

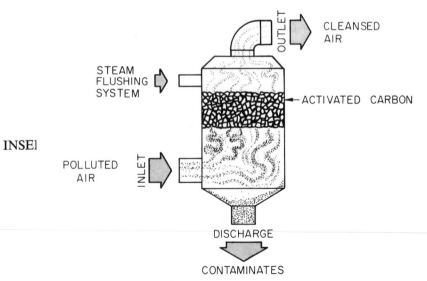

ADSORBING COLLECTOR SYSTEM

Although technology exists to eliminate many airborne agricultural contaminants, this problem has not received as much attention as industrial or automotive effluents. The toxicity of the chemical pollutants adds to the seriousness of agricultural contamination. Yet, in rural areas, air pollution does not irritate as many people as it does in urban environments. Since fewer people complain about agricultural air pollution, fewer technologists find it worthwhile to study ways to eliminate the problem.

The technology to eliminate the pollution is available for almost every form of air pollution. Yet, the social and cultural impetus required to put the technology to work is generally unavailable until an emergency or a disaster occurs. Legislation to place stringent guidelines on allowable pollution has been proposed and passed in some nations. But often clean air and economy are thought to be incompatible. As the disasters of air pollution show, some controls to curb pollution are necessary even if a slowdown in economic development results. The conflict between economic advance and quality of life ends when people can no longer breathe.

Noise Pollution

Possibly the loudest noise ever heard during the Stone Age was the eruption of a volcano. For most primitive people, thunder was the loudest noise they heard. Today, loud sounds produced by machines and vehicles sometimes create a condition known as noise pollution. It is a form of airborne pollution and can be as much of a health problem as other airborne pollutants. The level at which anything becomes a pollutant is that point at which it damages the natural conditions of things. As with other pollutants, it is difficult to determine exactly when noise becomes damaging. A complicating issue with noise is that aesthetic judgment enters into the consideration of what is pollution. Some consider hard rock music to be a form of noise pollution, while others consider it a pleasure.

Defining Harmful Levels. The difficulties associated with noise pollution, then, lie with the problem of judging what precisely constitutes pollution. Since aesthetic judgment enters into the consideration and is not quantifiable, some have looked to physiological measurement for help. If sound can be measured, and if physical damage to the human organism can be determined, judgments might be made about what noise levels constitute pollution.

Noise volume can be measured by decibels. Zero decibel is noise at the threshhold of hearing. Tests indicate that noise above 85 decibels heard for an extended period of time can cause some harm. However, many of the noises people are exposed to regularly in a technological society are above 85 decibels. For example, a large rocket engine produces a noise level of 175 decibels. A heavy truck can reach the 100-decibel level while accelerating.

The hazard of loud noise extended over a period of time is hearing loss. Some researchers suspect that more serious damage than hearing loss may result from noise pollution. They suggest that psychological disorientation, mental illness, and emotional instability may follow noise pollution. Some industries have reduced noise levels in factories on the assumption that workers function more effectively without the added stress of noise.

Solid Waste

Disposal of solid waste is another complicated environmental issue. Solid waste generated by agricultural operations, by industry, and by concentrations of people in cities is a persistent problem. Finding space to put junk is but one aspect of the problem. The pollution complications in both air and water are another aspect of the solid waste issue related to the necessary alterations of the lithosphere required for their disposal.

Garbage is an unpleasant but constantly present part of life in the modern world. The average American discards about five and one-half pounds of refuse per day. By-products of good production alone exceed two billion tons of waste per year in America, including agricultural wastes of residual pesticides, animal carcasses, and plant by-products. Animal manure accounts for about 75 percent of agricultural refuse. Food packaging produces more refuse in the form of discardable containers. Mining operations are responsible for one and one-half billion tons of discarded rock, dirt, sand, and sludge a year in the United States.

An Abundance of Trash. Industrial facilities generate one and one-quarter million tons of solid wastes in the United States per year. In every element of manufacture, from aluminium products to zinc products, from synthetic to natural materials, and from organic to inorganic resources, discarded waste results. Municipal wastes include household, institutional, and commercial materials discarded during consumption—wood, metals, glass, plastics, leaves, grass, paper, and food scraps. In the United States, about half of the two million tons of solid waste generated each year by municipalities is paper. Organic material such as wood, plant and lawn trimmings, and food scraps composed about 22 percent of the municipal waste; another 28 percent is primarily metal, glass, plastic, and rubber.

Small quantities of solid wastes present no disposal problems because much of the material is simply consumed or transformed by natural processes. Although all people in all societies have waste problems, technology contributes more to the problem:

> When we went from bucket of beer to returnable bottle there may have been no far reaching changes, except for the disastrous consequences of the diminishment of neighborhood, but when we went from returnable to throwaway, and now to recyclable, we fundamentally changed our relationship with the earth. The demon of convenience has us. (Kozlovsky, 1974, pp. 26, 27)

Nations that develop technology to levels comparable to that of the United States might be expected to confront the same waste disposal problems. And if technological development carries with it increased waste production, then the solid waste problem will soon become a world problem.

Methods of Disposal. The two traditional methods of disposing of solid wastes—open dumping on the land or in the ocean—are the least desirable for the environment. Open dumping on land contributes to both air and water pollution. Air is contaminated by constantly burning piles of flammable refuse, and water runoff pollutes lakes, rivers, and streams. Open dumps also encourage the breeding of rodents and flies.

Disposing of solid wastes in the ocean is also unsatisfactory. Presently, most solid wastes end up in the ocean; evidence of ocean pollution is apparent to all who watch an ocean liner dump its garbage and to all who find garbage piles floating near a beach. Two exceptions to the hazardous possibilities of ocean dumping indicate that the oceans can serve as a dump for some forms of waste. Research described by Curry-Lindahl indicates that "artificial reefs constructed of old tires may promote an increase in desirable species since many game fish require relief features such as reefs for protection and spawning grounds."

Similarly, a recent investigation of a massive dump of World War II material near the Caroline Islands (sixty ships with their equipment and supplies) demonstrates that marine life has adapted well to the dump. The tonnage of solid and chemical (fuel and oil) wastes did not permanently damage the oceanic life in that area. Rather, in the years since the dump, the ships have been transformed into a rich, productive reef.

A third and more acceptable method of disposing of solid waste is the sanitary landfill. Although it is far from sanitary, this method effectively controls the nuisance normally associated with open land dumps. Usually, a compacted layer of refuse from four to fifteen feet thick is laid in a confined area—ditch, ravine, trench—or on a hillside and is covered daily with a six-inch layer of earth. The layer of soil forms a protective cover between layers of compacted refuse. Some landfill areas that have reached their capacity as receptacles are easily converted to a recreation area or a building site. The sanitary landfill allows for biodegradation with minimal pollution, disease, and unsightly rubbish piles at a comparatively moderate expense.

Incineration, a fourth method of solid waste disposal, can be expensive and a source of air pollution. One expense is the incineration of resources and products that could be recycled. A greater demand is then put upon natural resources to create more goods to replace those destroyed. Yet, practically all refuse can be incinerated and reduced to an inert ash about 10–20 percent of its former volume. The ash is odor free and has practically none of the health hazards of raw wastes. Some of the heat generated by incineration can be utilized to produce steam. In addition, the use of electrostatic precipitators or electrical air cleaners can also reduce air pollution associated with incineration.

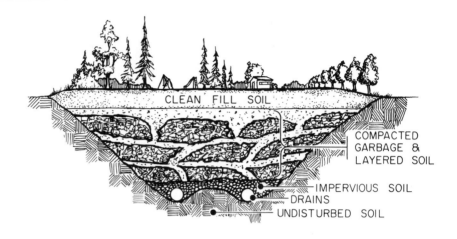

RECLAIMED SANITARY LANDFILL SITE

Recycling and Composting. In the efforts to alleviate the solid waste problem, recycling is the most environmentally sound process available. Yet, not all materials are recyclable. Composting is one process used to maximize recycling methods. This is a method of accelerating the biological action of decomposition in organic wastes, most of which will undergo a rapid decomposition if they are finely chopped, shredded, or ground before composting. In the commercial, open composting operations, long rows of compost material are frequently aerated by turning and plowing. This process, along with the addition of manure or sewage sludge, speeds the decaying process. The rapid decaying process in these piles often generates heat to temperatures around 150 degrees Fahrenheit. Many of the bacteria associated with disease are killed off at these temperatures. With weather permitting, the total process takes about seven weeks. The open composting operation requires sufficient land to handle the volume and must be far enough away from residential areas to avoid complaints about odor.

Closed, or mechanical, composting is usually done in large cylindrical receptacles that rotate constantly at a slow speed. Webs on the inside and spiraling the length of the cylinder aerate the prepared compost continually and speed the decaying process. This process requires no more than seven days and is relatively unaffected by weather conditions.

Inorganic wastes, such as metal, glass, and paper, can be separated, conditioned, and reused or reformed as a recycling process. While the quality of the recycled materials is usually below that of the virgin material, recycling does preserve natural resources.

In some municipal areas of the world, solid waste disposal is becoming a major problem. Neither New York City nor Chicago knows what to do with the increasing amount of garbage produced each day. And cities like Calcutta and Venice have the garbage problem compounded by poor city planning, inadequate disposal methods, and archaic sewage transport systems. How much garbage people of the world can learn to live with before taking serious action about its production or disposal is a question that remains to be answered.

Summary

Most informed people agree that the environment is in a precarious position. An expanding technology has mandated the excessive use of resources and has polluted land, water, and our atmosphere with the discharged wastes. Most environmentalists agree that the environmental crisis is possibly the most formidable obstacle to human survival ever encountered. At the same time, many persons are reluctant to believe the doomsday experts because they, themselves, are limited in their ability to foresee the future and unconsciously object to negative predictions.

Fortunately, solutions exist to many of the problems we face in restoring our habitat to a liveable state. Most of these solutions must come through the search for alternatives to current use of resources. Barry Commoner concludes *The Closing Circle* by saying that our options have been reduced to two: either the rational, social organization of the use and distribution of the earth's resources, or a new barbarism. It has been social mismanagement that has created our ecological problems, and it will take a change in these actions to restore harmony with nature. Yet, to change the state of our environment implies changing the course of history. This will require powerful economic, social, and political forces working together on a global scale. Singular efforts may aggravate situations and our environment cannot afford such actions.

Paramount in the process of survival is the philosophy of each individual and the inevitable collective judgments they must make. We, too, are an

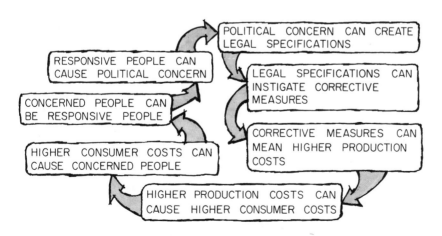

THE SEARCH FOR ECONOMICALLY SOUND AND
ENVIRONMENTALLY SAFE SOLUTIONS

expression of nature and cannot be separated from it. Therefore, we confront not only the lithosphere, the hydrosphere, and the atmosphere, but ourselves as well. It may be that dealing with ourselves is the greatest obstacle to saving our environment.

DISCUSSION QUESTIONS

1. If inquiry focuses on the economic consequences of environmental deterioration, should it be on specific industries, sectors, or the total economy?

2. Is it possible to deal with ecological issues considering our attitudes toward excessive productivity and reliance on products we really do not need?

3. What does our ecological dilemma imply for education at all levels?

4. What political adjustments are called for to handle global ecological harmony?

5. The law of supply and demand is a philosophical abstraction. Since supply is limited only by our ability to produce and demand is limited only by our ability to consume, can we hope to solve environmental issues with our insatiable drive for more tangibles?

6. What can you, an individual, do to solve current ecological problems and forestall future problems?

BIBLIOGRAPHY

Bernarde, M. A. *Our Precarious Habitat*. New York: W. W. Norton & Co., 1970.

Blaisdell, D. C. *Technology—the Key to Better Environment*. New York: Exposition Press, 1973.

Brown, L. et al. "The Population Problem in 22 Dimensions." *The Futurist* 10, no. 5 (October 1976): 238–45.

Brubaker, S. *To Live on Earth*. Baltimore: The Johns Hopkins Press, 1972.

Caldwell, L. K. "Environment and Administration: The Politics of Ecology." In W. W. Murdoch, ed. *Environment—Resources, Pollution and Society*. Stamford, Conn.: Sinauer Associates, 1971.

Carson, R. *Silent Spring*. Boston: Houghton Mifflin Co., 1962.

Christman, R. F.; Mar, B. W.; Welch, E. B.; Charlson, R. J.; and Carlson, D. A. *The Natural Environment—Wastes and Control*. Rev.

ed. Pacific Palisades, Calif.: Goodyear Publishing Co., 1974.

Clawson, M. "Land Resources." In W. W. Murdoch, ed., *Environment—Resources, Pollution, and Society*. Stamford, Conn.: Sinauer Associates, 1971.

Commoner, B. *The Closing Circle*. New York: Alfred A. Knopf, 1972.

Curry-Lindahl, K. *Conservation for Survival*. New York: William Morrow & Co., 1972.

Debell, G. *The Environmental Handbook*. New York: Ballantine Books, 1970.

Earle, S. A. "Life Springs from Death in Truk Lagoon." *National Geographic* 149, no. 5 (May 1976): 578–603.

Edmondson, W. T. "Fresh Water Pollution." In W. W. Murdoch, ed., *Environment—Resources, Pollution and Society*. Stamford, Conn.: Sinauer Associates, 1971.

Farb, P., and the Editors of Life. *Ecology: Life Nature Library*. New York: Time Inc., 1963.

Hardin, G. *Exploring New Ethics for Survival*. Baltimore: Penguin Books, 1972.

Herrscher, W. "How Do We Generate Environmental Attitudes?" *The Journal of Environmental Education* 4, no. 4 (Winter 1973): 18–19.

Hesse, W. H. *The Light at the End of the Tunnel*. Encino, Calif.: Dickenson Publishing Co., 1972.

Hungerford, H. R. "Myths of Environmental Education." *The Journal of Environmental Education* (Winter 1975): 21–26.

Kozlovsky, D. G. *An Ecological and Evolutionary Ethic*. Englewood Cliffs, N.J.: Prentice-Hall, 1974.

Livingston, J. A. *One Cosmic Instant*. Boston: Houghton Mifflin Co., 1973.

Masters, G. M. *Introduction to Environmental Science and Technology*. New York: John Wiley & Sons, 1974.

Maxwell, K. E. *Environment of Life*. Encino, Calif.: Dickenson Publishing Co., 1973.

McHarg, I. L. *Design with Nature*. Garden City, N.Y.: Doubleday & Co., 1971.

Meeker, J. W. *The Spheres of Life*. New York: Charles Scribner's Sons, 1975.

Odum, E. P. *Fundamentals of Ecology*. 3d ed. Philadelphia: W. B. Saunders Co., 1971.

Rodda, M. "Noise." In J. Rose, ed. *Technological Injury*. London: Gordon & Breach, Science Publishers, Ltd. 1969.

Segerberg, O., Jr. *Where Have All the Flowers, Fishes, Birds, Trees, Water, and Air Gone?* New York: David McKay Co., 1971.

Swan, J. A. "Attitudes and Values and Environmental Education." In T. R. Armstrong, ed. *Why Do We Still Have an Ecological Crisis?* Englewood Cliffs, N.J.: Prentice-Hall, 1972.

Turk, A.; Turk, J.; Wittes, J. T.; and Wittes, R. *Environmental Science*. Philadelphia: W. B. Saunders Co., 1974.

Chapter 11
Technology, Health, and Medicine

A Brief Overview of Medical History

Medicine, more than any other area, has been affected by technology. The study of medical technology—that is, the principles, methods, techniques, customs, and skills related to instruments and tools—requires at least a brief look at the history of medicine itself.

One of the earliest technological innovations in medical care was the discovery that opium kills pain. Its use was known as early as 1550 B.C. among the Mesopotamians and the Arabs, who also used mercury for treating leprosy and syphilis. But a long time passed before the early cures were generally used throughout the world.

The great leaps in Western medical technology did not occur until the seventeenth and eighteenth centuries of the Christian era. In the meantime, Chinese and Indian medicine may have been more developed than Western medicine. The oriental health practitioners combined religious, cosmological theories and speculative thought about the nature of the body to develop the fascinating theories associated with acupuncture and Ayurvedic medicine. The principles of such prescientific medicine continue to fascinate many today, not only because they sometimes bring unexplained relief from suffering and chronic illness, but also because they actually anticipate some recent discoveries about the interrelationships between mind and body—attitude and physical health. Today, medicine in the People's Republic of China combines the ancient theories of mind-body-world interdependence with modern medical technology.

Important Fundamental Discoveries

What is called modern medical practice began with the discovery of some fundamental medical tools still used in modified form today. The microscope, for example, was invented around 1600. Later, in 1674, Anton van Leeuwenhoek ground single lenses that could magnify to a point where microorganisms were visible. Although the thermometer, as a primitive instrument to measure body temperature and fever, was invented in the seventeenth century, neither it nor the microscope gained widespread use in medical practice until late nineteenth century.

The significant application of previously constructed instruments for precise measurement and the calculation of bodily functions took place in the nineteenth century. They led to: (1) the discovery of anesthetics; (2) the technique of antisepsis (destroying germs in the operating area); (3) the germ theory of disease; (4) the development of antitoxins; and (5) the discovery that certain diseases are transmitted by insects.

Anesthetics. Anesthetics—ether or chloroform—made surgery to remove organs, on damaged limbs, or on tumors a lifesaving technique in the mid-nineteenth century. Until such men as Dr. Crawford W. Long of Georgia in the United States and Sir James Simpson of Edinburgh, Scotland, used ether and chloroform as anesthetics for surgery, only the strongest, healthiest, and bravest could tolerate necessary surgery and survive.

With the increased use of anesthetics for surgery, the way was clear for scrutiny of the medical procedures of surgery itself. With or without anesthetics, surgery continued to be risky because of frequently occurring blood poisoning. The use of antiseptics to destroy germs in the operating field gradually reduced the risks of septicemia, erysipelas, tetanus, and hospital gangrene.

The germ theory of disease emerged from the work of Pasteur, Koch, and Klebs in their research concerning anthrax. The significant discovery was that a disease may be caused by a specific bacterial agent. Once a specific bacterial agent could be identified as the cause of a certain disease, the first step to control that disease was taken. Microorganism after microorganism was isolated and identified through the microscope, until the diseases of tuberculosis, cholera, bubonic plague, diphtheria, and others were controlled. Once the analytic step had been made—that is, the step that showed an identifiable bacterial agent as the cause of a disease—the way was clear for a general application of the germ theory of disease.

In the late nineteenth century, Theobald Smith demonstrated that the cattle disease called Texas fever was caused by a protozoan conveyed from sick to healthy cattle by a tick bite. This discovery allowed Walter Reed and his associates to show that yellow fever had its specific causal agent— the stegomyia species of mosquito. Later, Rocky Mountain spotted fever was shown to be spread by a tick bite and typhus by the bite of a louse. Medical technology not only isolated the specific causal agent of disease, but also identified the process of transmission as well.

X-ray Machines. Diagnostic techniques advanced considerably with the X-ray discoveries of Roentgen in 1895. The X-ray machine provided a way to scrutinize the internal parts of the human body such as the lungs, the gastrointestinal tract, the gall bladder, the kidneys, and the teeth. The electrocardiography machine—the photographic recording and measurement of electric currents flowing through the heart—provided a means to identify precisely the weakness, regularity, and strength of the heart beat.

Twentieth-Century Contributions

The twentieth century witnessed the expanded use of the vaccination process, which was originally discovered in the eighteenth century. Vaccination prevents a disease by building up natural inhibitors within the body which are formed by introducing weakened or dead bacteria to the body. The vaccination process stimulates antibodies that are already present in the body to protect against some specific disease. One of the greatest discoveries of the twentieth century was Dr. Jonas E. Salk's vaccine, which was a protection against the Brunhilde, Lansing, and Leon strains of poliomyelitis. Salk's vaccine provided a stimulus in the blood stream to produce three types of antibodies capable of destroying the polio organisms.

Another great leap in medical technology came with the discovery that certain foods are related to health and disease. The significance of nutrition in fighting disease had been known since the early eighteenth century, when it was observed that scurvy resulted from a specific nutritional deficiency. In the twentieth century, the term "vitamin" was coined to describe the active food elements essential for normal body metabolism and for good health.

Nutrition and Vitamins. The isolation of various vitamins and their functions, using the nomenclature of vitamin A, vitamin B, vitamin C, and so on began in earnest. The nutritional principle maintained in such research was that the deficiency of vitamins caused by diet or malfunction of certain organs could be corrected by the careful increase in food or vitamin supplements. For example, pernicious anemia, a disease in which red blood cells do not develop properly, was cured by increased dosages of one of the B vitamins found in liver extract (vitamin B_{12}). The precise relation of food to health is still a matter of research. Some nutritionists even hold that some diseases, such as cancer and heart disease, can be attributed at least in part to nutritional deficiencies.

A third medical innovation in the twentieth century is chemotherapy. In 1910, Paul Ehrlich prepared a chemical, Salvarsan, as a counter agent to syphilis. After three hundred or more chemical experiments, the chemical was later refined by Ehrlich into Neosalvarsan.

Sulfa Drugs. The next major chemical innovation was the discovery of the sulfonamide drugs in the 1930s. The sulfa drugs isolated and used were sulfapyridine, sulfathiazole, sulfadiazine, sulfaguanidine, sulfamaethazine. The sulfonamide drugs are antibacterials, which effectively kill disease-causing bacteria within the human system.

Antibiotics. The era of antibiotics—a technique which sets one type of organism against another—dawned with the discovery of penicillin. Penicillin gradually displaced the sulfa drugs as the treatment of many diseases because because by 1946 it was found to be less toxic and more generally effective than the sulfas. Other antibiotics followed the discovery of penicillin, including streptomycin from soil mold, bacitracin, polymyxin, and the general purpose antibiotic known as chloramphenicol and tetracylcine drugs.

Hormone Therapy. A fourth area of technological innovation was hormone therapy. Normal life processes require the secretions of the endocrine glands in proper amounts. Thyroxin, the hormone produced by the thyroid gland, adrenalin by the adrenal gland, and insulin by the pancreas, were isolated and studied. The chemical synthesis of such agents as preparations to be used by underproductive people increased the life prospects for many people suffering from debilitating diseases. The synthetic production of insulin to aid victims of diabetes helped to control a particularly distressing disease caused by a malfunction of the pancreas.

The wonder hormones of cortisone and adrenocorticotropic hormone (ACTH) produced sudden relief from a wide range of diseases and physical complaints. The symptomatic distress of rheumatoid arthritis, bursitis, infections, asthma, and hayfever was almost immediately relieved by the injection or addition of these hormones to the human body. Drs. Edward C. Kendall and Philip S. Hench of the Mayo Clinic in Minnesota received the Nobel Prize for medicine in 1950 for their use of cortisone. ACTH, a secretion of the pituitary gland, was found to be the agent that stimulates the adrenal gland to produce increased cortisone in the body. Although neither drug cures disease, both reduce uncomfortable symptoms associated with a wide range of diseases.

The sex hormones, testosterone (male) and estrogen (female), showed some favorable results in treating certain forms of cancer. Yet, all the hormonal compounds are found to have some distressing side effects. These include the growth of facial hair, pads of fat on the shoulder blades and hips, and often a depression psychosis. Recent studies suggest that the indiscriminate use of estrogen to treat a variety of complaints associated with aging carries the additional risk of cancer. So, while hormone therapy may help many sufferers, it is also risky for others.

Nuclear Medicine. A recent innovation in medical technology is nuclear medicine. The new discoveries create a complicated situation in which new techniques for diagnosis and treatment go hand in hand with some newly discovered diseases and injuries caused by exposure to radioactive materials. The diagnostic technique involves the introduction of radioactive material (isotopes) into the human body, generally through the blood system. Salt, iodine, or phosphorus are the materials usually used. The progress of the material through the body is traced by a Geiger counter, so that obstructions caused by tumors or malfunction can be located and examined.

Investigation of the brain, tracing blood through the heart and arteries and veins, the study and treatment of certain endocrine problems are all enhanced by radioactive isotopes. Some forms of cancer, virus infections, and blood diseases also are treated effectively.

But the nuclear age also brings with it the previously unknown problems of radiation injury. Knowledge of such injury came through study of the aftereffects of radioactive fallout from nuclear bombs both in wartime and in peacetime testing. Two aspects of injury have been discovered: First, the immediate damage to the central nervous system, the blood-forming organs and tissues, or the gastrointestinal tract; second, the genetic effects of radiation exposure. While genetic effects may not be apparent during the lifetime of the people exposed, damage and deformity almost always occur in their offspring. Recent studies indicate two discomforting facts: First, radiation exposure, no matter how small, shortens life to some degree. Second, radiation causes mutations or harmful changes in genes of germ cells. These changes may occur from exposure to cosmic rays or other natural sources of radiation, such as medical and dental X-rays or weapons testing. The mutations may be imperceptible immediately; but they may cause deterioration over decades, which shortens life, reduces fertility, and causes birth defects among offspring.

Studies indicate that most Americans use about one-third of their radiation safety limit simply by exposure to radiation in medical and dental X-rays. Moreover, effects of exposure are cumulative no matter how long the period of exposure. The body stores radiation, and, therefore, it would appear that all humans have a limit of exposure beyond which serious damage is sure to occur.

Medical diagnosis and treatment in nearly all branches of medicine have been dramatically influenced by technology. The influence has been one of significant development and aid in medical care. The results have been generally improved standards of living, the rise of public health movements, improved nutrition, and the possibility of a longer life for everyone able to enjoy modern medical technology.

As we have seen, however, there is a risk-benefit ratio in medical technology that is often difficult to measure precisely. The developments that can improve health care and increase longevity may also present risks sometimes not apparent until years later. Nuclear medicine and hormone therapy are two areas in which risk–benefit are difficult to assess. In the next section of this chapter, we shall look at other problems in modern medical technology.

The New Technology and Modern Medical Problems

The new technologies of medicine offer great promise both in the diagnosis and in the treatment of disease. The advance has not been without its risks, however. While modern medicine can do what people previously would have considered miraculous, it also faces new and complicated problems brought about by the new sophisticated technologies.

Old Diseases Mastered, New Diseases Encountered

The history of medicine involves technology and the changing picture of disease. As old diseases disappear, new ones always seem to appear. But we have no reason yet to believe that all diseases will be someday eliminated. The medical establishment feels considerable pressure to eliminate disease; people seem convinced that, in an age of technological miracles, death and disease also should be controlled technologically. Yet, disease does not disappear; it simply changes form.

Patterns of disease in countries that are not technologically developed are related to deficiencies, deprivation, and the poverty of all social, medical, and material resources. Infections and malnutrition kill many people in infancy or childhood. Other prevalent diseases are malaria, tuberculosis, gastrointestinal infections of various types including cholera, typhoid, dysentery, and the less specific infections of smallpox, bilharziasis, yellow fever, measles, scarlet fever, and whooping cough. Of the approximately sixty million deaths each year in the world, one-half of these are newborn babies, infants, and toddlers born chiefly in Africa, Asia, and Latin America. One-quarter of all deaths are caused by infections such as malaria, dysentery, typhoid, cholera, tuberculosis, smallpox, and pneumonia. The majority of deaths in the world, therefore, are caused by conditions that are subject to modification and control by abundantly available technological developments in other parts of the world. Some of the available technologies have nothing to do with medicine, but deal instead with economics, industry, and sanitation.

Even in the technologically developed nations of the world, disease is still not completely controlled. The leading causes of death in societies with highly developed technology are cardiovascular conditions such as coronary artery heart disease and high blood pressure; strokes associated with atheroma of the cerebral arteries; cancer; acute and chronic infections of the respiratory tract; rheumatism and various degenerative conditions of the locomotor system; mental disorders; congenital deformities and abnormalities; and accidents. These are conditions associated either with aging and degeneration or with stresses and risks caused by the pace and complications of life in society influenced by sophisticated technology. More people survive the early years because of the availability of technologies such as vaccination, nutritional additives, and available health care facilities. But the increased stresses and risks brought by urban crowding, modern transportation systems, processed foods, increased exposure to radiation, and the general fast pace of life take their toll eventually. In short, in a society with a highly developed medical technology, the old killers are controlled, but new diseases related to stress and old age become the new killers.

Disproportionate Medical Care

Another problem area related to technology is the uneven distribution of medical care in the world. Although technology makes a big difference in medical care, it is not the only variable in health care services. There are societies where medical–technical resources are abundantly available, but where health care is inadequate for many people. The striking case is that of the United States. Every president since Harry S Truman has affirmed the right of every American to high quality health and medical services. And given the financial and educational resources available in the United States, people might assume that the health of the average American matches or exceeds that of anyone in the world. Yet, the few quantitative measures available for comparing health care in different countries rank the United States well down the list of the developed nations of the world. Even more puzzling is the fact that health care is probably the largest industry in the United States, totaling about seventy-five billion dollars a year. Expenditures per individual average $375 a year, a figure considerably higher than in other developed countries. Yet, life expectancy in the United States is below that of Australia, Canada, Denmark, Finland, France, Greece, Israel, Ireland, Italy, Japan, the Netherlands, Norway, Sweden, Switzerland, and the United Kingdom.

Discrepancies Cited. Studies indicate a number of factors that may cause the discrepancy between the technological sophistication in the United States and the generally unsophisticated health care picture: Medical costs rise too high with medical–technical advance. Medical care costs have risen dramatically in the last twenty-five years. Some of those costs appear to be directly related to the technical complexities of treatment. For example, the technology of the artificial kidney machine is standard treatment for those whose kidneys do not function properly. The machine mechanically cleanses the blood; in some cases, the machine permits the patient's kidneys to recover sufficiently to perform their work again adequately. Almost all treatment with kidney machines takes place in hospitals, where machines are shared by a number of patients. The cost per patient is an average of $20,000 a year. However, the national supply of machines is limited; and it is estimated that as many as thirty thousand people a year die because they are unable to use a machine. Here is a case where technology for health care is known and operative. However, access to the technology by needy people is often impossible because of the high cost of treatment. The machines, themselves, are expensive to purchase, and their operation requires the added expense of training and paying personnel to operate them.

Kidney dialysis may be an unrepresentative case of medical expense, but other medical procedures are increasingly expensive too. A gall bladder operation in 1950 cost about $361 per patient. In 1975, that same surgery cost the average American patient $2,208. If the present rate of increase continues, by 1985 the operation will cost over $4,700. Clearly, the dramatic rise in cost for medical services certainly accounts for some of the uneven distribution of medical care in America.

Resistance to Subsidies. Many argue that federal assistance to patients would provide a more equitable distribution of medical service in America. When health care costs began to rise in the 1960s, 70 percent of the expenditures came from private sources; only 30 percent came from government sources. The ratio has not changed much since the 1960s. Resistance to increased government assistance to patients comes from two sources: The American Medical Association, which represents most doctors in the United States, has traditionally resisted government subsidy for most medical services. The case against the government subsidy ranges from opposition to socialized medicine, to fear that the historic principles of private enterprise will be threatened by government intervention in medical services.

A second source of resistance to government subsidy comes from the government itself. To nationalize any program requires that it go through two steps in the legislative process. The first step is authorization. The House of Representatives and the Senate must both pass an authorization bill that would permit spending government money for a new federal program. But even after this bill is signed and becomes a law, no money can be spent. An appropriations bill must accompany the authorization bill to appropriate the necessary money to the proper agency or department of government assigned to administer the medical program. Only when the appropriations bill is passed and signed by the president is a government actually able to begin a program. The two-bill requirement serves as a bureaucratic check on large expenditures and, in some instances, it probably saves the taxpayers a lot of money. However, it also allows a Congressman to speak and vote favorably *for* authorization of government expenditures in health care, but then vote *against* appropriation. The politician can effectively speak to both sides of an issue at once. To one group, he can indicate that he is in favor of health care. To another group, he can show that he is fighting against increased government intervention in the private lives of citizens, voting against higher taxes, and standing firm to protect the private enterprise system.

State involvement in medical care, however, is inevitable because of ever-increasing costs. State subsidies are practiced in some form everywhere, but countries differ in the scope or extent of subsidy. The U.S.S.R., for example, advocates and practices a complete state system for medical care, providing everything free to the public and paying physicians and medical expenses out of government funds. Medical education is also state funded; physicians owe their careers to the government, so they work for the government too. The National Health Service in the United Kingdom and in Scandinavian countries provides nearly complete health service to citizens and resident foreigners. Only special services, such as unusual treatment for rare diseases, are excluded. The United States government partially subsidizes special services, but ordinary medical and health care is the individual patient's responsibility. Although health insurance programs such as Blue Cross–Blue Shield defray some expenses for individual patients, not all people are able to enroll in health insurance programs. And usually those ineligible for enrollment (because of insufficient money or chronic illness) are the ones who need help the most.

Disproportionate Medical Services

Some argue that there is a critical shortage of physicians in the United States. Currently, the United States has about 325,000 practicing physicians, one for every 615 people. Sweden, which ranks higher on the life expectancy scale, has about 10,000 physicians for a population of eight million, one for every 800 people. However, Sweden considers itself to be inadequately serviced by physicians and has instituted a crash program in medical education to lower the ratio to one physician for every 500 people by 1980. Swedish people average three visits a year to a physician. In the United States, the average is five office visits a year for every person. The puzzling situation is that while the United States has more physicians available for the population and the population averages more visits to a physician a year, the life expectancy of citizens in the United States is lower. Moreover, in the United States, the probability of an infant dying during the first year of life is almost twice as high as in Sweden. Certainly, evidence does not seem to support the view that relatively poorer health for Americans is due to a shortage of physicians.

Geographical distribution of physicians is unbalanced. One hundred thirty-four counties in the United States—almost one-half million people— have no practicing physicians. It appears that physicians are located so that certain segments of the population are badly neglected. Some areas of major metropolitan centers have physician–patient ratios of one to twenty-five thousand. The Bronx area of New York City with a predominately black and Puerto Rican population has just such a ratio. Since only about 2 percent of all physicians in the United States are black (although blacks make up about 11.4 percent of the population), a racial discrepancy may compound the distribution problem. At any rate, the supply-and-demand principle does not seem to work in getting physicians into areas where they do not want to practice, whether these are in urban centers or in rural counties.

Overspecialization. Professional allocation of physician resources is inappropriate. This view maintains that health care is less than adequate in the United States because too many medical students are encouraged to specialize in fields in which they are not really needed. Surgery is one such field. A recent study by the National Bureau of Economic Research to determine the actual work load of the average surgeon in an urban environment concluded that the most common operation remains the tonsillectomy, and, that in terms of work capability, surgeons were working at 30 percent of their capacity (ten operations a week is considered a normal work load).

Too many surgeons or other specialists and too few general practitioners probably results from the tendency of many bright medical students to emulate their teachers. A career treating the complaints and sicknesses of the average citizen is not nearly so exciting as working with a surgical team that is experimenting with new techniques for heart transplantation. Many argue, however, that since medical education is so heavily financed by local and federal taxes, the government must initiate steps to force medical students into general practice.

In general, the allocation of physician-resource problem is one of establishing priorities in medical research and treatment. Cancer specialists, heart specialists, and immunology specialists all regard their areas as the most significant. It is to be expected that leaders in each field will do their best to attract the ablest and brightest students. And they will also seek as much government funding to subsidize their work as possible. Thus, the desire to be on the forefront of medical research and treatment, together with the promise of big mony, disproportionately loads certain areas of medical care and takes away from other areas. How to distinguish between the relative importance of medical research and medical treatment for citizens is not an easy matter; and once again, the normal law of supply and demand does not seem to regulate the allocation of physician resources.

It is important to remember that doctors, whose professional oath calls them to care for the sick and diseased, as individuals often go beyond their oath of duty to extend therapeutic and financial support for those in special need. The history of American medicine is replete with acts of individual self-sacrifice on the part of physicians for the welfare of their patients. The issue, however, lies beyond that of personal morality, sensitivity, or sacrifice. The issue is a complicated, corporate, institutional issue that requires a sophisticated manipulation of technical, political, and legal forces to work for moral and humane ends. How to do that without sacrificing personal freedom is something most of the nations of the free world are still trying to learn. Some have apparently learned better or more quickly than the United States.

Technology Obscures the Basic Objectives of Medical Practice

In the past, the objectives of the medical practice were rather clearly spelled out: Physicians were those who took as their life's task the care and cure of the diseased and the disabled. The "Oath of Hippocrates," dating from early Greece, states clearly the personal and therapeutic objectives of the physician.

> I will follow that system of regimen which, according to my ability and judgment, I consider for the benefit of my patients.... With purity and with holiness will I pass my life and practice my Art. Into whatever houses

I enter, I will go into them for the benefit of the sick, and will abstain from every voluntary act of mischief and corruption; and further from the seduction of females or males, of freemen and slaves. Whatever, in connection with my professional practice or not, in connection with it, I see or hear, in the life of men, which ought not to be spoken of abroad, I will not divulge, as reckoning that all such should be kept secret. [The Oath of Hippocrates]

The oath combines care, therapy, and a sense of loyalty and confidentiality. The work of the physician is to provide personal service to alleviate suffering and distress.

New technology has blurred this picture. The new technology forces the physician to make reeducation or continuing education a major professional preoccupation. Today's technology hastens the rate of professional obsolescence, so that all physicians must define their professional role as a commitment not only to patient care but also to education that must continue through the professional life. A generation ago a physician out of medical school for twenty years or more was still not technologically obsolete. Today, someone out of school for six or seven years is apt to be well advanced toward obsolescence unless some continuing education has been part of the medical practice itself.

A second factor blurring the objectives of medicine is the bifurcation of medicine into either technical procedures or medical care. If a physician wants to remain current in a field of practice, he must continue to develop technical prowess. If, on the other hand, the physician wants to maintain a caring relationship with patients, the time to keep current is often eliminated. And because medical procedures are increasingly technical, most patients when they are sick look for the physician who is most technically competent. It then becomes the responsibility of the physician to neglect the humanistic aspects of medical practice and concentrate upon technical skills. Personal care and concern are left for other members of the medical team, such as nurses, nurses aides, or volunteers. A physician who wants to take seriously the purely humanistic side of an historic profession is soon discovered to be either badly fragmented emotionally or technically obsolete.

The movement of medical practice from home or office to medical institutions such as hospitals or clinics further blurs the medical function. When pneumonia or a fractured bone could be treated at home or in the physician's office, the doctor and the patient relationship was personal and direct. When the doctor is replaced by the medical institution, particularly the hospital, the human dimension of the relationship is obscured and is often eliminated. The hospital is an impersonal, efficiently operated, financially obligated institution. It has to be maintained according to economic and technical requirements often established at state levels. As such, it cannot possibly provide care in the historic sense of medical care. The hospital—a building—cannot care. Care can be provided only by people. Yet, when there is an accident, the cry is not "Call a doctor," but "Take them to a hospital."

The Conflict of Interest Between Patient and Community

The remarkable opportunities that technology brings to the medical field for keeping people alive also raise some new problems about the relationship between the good of society and the good of the individual. For example, a remarkable reduction in mortality has occurred in the technologically developed countries, particularly in the early age groups. The chances for the survival of a newborn infant to late middle age is today vastly increased over what it was just two generations ago. The result of this development is a steady increase in the proportion of the population that lives well beyond the age of retirement. The over-75 age group is today the fastest growing group in the countries of Western Europe and North America. Yet, retired people find it difficult to contribute significantly to corporate life in technologically oriented societies. Most retired people, who have technology to thank for their long lives, also have technology to thank for the meaninglessness of their retirement years. And many of those who have been kept alive by machines or drugs are often reduced to docile and inactive people in retirement homes or nursing homes.

More serious, however, is the problem caused by the survival and reproduction of patients who carry genetic defects. The recessive defect of severe diabetes, a disease that usually leads to other diseases involving the eyes and the kidneys, can now be treated so that persons afflicted usually survive well into the reproductive years. The well-trained, intelligent diabetic can enjoy an expectation of life not so far short of the normal person. Yet, the genetic defect that causes diabetes is passed on to the diabetic's offspring, and diabetes continues with all of its liabilities toward serious companion diseases. The individual's life is saved and enhanced by technologcal advances. But the social cost is considerable if the afflicted individual reproduces two or three more people with the same affliction.

A second instance of the conflict between individual good and social good is that of the new treatment for the idiocy of congenital phenylketonuria. Rigid dietary restriction within the first few weeks of life holds the promise that infants suffering from this genetic disorder can be spared a life of institutional confinement. Yet, the genetic defect itself remains. And if reproduction occurs, the mentally subnormal increase at the expense of society.

Who Should Decide? The awkward fact is that modern medicine presents situations in which the interests of the patient and those of society are not identical and may even be contrary. The physician must wrestle with the problem of either denying therapy to the patient or treating the patient and placing upon society a new and growing responsibility for caring and supporting genetically defective people. Whether or not the physician should have the power to make such decisions or whether or not the physician is prepared to make such decisions is a question that demands attention. In one sense, the consequences of the physician's decision are not medical matters at all; they are human matters related to morality and to socio-economic issues. To withhold treatment or not, then, is probably a decision to be made by society and not by a physician. Yet, society tends to put the decision off and leave it to a physician. It is difficult to find politicians and officials who do not regard even discussion of such issues to be faintly indecent. Some attention must be given to just such questions in a society which aims at technologically sophisticated medical care.

New Technologies Create New Moral Questions

Organ Transplantation: An Illustration

The problem of deciding who shall live and who shall not live is even more poignantly presented by specific technologies of organ transplantation. The technology itself is surrounded with much more than the mere technical data of tissue matching, blood typing, and surgical procedures. Because organ transplantation, by definition, entails the giving of a vital bodily part, either by a living or a deceased donor, to a patient acutely in need of it, a complex exchange takes place involving psychological, sociological, and moral implications.

One side of the transplantation procedure is patterned on the ritual of gift exchange—an expressive act but not entirely a spontaneous act. The gift exchange in any situation is structured by three norms: a sense of obligation to give, to receive, and to repay. The obligations involved are reciprocal: The giver senses an obligation to present a gift, and the recipient senses a moral and social obligation to balance the exchange by giving the giver something of equivalent value. Failure of either side to perform acceptably in the gift exchange ritual strains the giver, the recipient, and others.

The specific problem associated with the technology of organ transplantation is that so long as the transaction is thought of in terms of a donation, it is subject to the social norms of giving, receiving, and repaying. But how can a recipient of a kidney or a heart possibly repay in kind? How are the psychological, moral, and cultural obligations that are placed on the recipient by the donation to be handled adequately? How are the families of donors and recipients to live with the new set of relations established by the act of organ donation? The giving of an organ is probably the most dramatic and supreme form of gift exchange in the history of the human race. How, then, can this act be put into the old cultural framework of gift exchange without destroying the participants?

Complicated Obligations. Relatives and family members of the patient, as well as the physicians on the surgical team, face equally complicated obligations. In their book *The Courage to Fail,* Renee Fox and Judith P. Swazey refer to the obligations put upon family and physicians as "gate-keeping." Gatekeeping has two sides: preparation for donation, and protection and sustenance of those who for some reason cannot make a donation. In the case of the kidney failure of a family member, psychological pressure to donate a kidney is felt by all members of the family. How to include those who might satisfactorily live with the actual complications of the gift exchange, and how to exclude those who for any reason cannot, are the gatekeeper's difficult decisions. The gatekeeper decides who is allowed to donate organs.

Many questions arise that have never been asked in normal medical situations before. Should live organ transplants between close relatives be prohibited because of the stress entailed for the donor, the recipient, and the relatives? Are the postoperative lives of people who receive transplants sufficiently long and meaningful to be deemed worthwhile in the face of the emotional and moral stress inherent in the gift exchange? What moral guidelines should physicians and others in the medical profession follow?

Who Should Select? There is yet another aspect to the problem. How is anyone to select from the pool of afflicted patients who should be given the special lifesaving therapy? If among thirty thousand patients needing kidney transplants only seven to fourteen thousand are likely to actually receive a kidney because of the shortage of donors, how is anyone to decide which of the thirty thousand they should be?

Traditional medical guidelines insulated the physician from this problem. The Hippocratic Oath commits the physician to work for the benefit of the sick "in whatever houses I enter." The oath does not anticipate the situation in which one must choose to save certain lives and leave others for death. Physicians probably have always had to make difficult choices, particularly on the battlefield and in times of disaster. However, the pressure of circumstances on the battlefield and in disasters forces a hurried decision which few people would criticize. The new technology presents, for the first time, situations that call for calm, deliberate, reasoned choices. Yet, the choices are not fundamentally medical ones, any more than the choices about when and where to construct a new hospital might be medical ones. Many factors, other than medical factors, play a part.

Nicholas Rescher, in an article for the journal *Ethics,* notes some criteria that might help people who must decide who shall live and who shall die. General criteria for including some patients and excluding others constitute the first phase of decision making. Three criteria should be applied for including patients in the group eligible for unusual lifesaving therapy.

1. The constituency factor. Since unusual technological medical treatment requires an institutional setting, only those people in the area of the institutional setting, who pay taxes to support the institution should have priority for treatment. Some other constituency principles may be indefensible or even illegal, such as race, religion, sex, party membership, or ability to pay. Yet, state or even national constituency may be a defensible principle to include some and eliminate others from the group of patients. Only those within a certain geographic area may be considered eligible for this lifesaving therapy.

2. The progress of science factor. How well will a patient serve the needs of science? Will the patient offer to return at designated times for tests and examinations that may improve the techniques? Which case among many cases will improve a therapy?

3. The prospect of success factor. If the technique in question has a statistical record of survival in favor of certain patients within age or sex categories, this factor may be a basis for including or excluding some patients from the group.

The final selection phase requires further criteria to allow decision makers to compare those who pass the criteria of inclusion.

1. The relative likelihood of success factor. It makes sense, for example, to give kidney transplants first to those patients whose blood type or tissue type indicate a high chance of success.

2. The life-expectancy factor. How long can it be assumed that a patient will live after the treatment? An elderly patient might have to be excluded in favor of a younger patient, all other factors being equal.

3. The family role of the patient factor. The nature of the relationship to family, children, and/or parents of the patient, as well as the financial dependence of others upon the patient, matters and deserves some consideration. According to this factor, a mother of small children would have priority over the middle-aged bachelor.

4. The potential future contribution factor. A valid consideration is the likely future service to be rendered by the patient if recovery occurs. Society invests something in one person against another in rare medical–technical procedures and is entitled to look for some return. It is complicated to try to determine who might make the greatest contribution to society or whose loss would leave behind the greatest burden for society to bear.

5. Past services rendered factor. Services rendered by a prospective recipient should not be forgotten because they remain of value in the present and into the future. How to determine the relative contributions of a librarian over a musician, however, poses further problems. (Rescher, 1969, pp. 173–80)

These criteria do not make the choices easy for those who work with the lifesaving technologies. Yet, if criteria are stated and known by all involved, some comfort can be taken in the fact that a decision is made only after some calm, rational, and deliberate reflection. It must be remembered, however, that decisions of this sort must be made. To confront a decision-making situation and choose not to choose is still to choose.

Medical technology in the last one hundred years has enhanced life in many ways. Age-old infirmities are now controlled or eliminated completely. And the future promises even better and fuller lives for all humans. Yet, the new technologies are not without their human problems, which seems to suggest that the greatest problems may not be technical, but human ones.

DISCUSSION QUESTIONS

1. Why were the microscope and the thermometer not used in medical practice for such a long time?

2. What risk–benefit problems exist in medical–technical procedures? Do you think a patient always has the right to know about risk–benefit factors in treatment?

3. Is technology the principle factor distinguishing various patterns of disease in the world?

4. What forms of government subsidy, short of socialized medicine, might lessen the cost of modern medical services?

5. Do you prefer a technically competent, but impersonal physician to a friendly, compassionate, but technically obsolete one? Do both of them have an important function in medicine? Why?

6. Does society have a right to prevent people who carry genetic defects from reproducing?

7. Should a recipient of a donated organ be prevented from knowing who donated the organ? Why?

BIBLIOGRAPHY

Allen, F. R. "Technology and the Practice of Medicine." In F. R. Allen; H. Hart; D. C. Miller; W. F. Ogburn; and M. F. Nimkoss, eds. *Technology and Social Change*. New York: Appleton-Century-Crofts, 1957.

Anders, G. "Burning Conscience—Commandments in an Atomic Age." In C. Mitcham and R. Mackey, eds. *Philosophy and Technology: Readings in the Philosophical Problems of Technology*. New York: The Free Press, 1971.

Baier, K., and Rescher, N., eds., *Values and the Future*. New York: The Free Press, 1969.

Barbour, I. G. *Science and Secularity: The Ethics of Technology*. New York: Harper & Row, 1970.

Beeson, P. B. "Some Good Features of the British National Health Service." *Journal of Medical Education* 49, no. 1 (January 1974): 43–49.

Berger, P. L.; Berger, B.; and Kellner, H. *The Homeless Mind: Modernization and Consciousness*. New York: Random House, 1973.

Ebling, R. J., and Heath, G. W., eds. *The Future of Man*. London and New York: Academic Press, 1972.

Experiments and Research with Humans: Values in Conflict. Washington, D.C.: National Academy of Sciences, 1975.

Fletcher, J. *The Ethics of Genetic Control*. Garden City, N.Y.: Anchor/Doubleday, 1974.

————. *Morals and Medicine*. Boston: Beacon Press, 1954, 1960.

Fox, R. C., and Swazey, J. P. "Gift Exchange and Gate-Keeping: An Interactive Perspective on Organ Transplantation." In D. Callahan, ed. *Freedom, Coercion and the Life Sciences*. Cambridge, Mass.: Harvard University Press, 1971.

————. *The Courage to Fail: A Social View of Organ Transplants and Dialysis*. Chicago and London: University of Chicago Press, 1974.

Freund, P. A., ed. *Experimentation with Human Subjects*. The Daedalus Library of the American Academy of Arts and Sciences. New York: George Braziller, 1970.

Fry, J., and Farndale, W. A. J., eds. *International Medical Care: A Comparison and Evaluation of Medical Services Throughout the World*. Oxford and Lancaster: Medical & Technical Publishing Co., Ltd., 1972.

Govoni, L. E., and Hayes, J. E. *Drugs and Nursing Implications.* 2d ed. New York: Appleton-Century-Crofts, 1971.

Hatcher, R. A. et al. *Contraceptive Technology 1976–77.* 8th rev. ed. New York: John Wiley & Sons, 1976.

Jonas, H. *Philosophical Reflections on Experimenting with Human Subjects. Daedulus* 98, no. 2, (Spring 1969): 219–47.

Kass, L. R. "The New Biology: What Price Relieving Man's Estate?" *Science,* 174 (November 19, 1971): 779–88.

Knowles, J. H. "The World of Health and the American Physician." *Journal of Medical Education* 49, no. 1 (January 1974): 50–56.

Magraw, R. M. *Ferment in Medicine: A Study of the Essence of Medical Practice and of Its New Dilemma.* Philadelphia and London: W. B. Saunders Co., 1966.

Mayer, E. "Biological Man and the Year 2000." In D. Bell, ed. *Toward the Year 2000: Work in Progress.* Boston: Beacon Press, 1967, 1978.

Mendolsohn, E.; Swazey, J. P.; and Taviss, I., eds. *Human Aspects of Biomedical Innovation.* Cambridge, Mass.: Harvard University Press, 1971.

"New Dimensions in Legal and Ethical Concepts for Human Research. *Annals of the New York Academy of Science* 169, no. 2 (January 1970).

Piel, E. J., and Truxal, J. G. *Man and His Technology: Problems and Issues.* New York: McGraw-Hill Book Co., 1973.

Rescher, N. "The Allocation of Exotic Medical Lifesaving Therapy." *Ethics* 79, no. 3 (April 1969): 173–80.

Rexed, B. "The Role of Medical Education in Planning the Development of a National Health Care System." *Journal of Medical Education* 49, no. 1 (January 1974): 27–42.

Wallia, C. S. "Science, Technology, and Human Values." In C. S. Wallia, ed. *Toward Century 21.* New York: Basic Books, 1970.

Chapter 12
Technology, Work, and Leisure

Introduction

Technology creates tools that human beings use to make their work easier, which often results in reducing the time spent working. If tools are found to reduce the number of hours one spends working, then some other ways must be found to spend that free time. Either more work or some other things to do can fill that time created by technology.

How people spend the time released by technology is the subject of this chapter. Since working is how most people spend most of their time, any discussion of technology, work, and leisure soon leads us to consider meaning, fulfillment, happiness, and security for humans. Modern tools and machines offer new powers to all mankind: To some people, tools promise liberation from drudgery. To others, new tools and machines represent unemployment, idleness, and economic hardship. In short, the same technologies that produce abundance and order in the world of work also produce fear, awe, and despair.

We shall examine this complexity in the world of work and technology first by looking at work from an historical perspective and then by looking at some of the problems modern technology creates for work.

An Historical Perspective on Work

Scarcely anyone in the history of the human race has liked to work. The earliest mythologies characterize golden ages of the past or paradises of the future as worlds in which humans do not work. In Christian, Jewish, and Buddhist religions, heaven is described in many different ways, but all include the promise of no work.

It is doubtful that prehistoric peoples had any concept of work at all. For them, to live was to work. Preliterate societies often have elaborate vocabularies for the activities and objects in hunting, gathering, and toolmaking, but no word can be found for work. Eskimos, for example, have over twenty different words for "snow." But work appears to be such a natural activity, akin to breathing or sleeping, that it does not require a term to describe it or to distinguish it from nonwork.

Such information about preliterate societies comes to us from contemporary hunting and gathering societies in southwest Africa and the far north of the Americas, and from certain Amerindians in the high, western plateaus adjacent to the Rocky Mountains in the United States. If contemporary, preliterate societies are Stone Age survivors and not simply remnants of some more complex culture, we must conclude that the prehistoric person had no clear concept of work.

Work as a Curse

The ancient Greeks regarded work as a curse. The Greek word for work is closely related to the word for sorrow, *ponos;* the concept work connoted drudgery, heavyheartedness, exhaustion. The Greeks thought that work enslaved mankind, and by the golden age of Athens in the fifth century B.C., all work had been relegated to the forced labor of slaves. Work was for the unfree, and the independence so highly valued by classical Greek thought was seen threatened by work.

The ancient Hebrews considered work in much the same way as the Greeks, but with one slight difference; to the Hebrews, work was part of a divine curse put upon mankind because of Adam's sin. The Garden of Eden story suggests that before Adam sinned, human habitat was a paradise. After the disobedience and rebellion, God condemned Adam and Eve to a life of toil. Thus, work is a human necessity because of the fall. But for the Hebrews, work might also be a means of atoning for the original sin.

It was with Christianity that the Western world slowly began to build the meanings that evolved into what is commonly called the "work ethic." The early Christians accepted the Jewish conception of work as punishment combined with possibilities for atonement. St. Paul wrote that "Every man's work shall be made manifest: for the day shall declare it, because it shall be revealed by fire; and the fire shall try every man's work of what sort it is." [1 Cor. 3:13] Work is something God will examine and judge according to divine standards.

Gradually, less threatening meanings filtered into the Christian concept of work. The early monks, following the rule of St. Benedict of the sixth century, believed that "idleness is the enemy of the soul." Manual labor was seen by the monks to aid in maintaining the spiritual health of the soul and the physical health of the body. Evil thoughts have difficulty penetrating the mind of one who is preoccupied with labor. St. Benedict insisted that "then are they truly monks when they live by the labor of their hands, as did our Fathers and the Apostles." [1] Lay Christians were taught to see work as good because it provided goods that might benefit others in need. Work might be an expression of Christian charity.

---

[1] "The Rule of St. Benedict." Collegeville, Minnesota: The Liturgical Press. Copyrighted by the Order of St. Benedict, Inc.

The great medieval theologian St. Thomas Aquinas integrated work with profit making. The concept of the "just price" espoused by Aquinas allowed for a monetary reward above the cost of the production of goods exchanged at the marketplace. Yet, "just" price meant what it said. Christians could exchange the products of their labor for a fair price that would allow them to provide for their own and their family's immediate needs. But in the society of Aquinas' time, the rare person lucky enough to live without working was not scorned. Nor did hard work acquire any special merit. Work was an unfortunate necessity for eking out a livelihood for most people.

Protestantism of the sixteenth and seventeenth centuries gave impetus to a conception of work that is highly moral. Martin Luther, the German Protestant reformer, took the decisive step when he eliminated the distinction between working and serving God. Luther insisted that what a person did in his daily work ought to be an act of worship to God. Work is one way to serve God. Luther condemned the monks of his time because they considered spiritual contemplation and prayer superior to the activities of working people. The cobbler at his work bench engages in as devoted an act as the monk in his cell, according to Luther.

Work as a Religious Mission

For the Calvinist reformers, a person's vocation constituted a religious mission. Conscientious fulfillment of the daily task was a deed pleasing to God. Moreover, sucess in one's trade was a sign that God accepted the work. Thus, to a Calvinist Christian, dislike of hard work makes damnation all but inevitable. Since work is in effect God's work, all men, rich or poor, ought to work. The better one can do his work, the more closely he conforms to God's will. Thus, efficiency, rationality, and diligence come to be characteristics of the dedicated Christian in Calvinist theology.

It is important to note the strong moral and religious importance Protestant reformers attached to work. Not everywhere has work had such connotations. In primitive, survivalist societies, work is simply a condition of human life; one must work to survive. In other societies, work is a curse, something everyone will avoid if possible. In still others, work is an outlet for man's energies—a better outlet than giving in to the temptations of idleness. But with Protestant Christianity, work becomes a mark of moral worth and religious devotion.

Even though the religious issues that gave rise to Protestantism have faded for many people in the Western world, the moral connotations given to work by the Reformers have not faded. A study by Daniel Yankelovich, Inc., in the mid-1960s found that a majority of adult Americans associated four highly moralistic themes with work: They tended to identify work with "the good provider" theme, which links making a living with a social definition of masculinity. The real man provides a living for his family. Masculinity does not have to do primarily with sexual prowess, physical strength, or virile appearance to most Americans. For almost 80 percent of the population, to be a man means to be a good provider for one's family.

A second theme was the "independence" theme. To make a living by working is to gain freedom from want, from hardship, and from dependence upon welfare aid. A third theme discovered was the "success" theme. Most Americans believed that hard work leads to success. Such success may come in the form of home ownership, a rising standard of living, or a solid position in the community. A fourth theme was the "self-respect" theme. Hard work carries with it human dignity. To work hard at whatever sort of work one must do is to gain self-respect, worth, and a feeling of well-being.

Thus, for the majority of Americans, manhood, responsibility, economic security, independence, success in life, self-esteem, and human dignity are closely associated with work. And it is, no doubt, from this moralistic attitude toward work that strong resistance to welfare legislation, unemployment, idleness, and excessive leisure stem. To assist the unemployed too much might suggest that not working is morally acceptable. Moreover, to remain unemployed too long threatens the self-respect and social esteem of many Americans.

It is against this background of the moral significance of work and leisure that any discussion of modern technology and its implications for work must develop. If technology brings about laborsaving devices, is it right and good that people no longer need to work? Or, if machines displace humans from jobs, is it right that people be deprived of their work? Is technologically forced unemployment bad or good? And should nonworking people be compensated for being deprived of work?

Work in Technological Societies

As we have seen, technology has a variety of meanings. When the word "technology" is used to describe changes in the world of work, many connotations appear. Technology means industrialism, mechanization, automation, cybernation. It also means continuous-flow operations, alienation from work, and unemployment. These terms are all "loaded" terms—that is, they connote much more than a simple, dictionary definition might. For example, although the introduction of machines into a factory may make work easier, it may instill fear into the factory employees who suspect the machines will replace them. Thus, some workers may be laid off. Other machines will be retooled for different jobs.

Automation and Mechanization

Much of the debate about technology in modern societies stems from a failure to define the meanings and implications of the terms mentioned above. Two words that need clarification are "automation" and "mechanization." Mechanization is the use of machines to do what humans formerly did. It substitutes mechanical for human handling of materials. Automation, on the other hand, is the automatic, centralized control of an integrated production system to the point where humans no longer are needed, except to watch and maintain the machines. Industries may be classified into degrees of technological sophistication through reference to the terms mechanization and automation. The highest degree of technological sophistication in industry is advanced automation, where all processes are mechanized and integrated by machines from beginning to end. A second degree is beginning automation. The third is advanced mechanization, where machines produce, process, and control quality. And the fourth is beginning mechanization.

Advanced automation is the direction toward which many industries in the Western world want to move. But in the United States, only a small portion of the labor force is employed in industries using advanced automation, which include industries associated with communications, data processing, and electronics. The majority of industrial workers in America work in areas where some form of beginning automation is being used; and many are currently working in industries with advanced mechanization. Chapter 6, "Levels of Technological Societies," discusses this issue thoroughly in the context of world development.

The Assembly Line

The implications of automation and mechanization together with continuous-flow operation, alienation, and depersonalization can be seen by a brief examination of assembly line work. Although the assembly line was not Henry Ford's invention, he and his automobile manufacturing methods have been closely associated with it because he adapted the assembly-line technology to produce the automobile. After Ford, it became a dominant method of mechanized production.

Frederick W. Taylor, the first man to systematically investigate the principles of scientific management of the technology of mass production, laid down the principles for assembly-line production. Taylor wrote in 1911 that "the man has been first; in the future the system must be first." He maintained that machines and rational ordering of human effort can make production more efficient and economical. In his book, he set out the basic rules for time–motion study. First, he said, ten or fifteen men must be found who are especially skilled in the particular task to be analyzed. Second, each man's series of moves and operations and the tools he uses must be studied. Third, a stop watch should time each movement required for the task, and the quickest moves should be selected. Fourth, all unnecessary moves should be eliminated. And fifth, the best movements and the best tools should be combined into one series of movements for each worker to copy. This new method of doing the task is then substituted for the ten or fifteen inferior series of movements formerly used.

Taylor's method is today called time-and-motion study, and the people who use it are considered efficiency experts. The assembly line is the result

A craftsman's work is fragmented into a series of moves performed by a number of people repeating the moves over and over. The result is a redefinition of work in terms of multiple motions of lifting, pushing, pulling, turning, and so on. The subdivision, fragmentation, and simplification of tasks call for careful organization, functional interdependence, and rationalization of the production process. The goal of the efficiency expert is to reduce a task to a series of motions that can be measured with precision. Once the task can be measured against time, a manager or engineer can measure the task against money values. The assembly line greatly increases production since each worker needs to do only a part of the work of a craftsman, and it also increases profits because more can be produced to be sold on the market. Often assembly-line production helps raise the standard of living in a society where it is used because it makes more products available to more people at a cheaper price than if they were to rely on craftsmen.

Cadillac automobiles move along the assembly line while workers install interior parts and equipment. Some phases of the assembly operation still require human workers. Photo courtesy of Fisher Body Division, General Motors Corporation.

Some Negative Aspects

The negative side of the technology of the assembly line is that it abstracts work in order to subject it to rational precision. Abstracting work depersonalizes it; the worker cannot identify with the work, and consequently cannot identify with the product. The result is what social psychologists call "alienation." The worker can identify himself only with a series of movements he performs at one stage in a whole process of production.

Although assembly-line workers comprise less than 2 percent of the work force in America, Taylorism and its emphasis upon efficiency is not restricted to assembly lines or even to manufacturing. A report of the Special Task Force to the Secretary of Health, Education, and Welfare noted that even the service sector of the economy is not exempt from the general principles of Taylorism. For example, the study noted that the greatest growth in the medical care industry has occurred in lower-level occupations. The growth occurred generally as an attempt to increase the efficiency of the upper-level occupations by delegating tasks downward. The result has been an increase in efficiency and a reduction in the range of skills necessary for low-level jobs. The routinizing, boredom, and discontent among people in the lower levels of medical care are as serious as those of the automobile assembly-line workers. Moreover, Taylorism in the service occupations tends to decrease opportunities for advancement for low-level workers. A laboratory technician or a nurse cannot expect to be advanced to the position of medical doctor.

A move toward eliminating the negative factors in assembly-line work was made in the automotive industry in the 1960s. A new production machine was introduced to the assembly line to take the place of certain routine, dangerous, and tedious tasks. The machine was the industrial robot —an automatic manipulator preprogrammed to perform given tasks. The

An industrial robot with its own memory bank. The robot can be used for loading and unloading, transferring materials, welding, or casting. An operator pushes buttons which activate the arm, hand, and fingers of the robot. Once programmed the movements are repeated automatically, sequentially, and precisely. Photo courtesy of Unimation, Inc.

robot retains the program in its electronic memory. Typically, the robot has a pivoted mechanical arm with a handlike gripper at one end. Its arms can move vertically and horizontally or they can rotate. The grip can move like a hand and a wrist. The robot never tires, does not feel pain, and can work a twenty-four-hour day without a break. In General Motor's Lordstown, Ohio, plant, at least twenty-six robots spotweld about 390 areas of the Chevrolet Vega automobile.

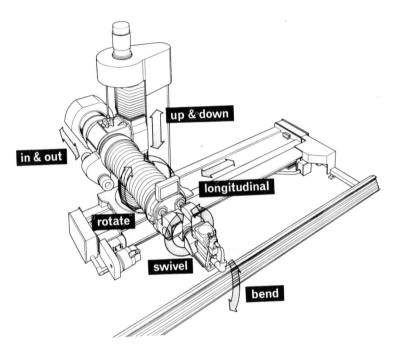

Diagram of robot movement. Fisher Body Division of General Motors uses a six-axis manipulator (SAM) to perform six directional motions in welding automobile frames and bodies. Courtesy of Fisher Body Division, General Motors Corporation.

Both the efficiency and the economy brought by the technology of the assembly line is illustrated by statistics provided by the Zenith Corporation experiments in automation. A recent Zenith Corporation plant cost $5 million, and its implementation of full automation resulted in a halving of the labor force needed to construct television sets. The output per worker increased approximately twenty to thirty times beyond that of the previous plant operation. The plant was able to insert 155,000 components per hour into a variety of television circuits, enough to produce seven thousand television sets per day. The system used small digital computers for seventeen automatic sequencers and thirty-one insertion machines. To change from one circuit to another, the computer program was simply altered to make the change. Thus, machines performed the normally tedious tasks at a great savings to the corporation.

Robots in an automobile assembly plant spot weld as many as 24 times as they swing around, twist, and move backward and forward. A complete operation of 24 welds takes 27 seconds. Formerly it took two welders eight hours to make the same number of welds that require fewer than six robot hours. Photo courtesy of Unimation, Inc.

Employee Alienation

The alienation felt by workers is manifested in many ways, including dislike for jobs, resentment toward management, rebellion against union leaders, tardiness, absenteeism, turnover, and inattention on the job. Machines that can do the tedious and dangerous tasks sometimes reduce alienation. But alienation is not simply a matter of boredom or danger. Recent studies indicate that alienation is the result of a deeper conflict that exists between changing employee attitudes and the expectations and demands of businesses.

Employees, particularly in highly industrialized countries, tend to demand a good deal more than simply a paycheck in exchange for their time and effort. A recent study by Walton lists six problem areas in modern industrial organizations and employee relationships.

1. Employees want their jobs to challenge them; they want to improve their skills while at work. Industry, on the other hand, tends to simplify and fragment jobs in order to increase efficiency, speed, and productivity.

2. Employees want to be included in decisions that affect their working life. But organizations in modern industry are characterized by bureaucratic hierarchies and chains of command that reduce worker participation significantly.

3. Employees want to take an interest in work itself and to make their commitments to the industry in terms of that interest. Organization practices, however, still assume that economic reward and employment security are the most important factors for workers.

4. Employees want some tangible indications of what they can get from a career *right now.* But when organizations design job hierarchies and career paths, they assume that workers are willing to postpone gratification in much the same way workers of the past did.

5. Employees want greater attention given to the emotional aspect of an organization—such matters as self-esteem, pride, openness between people, and expressions of warmth. Yet, organizations tend to emphasize rationality in management and seldom consider sentiment and emotion in dealing with employees and their work.

6. Employees are less likely, today, to identify competition as the way of progress in their lives or on the job. Nevertheless, management continues to plan career patterns, work, and rewards as if employees valued competition. (Walton, 1974)

Worker alienation is probably best understood by many through firsthand accounts of worker dissatisfaction. The following excerpt [2] from Studs Terkel's *Working* is a personal statement from an assembly-line worker at the General Motors Corporation plant in Lordstown, Ohio. While reading the statement, note the references the worker makes to machines, to his own sense of his identity as a human being, and to his alienation from his job and the employer.

Gary Bryner

He's 29, going on 30. He is president of Local 1112, UAW. Its members are employed at the General Motors assembly plant in Lordstown, Ohio. "It's the most automated, fastest line in the world." A strike had recently been settled "for a time." After graduating from high school in 1959, he "got a job where my father worked in Republic Steel." He was there four years—"dabbled with the union, was a steward. . . . I started on the track gang. I went into the forging department, a blacksmith's helper. Then, a millwright's helper. Then a millwright until I was laid off in '63." He worked at another factory in Ravenna for three years. "That's where I really got involved in the union." In 1966 he "went to General Motors at Lordstown."

2 Reprinted from *WORKING: People Talk About What They Do All Day and How They Feel About What They Do,* by Studs Terkel. Copyright © 1972, 1974 by Studs Terkel. Reprinted by permission of Pantheon Books, a Division of Random House.

I took on a foreman's job, some six or seven weeks and decided that was not my cup of tea. The one thing they stressed: production first, people second. . . .

I went back as an assembly inspector—utility. I relieved six or seven guys. I was able to get around and talk to a lot of people. I was very dissatisfied the way things were going. People being pressured, being forced to run. If a guy didn't do it they fired his butt. It was a mail-fisted approach by management because everybody was new. The way they treated us— management made more union people in 1966 and 1967 than the union could ever have thought of making. . . .

You go on to '68, '69, and they had sped up the line. They had started out at 60 cars an hour. Then they went on to a model 6, two models. We had a Pontiac, what was it called?—Firebird. And a B body on the same line. That presented difficulties. On top of it, '72 is not '66. There was a lot of unemployment then. Now there isn't. The turnover is almost nil. People get a job, they keep it, because there's no place else. . . . It was boring, monotonous work. I was an inspector, and I didn't actually shoot screws or tighten the bolts or anything like that. A guy could be there eight hours and there was some other body doing the same job over and over, all day long, all week long, all year long. Years. If you thought about it, you'd go stir. People are unique animals. They are able to adjust. . . . Can you imagine squeezing the trigger of a gun while it's spotted so many times? You count the spots, the same count, the same job, job after job. It's got to drive a guy nuts.

When General Motors Assembly Division came to Lordstown, you might not believe it . . . They use time, stopwatches. They say, It takes so many seconds or hundreds of seconds to walk from here to there. We know it takes so many seconds to shoot a screw. We know the gun turns so fast, the screw's so long, the hole's so deep. Our argument has always been: That's mechanical: That's not human. . . .

When they took the unimates on, we were building 60 an hour. When we came back to work, with the unimates, we were building a hundred cars an hour. A unimate is a welding robot. It looks just like a praying mantis. It goes from spot to spot to spot. It releases that thing and it jumps back into position, ready for the next car. They go by them about 110 an hour. They never tire, they never sweat, they never complain, they never miss work. Of course, they don't buy cars. . . .

There's 22, 11 on each side of the line. They do the work of about 200 men—so there was a reduction of men. Those people were absorbed into other departments. There's some places they can't use 'em. There's some thinking about assembling cars. There still has to be human beings.

If the guys didn't stand up and fight, they'd become robots too. They're interested in being able to smoke a cigarette, bullshit a little bit with the guy next to 'em, open a book, look at something, just daydream if nothing else. You can't do that if you become a machine.

Thirty-five, thirty-six seconds to do your job—that includes the walking, the picking up of the parts, the assembly. Go to the next job, with never a letup, never a second to stand and think. The guys at our plant fought like hell to keep that right. . . .

Assembly workers are the lowest on the totem pole when it comes to job fulfillment. They don't think they have any skill. . . . They have no enthusiasm about pride in workmanship. They could care less if the screw goes in the wrong place. Sometimes it helps break the monotony if the screw strips. . . .

In some parts of the plant, cars pass a guy at 120 an hour. The main line goes at 101.6. They got the most modern dip system in paint. They got all the technological improvements. They got unimates. But one thing went wrong. (Chuckles.) They didn't have the human factor. We've been telling them since we've been here: We have a say in how hard we're going to work. They didn't believe us. Young people didn't vocalize themselves before. We're putting human before property values and profits. . . .

Their idea is not to run the plant. I don't think they'd know what to do with it. They don't want to tell the company what to do, but simply have something to say about what *they're* going to do. They just want to be treated with dignity. That's not asking a hell of a lot.

I weave in on both sides of the assembly line. From the right side, the passenger's side, to the driver's side. Talking to guys. You get into a little conversation. You watch the guy, 'cause you don't want to get in his way, 'cause he'll ruin a job. Occasionally he'll say, "Aw, fuck it. It's only a car." It's more important to just stand there and rap. I don't mean for car after car. He'd be in a hell of a lot of trouble with his foreman. But occasionally, he'll let a car go by. If something's loose or didn't get in-stalled, somebody'll catch it, somebody'll repair it, hopefully. At that point he made a decision: It was just a little more important to say what he had on his mind. The unimate doesn't stand there and talk, doesn't argue. With us, it becomes a human thing. It's the most enjoyable part of my job, that moment. I love it! (Terkel, 1972, pp. 256–65)

The Humanization of Work

"The first big step in humanizing the workplace is for the employers and their representatives to accept their employees . . . as human beings." [3]

Noneconomic Demands

To combat alienation produced by technological innovation in manu-facturing, assembly, and processing, management and labor unions are taking some new measures. One change is an increase in noneconomic demands by labor unions representing workers at the bargaining table. Tra-ditionally, economic issues—pensions, health insurance, protection against layoff, compensation for disability incurred on the job, and cost-of-living protection—have been the focal point of union–management bargaining.

Noneconomic issues presently demanded by labor unions include shop conditions, noise levels, pollution controls. Generally, it has been difficult for such demands to reach top-level negotiations since the bargaining pro-cess itself requires that local union demands be consolidated to a manage-able list for the actual negotiations. Noneconomic issues generally tend to

[3] Leonard Woodcock, President of the United Auto Workers of America, 1973.

deal with work conditions at a particular plant, and such matters are often forgotten or ignored when the negotiations themselves begin. That is, non-economic concerns do not have the same universality or predictability that economic issues have. Moreover, more pay is usually the easiest thing for management to surrender. Restructuring a plant to make it more comfortable or redesigning an assembly line to make it more humane are more costly and less predictable in outcome.

However, since 1970, issues such as voluntary overtime, health and safety on the job, noise, and pollution issues have become more important demands for American workers than increases in wages. And serious consideration by both union leaders and management has been the result.

Restructuring of Work

A second change resulting from widespread worker alienation brought about by technology has been the restructuring of work. Here, often enlightened management rather than union leadership initiates change. Such measures usually call for radical redesign of a plant and often entail construction of new plants. Three general areas of restructuring of work have appeared recently. The three are not mutually exclusive, but are often combined to create a whole new work environment.

Self-managing Work Teams. This form of restructuring work eliminates the assembly line and makes groups of workers responsible for the assembly rather than individuals on a line. The group performs a set of tasks generally under some form of self-management. The typical size of the groups ranges from seven to fifteen workers, teams small enough for face-to-face meetings and for group decision-making and coordination of the work assignment.

The Volvo automobile assembly plant in Sweden initiated this approach to automobile assembly. An increased contact with fellow workers and individual identification with the production process tended to increase both worker satisfaction and productivity, the Volvo Corporation discovered. The added responsibility of self-management for the work teams improved quality control procedures as well.

Whole Tasks. Instead of fragmenting work into simple operations as the assembly-line procedures do, the work is organized into wholes that require more knowledge and skill to complete. This might mean that one worker could assemble a whole unit rather than merely add one small part of the unit. The whole-task innovation allows the worker to learn a major segment of the production process. In some cases, planning the assembly process that concerns the worker is given to him; at the same time, quality control, inspection, and implementation of the process are made his responsibility.

Flexibility in Work Assignments. Instead of assigning a worker to one specialized task, the assembly process provides: (1) temporary work assignments and reassignments from one task to another; (2) temporary redivision of work from one cluster of jobs to another; (3) movement from one task to another to allow a worker to master an increasingly greater amount of work; (4) systematic rotation through set positions. Flexibility in assignments allows workers to develop new skills, which, in turn, reinforce coordination and teamwork. Usually, the team itself decides how its members will rotate.

This restructuring of work into teams makes it possible for individual workers to identify with whole tasks, learn new jobs and skills, and participate in decision making that affects the individual's day on the job.

Restructuring of Management Operations

Restructuring work at the level of labor also requires that management restructure its own operations. In the first place, supervisors must redefine their responsibilities. They must become facilitators rather than simply supervisors. They facilitate planning and decision making of the work teams and coordinate relations between one team and others.

A second restructuring of the management's role occurs when it becomes apparent that productivity of work teams depends upon their receiving information not automatically available to them. Management must assume responsibility, therefore, for providing the work teams with economic and technical information concerning the production process so that they can plan and decide.

A third responsibility of management is to educate and train workers. Recruiting workers with interests and skills to match the work, and supervising the training process required for the worker to function adequately on the job, become an important part of management. Such a responsibility is quite different from what is expected of management when production operations are the assembly-line technique with a one man–one job ratio.

A fourth responsibility for management is to pattern leadership to allow teams autonomy and self-regulation. In other words, supervisors with authoritarian personalities might not easily adjust to a new role as facilitator, information gatherer, and educator. Thus, not only must a plant be restructured physically to permit a redefinition of work, but the worker must be retrained to fulfill a new function and the supervisor must redefine his own role in the new autonomy and responsibility given to workers.

An innovative restructuring of work and the workplace occurred at the General Foods Corporation plant in Topeka, Kansas, in 1971. Rather than restructure small work groups, General Foods redesigned a whole plant, putting into operation eight principles of redesign.

1. Autonomous work groups. Work teams were given collective responsibility for larger segments of the production process. The teams, composed of eight to ten members, decided who would do what tasks, how to inter-change jobs, and who would cover for sick leaves.

2. Integrated support functions. The teams took responsibility for tasks nor-mally performed by maintenance, quality control, custodial, and industrial engineering; all duties for the continuing operation of the plant were in-tegrated with the individual work teams.

3. Challenging job assignments. The attempt was made to eliminate dull and routine jobs insofar as possible. Nonchallenging jobs basic to the pro-duction goals, however, were either rotated or integrated into the general task assignments for a shift's work.

4. Job mobility and rewards for learning. Since the aim was to make all sets of tasks challenging, single job classifications had built into them pay increases based on mastering additional skills for more jobs within the team and within the whole plant. Thus, individual team members were rewarded for learning more about the total manufacturing system, and teams were rewarded for increasing the skills of individual members.

5. Facilitative leadership. The team leader position was created to facilitate team development and decision making. This replaced a supervisor respon-sible for directing, controlling, and planning the work project. The team leader approach envisioned the time when no leader position might be required.

6. Managerial decision information for operators. The design of the plant called for operators to have economic information and managerial rules to make decisions so that they could perform tasks ordinarily done at a higher level of supervision.

7. Self-government for the plant community. No plant rules were stated prior to the opening of the plant. Rather, the rules for operation evolved from the collective experience of the workers operating the plant.

8. Congruent physical and social context. Status symbols, which normally set apart management and workers, were eliminated as far as possible. Park-ing lots, for example, were open to all workers regardless of position. Plant entrances were common for all employees. And the architecture and tech-nology were designed to facilitate, rather than to discourage, the congrega-tion and interaction of work teams and management.

The General Foods Corporation redesign proved highly successful. Almost immediately a 40-percent reduction in personnel needed to run the plant took place because of the increased productivity and efficiency in operation caused by reducing employee discontent. The economic benefits to General Foods provided by a reduction in personnel were enhanced by improved yields, minimized waste, and avoidance of plant shutdowns. Pro-duction matters normally related only to technology were highly sensitive to worker attitudes also. When the workers were challenged, rewarded, and integrated, technology that was designed for efficiency became even more effective in increasing economic rewards for the corporation.

Toward a Leisure Society

One consequence of the increased efficiency of new technology is the increase in free time off the job for workers. Historically, if time has been consumed by work for most people, the future promises a great change. It is possible in the future that more time will be consumed by leisure than by work. But if people continue to seek personal meaning and significance in their work, the possibility of not working can be more of a threat than a promise. How to handle leisure time may be a real problem for mankind in the future.

De Grazia said that leisure is "the state of being free of everyday necessity." Leisure time is not simply free time, however. It is a state or condition in which time need play no part. Although free time can and probably should be turned into leisure, it need not be. Actually, free time has not increased as much as might be expected in advanced technological societies. Many argue that leisure is rarely to be found, in spite of industries devoted to leisure activities. Even though work time has significantly decreased in the past century, much supposedly free time off the job is taken up with traveling to and from the job, with grooming, and in getting ready for the job. Shopping and maintaining the home are other activities that are not really leisure activities: They are necessities.

Adequate Preparation Is Vital

Some psychologists maintain that if humans are unable to prepare adequately for the increased free time that technology promises, civilization faces a danger of self-destruction as great as that inherent in nuclear war or overpopulation. The tendency of many to fill up free time with frenzied activities that have nothing to do with leisure, seems to suggest that technological societies have not yet adequately prepared themselves for the future.

The interesting thing about free time created in technological societies is that it promises increased leisure for the lower echelon of workers only. Whereas in the past it was the aristocratic elite who did not have to work and could enjoy leisure, the new society marked by advanced technology will free the unskilled workers. The new elite will be the management class of professionals needed to run the sophisticated machinery of the future. The professionals of the new society will have little free time; all their time will be filled with thinking about their work, even if they are not actually doing it.

The social inversion that provides the masses with an abundance of free time and the professional class with much work creates problems. Since, in the past, the masses worked while the elite enjoyed free time, there are few historical models to guide mankind in the future.

Yet, thinkers such as Norbert Wiener, who is perhaps the leading theorist of computer technology, are convinced that full automation is imminent and that it will force extended free time on a whole segment of the human population. Complete automation will abolish the need for any slightly skilled or semiskilled workers. Wiener maintains that:

> The automatic factory and assembly line without human agents are only so far ahead of us as is limited by our willingness to put such a degree of effort into their engineering as was spent, for example, in the development of the technique of radar in the Second World War. . . . There is no rate of pay [now] at which a pick and shovel laborer can live which is low enough to compete with the work of a steam-shovel as an excavator. The modern industrial revolution is similarly bound to devalue the human brain, at least in its simpler and more routine decisions. . . . [In] the second revolution . . . the average human being of mediocre attainments or less has nothing to sell that is worth anyone's money to buy. (Wiener, 1961, pp. 27–28)

How to prepare for enforced idleness may soon be one of the major social issues of the Western world. If work has been a prominent feature of the human condition for so many thousands of years, will life not become intolerably boring and meaningless without it? With so many social institutions centering around work, what will happen if the majority of the population remains idle? But if extended free time is to be the case, how are societies to educate people for leisure? How can the work ethic be displaced? Or, how can one segment of society be educated to have and to use free time productively at the same time as another segment is educated to expect little or no free time? How can some students be encouraged to study longer and harder while other students are taught how to appreciate and to use free time responsibly?

A Redefinition of Work

The increased importance of leisure is a new phenomenon, limited as yet to relatively few people. Workers in less technically developed countries will continue to work long hours simply to stay alive. For thousands of years work has had to do with material gain; one solution to the problem of free time may be to redefine work. Since industrialism, work has been understood in terms of pay. It might be time to regard voluntary labor associated with housework, hobbies, art, and recreation as part of legitimate work. Our views of work are, as we have seen, beliefs that stem from certain value commitments, and they are changeable. Some more subtle meanings of work might be emphasized, such as work as a way of helping others, work as an antidote to boredom, work as a factor in self-esteem, or work as creative activity. These meanings may already play a part in work, but in the fact of more free time off the job, people may need to think seriously about motives for work and leisure in a technological society.

DISCUSSION QUESTIONS

1. How pervasive do you think the work ethic is among young people today? Do you find it peculiar that the same values that helped produce our laborsaving technology may prevent people today from enjoying their free time?

2. Should people who are forced into unemployment be compensated for not being able to work? Is there a conflict between values that create laborsaving machines and values that say people ought to work?

3. What are the benefits and what are the costs of the assembly line technique in industry? Are economic gains more important than human loss?

4. Why is it important for Gary Bryner in the automobile factory to pause to talk to a fellow worker and let a car or two go by on the assembly line?

5. What evidence can you offer of worker alienation in industries other than production industries? Are government workers alienated also? Why? Are service workers? Why?

6. What activities are leisure activities? Is it possible to find oneself working at enjoying leisure?

7. Is it possible that extended free time created by modern technology might be as destructive socially and psychologically as nuclear war?

8. What changes might be made in university and college curricula to prepare people for more free time from work? Is it possible that vocational education might, in the long run, be more irrelevant to people than the traditional liberal arts education?

BIBLIOGRAPHY

Berger, P. L.; Berger, B.; and Kellner, H. *The Homeless Mind: Modernization and Consciousness.* New York: Random House, 1973.

Burke, J. G., ed. *The New Technology and Human Values.* Belmont, Calif.: Wadsworth Publishing Co., 1966.

Burns, T., ed. *Industrial Man: Selected Readings.* Baltimore: Penguin Books, 1969.

de Grazia, S. *Of Time, Work, and Leisure.* New York: Twentieth Century Fund, 1962.

Dorf, R. C. *Technology, Society and Man.* San Francisco: Boyd & Fraser Publishing Co., 1974.

Freeman, D. N. *Technology and Society: Issues in Assessment, Conflict, and Choice.* Chicago: Rand McNally, 1974.

Kaplan, M., and Bosserman, P., eds. *Technology, Human Values, and Leisure.* Nashville, Tenn.: Abingdon Press, 1971.

Katz, E., and Burevitch, M. *The Secularization of Leisure: Culture and Communication in Israel.* Cambridge, Mass.: Harvard University Press, 1976.

Kelly, K. D. *Youth, Humanism, and Technology.* New York and London: Basic Books, 1972.

Mueller, E. *Technological Advance in an Expanding Economy: Its Impact on a Cross-Section of the Labor Force.* Ann Arbor, Mich.: Institute for Social Research, The University of Michigan, 1969.

Muller, H. J. *The Children of Frankenstein: A Primer on Modern Technology and Human Values.* Bloomington, Ind.: Indiana University Press, 1970.

Neff, W. S. *Work and Human Behavior.* Chicago: Aldine Publishing Co., 1974.

Rosow, J. M., ed. *The Worker and the Job: Coping with Change.* Englewood Cliffs, N.J.: Prentice-Hall, 1974.

Taviss, I. *Technology and Work.* Cambridge, Mass.: Harvard University. Research Review

No. 2, Harvard University Program on Technology and Society, 1969.

Taylor, F. W. *The Principles of Scientific Management.* New York: Harper & Row, 1911.

Terkel, S. *Working.* New York: Random House, 1972.

Thrall, C. A., and Starr, J. M., eds. *Technology, Power, and Social Change.* Lexington, Mass.: D. C. Heath & Co., 1972.

Vaux, K. *Subduing the Cosmos: Cybernetics and Man's Future.* Richmond, Va.: John Knox Press, 1970.

Walton, F. W. "Innovative Restructuring of Work." In J. M. Rosow, ed. *The Worker and the Job: Coping with Change.* Englewood Cliffs, N.J.: Prentice-Hall, 1974.

Wiener, N. *Cybernetics.* 2d ed. Cambridge: M.I.T. Press, 1961.

Work in America. A report of a special task force to the Secretary of Health, Education, and Welfare. Prepared under the auspices of the W. E. Upjohn Institute for Employment Research. Cambridge, Mass.: M.I.T. Press, 1973.

Chapter 13
The Search for Alternatives: Technological Assessment and Forecasting

Not all potential future technology will make life more comfortable or enjoyable; it can just as easily impair the quality of life as enhance it. But how do we design, implement, and adapt to new technologies when they come so quickly? At times, we are bombarded with so much change that we see how startling it is only if we look backwards. Technological change produces numerous effects, some of which are very negative. In some cases, however, a cause-and-effect relationship is never clearly established. Our attempts at forecasting and assessing these relationships has been haphazard because we have never fixed the responsibility for the impact of technology.

Some writers have suggested that we establish a meritocracy in which engineers and scientists, as philosopher–kings, control our political systems. Others have suggested that we declare a moratorium on the growth of technology. Still others have suggested that we use our rational processes to anticipate the technology of the future and assess it to fit humane ends. In the past decade, the human has conceived disciplines and organizations, and has made conscious efforts to foster these goals. Today the technological forecasting and technology assessment movements are well ingrained into our culture and throughout the entire world.

A Case in Point: Cross-Florida Barge Canal

In the early 1900s, large water resource projects became common in the United States. Experience transformed these projects from single-purpose endeavors (for example, irrigation) to multipurpose endeavors (power generation plus irrigation plus recreation), which brought to public attention such issues as ecological degeneration, cost overruns, and changing values. In many cases, the projects became irreversible in spite of human concerns and attempts to discontinue them.

The Cross-Florida Barge Canal project, one project that received extensive assessment, was finally halted because of its ecological implications. The project's goal was to construct a barge canal from the Atlantic Ocean, across Florida, to the Gulf of Mexico. Early project proposals have been attributed to Philip II of Spain, to Andrew Jackson, and to John Quincy Adams. However, it was not until 1935 that the Emergency Relief Act allowed President Roosevelt to allot funds for river and harbor projects. In that year, the U.S. Geological Survey assessment of the project was that the canal would cause tremendous ecological damage. The salt water would irreparably damage the geological features of the inner waterway. In spite of the report, the president requested $5 million, and work began in September 1935. In June 1936, with an apparent cost overrun, work was stopped after the Department of Commerce pointed out that local fresh water supplies were threatened. Five years of bitter debates continued in Congress. When World War II broke out, the military suggested that the canal would help protect shipping by eliminating the long voyage around the southern tip of Florida. Although Public Law 675 authorized continued construction at an estimated $93,000,000, other national priorities halted the project.

The 1950s brought renewed interest in the canal, especially from the Secretary of Defense, who maintained that the canal would lessen the risk of submarine attacks. Construction was renewed in February 1964, during the Johnson administration, despite objections from environmental groups. The Florida Defenders of the Environment was organized in July 1969, with support from trained ecologists and economists. In February 1970, President Nixon received a letter signed by over one hundred fifty environmental specialists requesting a moratorium on construction. The president referred the letter to the council on Environmental Quality, which recommended ending the project. Finally, after a cost of millions of dollars and almost forty years, the project was abandoned.

Before the mid-1960s we had few channels for forecasting and assessing technology. Fortunately, channels were discovered in time to provide information for rational decision making. The question remains, however: Can the technology of today and tomorrow be predicted and assessed before it is in its formative stages?

Historical Development of Technological Assessment

Assessment is an inherent part of all innovations: It is not new to society. Kranzberg finds evidence of the first assessment in prehistoric times. Once random invention gave way to systematic innovation and accumulation had intensified, individuals began to look beyond first-order effects of their innovations. At this point, it was realized that many effects of innovations could be calculated in advance.

At the beginning of the nineteenth century, overzealous acceptance of technology met with a great deal of public hostility. Some objected to the spoliation of the countryside by railroads infringing upon hunting rights. More dramatically, the Luddite workmen destroyed laborsaving machinery to protest against the dehumanization of industrial production. That was one of the first major challenges to technological change.

It became apparent to many people about a century ago that the government needed to protect individual rights and those of society as a whole.

As the democratization of society took place in the United States and Europe in the nineteenth century, people began to express their feelings. At that stage, the government placed some restrictions on technological imperfections. In 1824, for example, the steamboat *Aetna* exploded in New York Harbor killing thirteen persons and injuring many more. The House of Representatives considered a bill barring the issuance of a certificate of navigation to any boat operating at high steam pressures. Although the bill never passed, it prompted an investigation into the cause of boiler explosions. In 1830, the government granted the Franklin Institute a research grant to study the problem—the first grant of a technological nature issued by the federal government. It took six years for the Institute to make its recommendations and another two years for a law to be passed. However, the law was written so poorly that the inspection criteria for steamboat engineers was eliminated. More boiler explosions resulted in legislation in 1852 with a regulatory agency to enforce the law. In this case, it took twenty-eight years from awareness to viable legislation.

Government Involvement

The first governmental attempt to institutionalize scientific advice occurred in 1863, when the National Academy of Science was established. While this group was interested in scientific research, it gave little attention to social issues. It was not until December of 1938 that the hearings of the Temporary National Economic Committee resulted in a thorough investigation of technology and its impact on society. In the 1960s, the President's Commission on Technology, Automation, and Economic Progress conducted a similar investigation.

During the 1950s, most large firms had research and development organizations, many of which were supported by governmental agencies. In 1958, the Federal budget included $4 billion for research and development in military and atomic energy pursuits. As the space program escalated, this budget rose to $14 billion in 1966. The Department of Defense, the Atomic Energy Commission, and the National Aeronautics and Space Administration used 90 percent of these funds. This surge of research prompted the sophistication of research technique and technology assessment. In 1963, in an address to the National Academy of Science, President Kennedy said, "Every time you scientists make a major invention, we politicians have to invent a new institution to cope with it. As we begin to master the destructive potentialities of modern science, we move toward a new era, in which science can fulfill its creative promise and help bring into existence the happiest society the world has ever known."

International Formulations

It was also in the 1960s that individuals and groups throughout the world formulated early warning systems to stop the destruction of natural resources. It was a move toward anticipatory planning as opposed to reaction planning and led to worldwide concern for technology assessment. For example, the Organization for Economic Cooperation and Development met in Paris in 1972 to discuss technology assessment. That same year, in Milan, representatives from NATO, the National Science Foundation, and the International Institute for the Management of Technology met, and the Third World Future Research Conference was held in Bucharest with technology assessment its primary concern.

The boiler explosions described earlier were just one example of assessment after the fact. Tragedies such as the sinking of the nuclear submarine U.S.S. *Thresher,* the fire aboard the Apollo spacecraft, oil spills, power failures, and so on were very visible technological failures. Others were very subtle and in many cases have yet to be tested for potential side effects. For example, what will come from the array of pharmaceutical products consumed today? Will other thalidomides appear? What will be the long-range consequence of the sonic boom? What about current research in genetic manipulation? Are current concepts of assessment adequate for the challenges ahead of us? Questions such as these caused the U.S. Congress to create the Office of Technology Assessment.

Technology Assessment Organizations

Office of Technology Assessment (OTA)

In October 1966, a congressional subcommittee on Science, Research, and Development examined the consequences and secondary impacts of technical innovations. Its report first used the term "technology assessment." The authors cited technological unemployment, toxic pesticides, pollution, exhaustion of resources, the disposal of radioactive wastes, and invasions of personal liberty by electronic snooping and computer banks as examples of the potentially dangerous consequences of technology. The committee concluded that an early warning system would be a boon to Congress.

On March 7, 1967, Representative Emilio Q. Daddario proposed that Congress create a "Technology Assessment Board." He offered the following definition of technology assessment:

> Technology assessment is a form of policy research which provides a balanced appraisal to the policymaker. Ideally it is a system to ask the right questions and obtain correct and timely answers. It identifies policy issues, assesses the impact of alternative courses of action and presents findings. It is a method of analysis that systematically appraises the nature, significance, status, and merit of a technological program . . . It is designed to uncover three types of consequences—desirable, undesirable, and uncertain. . . .

Rep. Daddario developed a number of themes:

> The urgency of assessment due to the population explosion and the growing power of technology to effect changes in the human environment.

Many major impacts of technology were irreversible. Science and technology had become a way of life, with $157 billion of public and private funds invested over the past decade. (*O.T.A.: Background and Status,* 1973, pp. 10–11.)

To explore technology assessment, the subcommittee proposed a series of hearings and seminars, which resulted in three major reports that formed the basic framework for later works on technology assessment. These reports, all of which were completed in 1969, were:

1. Technical Information for Congress, by the Legislative Reference Service. This report examined fourteen technology assessments performed for Congress.

2. Technology: Processes of Assessment and Choice, by the Committee on Science and Public Policy. This report discussed the philosophic content of assessment and concentrated its effort on the design of an organizational framework for technology assessment within the federal government.

3. A Study of Technology Assessment, by the Committee on Public Engineering Policy. This report consisted of three experiments in technology assessment which provided possible techniques for future assessments.

After five years of persistent effort, Rep. Daddario's dream had come true. In October 1972, the Office of Technology Assessment was signed into law by the president.

Structure of the OTA. The OTA is located within and responsible to the legislative branch of the government. Within this jurisdiction, the office was charged with providing early indications of the probable adverse and benefical impacts of the applications of technology. Specifically, it was to:

1. Identify existing or probable impacts of technology or technology programs.

2. Where possible, ascertain cause-and-effect relationships.

3. Identify alternative technological methods of implementing specific programs.

4. Identify alternative programs for achieving requisite goals.

5. Make estimates and comparisons of the impacts of alternative methods and programs.

6. Present findings of completed analyses to the appropriate legislative authorities.

7. Identify areas where additional research or data collection is required to provide adequate support for all the assessments of estimates.

8. Undertake such additional associated activities as the appropriate authorities may direct. (Public Law 92–484, 1972)

Assessment activities may be initiated by: (1) the chairman of any standing committee, special, or select committee of either house of the Congress, or of any joint committee of the Congress, acting for himself or at the request of the ranking minority member or a majority of the committee members; (2) the board; or (3) the director in consultation with the board.

The board consists of thirteen members, made up of six senators, six representatives and a nonvoting director. In addition the board has an advisory council made up of twelve members. Ten of these, who are eminent in one or more fields of the physical, biological, or social sciences or engineering, must be from the public sector and must be experienced in the administration of technological activities. (Public Law 92–484, 1972)

The OTA is a liaison between Congress and the contracted assessment team. Ad hoc task forces carry out the actual assessments since the OTA, by law, cannot operate any laboratories, pilot plants, or test facilities. The office may enter into contract with any person, firm, association, corporation, educational institution, or with any agency of the United States, with any state, territory, or possession.

Speaking at the Second General Assembly of the World Future Society in 1976, Senator Edward M. Kennedy announced that the OTA has major programs underway in energy, especially solar energy; food; oceans; transportation; and materials. New programs are being developed in health, technology and international trade, and national research and development planning. As the first chairman of the OTA, he concluded his remarks by saying, "Perhaps its chief value will come as a spur to institutional innovation in other parts of the society."

Office of Technology Assessment and Forecasting

The Commerce Department instituted a new program in 1973 called the Technology Assessment and Forecast Program. This was established under the Office of the Assistant Secretary for Science and Technology and constitutes a new information source for busines, industry, and the government. A basic premise of the program is that the changing patterns of patent activity, now listed in 85,000 subclasses, can be an accurate indicator of technological activity throughout the world; it can be used to help appraise the comparative technological strentghs and weaknesses of the United States and competitive trading nations. The program has two basic objectives:

1. To identify those areas of technology in which a high proportion of the activity is of foreign origin.

2. To spotlight areas of technology exhibiting unusually rapid overall growth. (U.S. Dept. of Commerce, *Early Warning Report,* p. 2)

The data in this program consist of over eleven million U.S. patent documents, classified into three hundred broad divisions of technology, called classes. These are subdivided into the 85,000 subclasses. Each year, approximately 250,000 new U.S. patent documents are added to this file. This activity makes it possible to study the interdependence of patents, technology, and the economy. Eventually, requests for the information from this data base will take many forms. For example, the user may wish to have data on such factors as:

1. Overall growth (rate at which patents are being added to an area).

2. Foreign share (percentage of patents in an area obtained by residents of foreign countries).

3. Extent of government ownership (percentage assigned to the U.S. government at the time of issuance).

4. Country profiles (effort that a country is devoting to different divisions of technology).

5. Research and development expenditures.

6. Export–import figures.

Although the technology assessment and forecast program is new, like the OTA, it has valuable information for government and private groups. Decision making has been enhanced by the identification of trends and comparative efforts throughout the world. This function will become increasingly important at a time when other countries move into new technologies and as the number of multinational corporations grow.

Assessment by the Private Sector

One should not be led to believe that assessment is solely a federal government function or concern; the private sector is very much involved in making assessments. Citizen and student groups have joined in the quest for technology that has been tested and proven safe for humans, animal life, and our total ecology. Testimony before the Subcommittee on Science, Research and Development in 1970 revealed that there was a severe shortage of trained personnel to make assessments. Since that time, however, new university courses and degree programs train persons in the technological assessment.

The National Environmental Policy Act of 1969, which required environmental impact statements, stimulated interest in technology assessments within the private sector. Corporations are learning that an assessment must move beyond economic and legal impacts.

Years ago, corporations applied the theory of Adam Smith, which stated that when corporations pursued maximum profit, they were led as if by an invisible hand to serve society's best interests. Today, such theory no longer commands respect by the consumer. What are the obligations of business to individuals and society as a whole? There really is no ready-made answer to this question. What is important is that the question is not merely a threat, but a consciousness-raising element that must be dealt with in board meetings and that must respond to legislation. Since the economic system plays an important role in the process that technology develops, assessment must become an essential part of that system. If corporations can accept the assessment process as a balanced analysis of how productivity can proceed, the process will provide a list of future courses of action supported by analyses of the consequences.

Technology Assessment in Foreign Countries

Although technology assessment has progressed further in the United States than elsewhere, other countries have begun assessments on a large scale. In the early 1970s, the International Society for Technology Assessment was formed to foster assessments worldwide. The First International Congress of Technology Assessment, held from May 27 to June 1, 1973, at The Hague, the Netherlands, was attended by two hundred twenty-five persons from twenty-one countries, making the movement global. This group held its Second International Congress from October 24 to 28, 1976, at the University of Wisconsin.

The Office of Technology Assessment in the United States launched its effort ahead of most other countries. However, assessments in Canada, Japan, the U.S.S.R., and many other countries are being made with vigor. Also highly visible are the written materials attributable to foreign writers. The first issues of the *Technology Assessment Journal* contained articles from writers in Great Britain (Technical Change and Risk Distribution), Japan (A New Approach to Societal Development), U.S.S.R. (Technology Assessment in the U.S.S.R. or the Science of Science).

Since technology is evident in all cultures, assessment cannot be restricted to any one area of the world. The transfer of technology from country to country, the concept of the multinational corporation, and the increased awareness of our finite resources mandate the need for assessments in every country on earth. For example, can the world tolerate nuclear fallout from detonations in China such as occurred in the fall of 1976? Can the United States continue to use one-third of the world's resources when it has only 6 percent of the population? Are we assessing the new alternatives that we are choosing as a result of the energy crisis (for example, nuclear power)?

Assessing Technology Assessment

In theory, technology assessement is easy to understand, and it is difficult to take issue with its intent. It is an attempt to make sense of radical change and to humanize its consequences. It is an attempt to learn whether a new development will provide a viable option for the human race or whether it will accelerate problems over which we have no control.

The novelty of technology assessment is the identification of second, third, and fourth effects that may affect society more deeply than the primary effects. If these can be identified before being dumped upon the human race, there may be time to eliminate the problem. Obviously, success depends upon a social conscience in big business and the consumer. Hopefully, this movement will also identify trends while suggesting where new developments will occur, implying that forecasting is a necessary part of the assessment process, and forecasting, too, is a very young discipline.

Many questions need to be answered if both assessment and forecasting are to reach their full potential. For example, who is to do the assessment and forecasting? Who will evaluate the results? Who will enforce the legislation written to accommodate the new technology? Can bias and self-interests be eliminated from the process? Most importantly, can social responsibility be taught at a time when technology seems to have depersonalized society? Can accurate assessments and forecasts be made if technology is feared?

One thing is certain: Technological decisions must be made today and in the future. There is no way to escape the consequences of decisions or indecisions.

Technological Forecasting

In the last decade, we have observed a startling increase in the study of the future. New books, such as *Future Shock;* new journals, such as *The Futurist;* and new societies, such as the *World Future Society* have appeared to enhance this awareness. Just as the year 1976 prompted an assessment of the progress of this country, the closeness of the year 2000 prompts us to predict the future. The climate of this era is based on the discovery that the future can be designed and managed to meet human goals. Increasingly, social scientists are becoming aware that because of the growth of technology we face profound decisions if our children are to enjoy a world compatible with their needs.

In 1964, Kenneth Boulding described an invisible college of people throughout the world who had come to the realization that we stand precariously in the midst of a great transition in human history. He indicated that the situation will require a commitment of energy and resources and a level of enlightenment beyond any brought forth by any era. This college is no longer invisible. Today, there is a proliferation of courses and degrees being offered in our school systems. Many formal groups have been organized solely for the purpose of studying the future.

Curiosity About the Future

The human has been curious about the future for thousands of years. The earliest records that deal with the future appeared in Egypt in 3500 B.C. The *Book of the Dead,* for example, was written to express beliefs about individual's immortality, allegedly determined by one's conduct on earth.

This book was a kind of manual for the use of the soul in its journey to Amentit or Hades and contained the correct answers to questions that the dead person would be asked. Astronomy represents one of the first scientific uses of forecasting the future. In addition to providing navigation, the annual floods of the Tigris and the Euphrates were found to have a correlation with the constellations. Oracles were often backed by myth and allusive pronouncements because of their unreliable knowledge, but they continued to direct the decision-making process.

Near the close of the tenth century, the first modern mechanical clock was invented by a monk named Gilbert, who later became Pope Sylvester II. The monastery was such an important part of life at that time that a prediction of time was necessary to maintain order. The clock used by the Benedictines became a means to keep track of hours and to synchronoize the actions of people. Today it still serves this function.

Prior to the Renaissance, people were past-oriented; they remained satisfied with the knowledge from the Greeks and Romans. Science was assumed to be in the hands of alchemists, necromancers, and heretics. Few people used the store of knowledge available in nature. The fifteenth century, however, awakened the human senses and produced such great scientists as Leonardo da Vinci, Newton, and Galileo. Leonardo, living at the beginning of the Renaissance, produced countless theories and models of scientific inquiry. His solutions to practical problems were enhanced by his ability to search for future possibilities. His studies of airplanes, automobiles, and automation during this period (1452–1519) were remarkable and were a forerunner of the future. This period was considered by many as the period of synthesis—that is, the period when people took bits of knowledge and related them to problems of the day and of the future. At that time, an individual could come close to mastering the range of human knowledge, and Leonardo came close to this level of absorption. In that age of discovery, many adventurers (Columbus, Copernicus, Galileo, Newton) had one thing in common—a dream of a limitless future.

History shows us that Thomas Jefferson looked to the future politically and scientifically. His hopes and actions were designed to improve the lives of two and one-half million colonists. He predicted the eventual conquest of air and went so far as to predict that balloon travel, invented by the Montgolfier brothers, would carry humans across inaccessible locations. Following this period, came countless inventions designed to strengthen the idea and desire for progress. By 1870, such thinkers as Darwin, Marx, and Spencer expressed their beliefs about social and technological progress. Even today, their ideas about the future are reviewed by scholars in the study of the human race.

Literary Forecasting

The twentieth century brought another trend—that of the predictive science fiction writers. Jules Verne popularized oceangoing submarines and space travel. H. G. Wells, obviously influenced by Verne, wrote about a better social order. His predictions, the most notable of which appeared in his book *Anticipations,* were mind-boggling. His ideas concerning submarines and aircraft were false, but his predictions for ground travel were quite accurate. For example, he predicted turnpikes allowing speeds of 60–80 miles per hour. His lack of knowledge of contemporary engineering and the social sciences prohibited perfection in these forecasts. However, his greatest contribution was to call for a science of the future.

In 1911, Thomas Edison predicted many applications of electricity. His enthusiasm for the electric car may soon be shared because of the shortage of fossil fuels. Supporting his theories on electricity was Charles Steinmetz of General Electric, who predicted electric kitchens, air conditioning, legislation to control combustion in the cities, and radio broadcasting. *Scientific American* published an editorial in 1920 with sixty-five predictions aimed at the year 1995. Fifteen years later, only seven of these seemed unlikely and twenty-five were already a reality. Even Edgar Allan Poe, in "Mellonta Tauta," wrote about the future. This piece of work, about the year 2848, described elaborate communication and transportation systems.

Many other sources of that period could be cited that contain serious predictions about the future. The 1920s and the 1930s offered many classics well worth the time to consider. Martino indicates that these early twentieth-century personalities introduced a trend—that of using forecasting as propaganda or special pleading. Writings were intended to warn society of inherent dangers in technological development or to extol the benefits of the technology. Many forecasts were designed to influence decision makers, but the appeal was normally made to the public at large. The forecaster, even when trained as a scientist, served more as a philosopher than a forecaster as we know him today. Notable persons in this category were Aldous Huxley, Bertrand Russell, and even such recent writers as Arthur C. Clarke.

The Forecasting of Technical Events

Within the futures movement is a specialized area of forecasting known as technological forecasting. Cetron defines a technological forecast as a realistic estimate by technically knowledgeable persons of the rate, direction, and extent to which a particular technology or group of technologies will develop in a specific period of time. Its purpose is to separate clearly the more likely technical states from the less likely. By this definition, a forecast does not predict breakthroughs nor describe the innovation. It does indicate that a significant advance is in the offing and suggests probable timing of the advance.

A forecast must communicate and influence those in the decision-making process. Obviously, to be effective, the forecast must permeate the total management system. Within this framework, it must become a tool which yields consistent conclusions. Normally, the forecaster will forecast how soon certain technologies will be possible and what characteristics they may have. The actual technology is dependent upon many facts: economic, social, political. In many cases, these are beyond the province of the forecaster. Nontechnological considerations may raise havoc with even the most carefully made forecast. Forecasting is, therefore, not an end in itself, but a powerful tool that materially helps in the planning function. In short, it is a probabilistic prediction of future technology.

The version of technological forecasting we know today became prominent in the 1960s. However, the concept of systematic forecasting designed to provide information for specific decision makers was born in 1937 when the National Research Council established the National Resource Committee under the leadership of William F. Ogburn, who is referred to in Chapter 2. This council recognized that long-range planning requires insight into technological, social, and related environments in the future. Ironically, this group failed to predict atomic energy, radar, jet propulsion, and antibiotics, all of which were a high priority within five years.

Since that time many technological forecasts have been made in the military services. A few of these were the Von Karman Report done for the Air Force in 1944; Project Forecast done for the Air Force in 1963–64; the University of Syracuse Research Corporation forecast of science and technology done for the U.S. Marine Corps in 1964; and several projects done for the Department of Defense in 1965. Today, most of the armed forces have long-range forecasts completed annually: The military has taken the leadership in this movement. In 1967, when the First Industrial Management Conference on Technological Forecasting was held, two-thirds of the papers presented were from the department of defense or from defense contractors.

The forecasting movement has prompted the development of vast literary holdings, professional organizations, and conferences. The *Technological Forecasting and Social Change Journal* had subscribers from forty-three countries in 1974. Once again the evidence is clear: The impact of technology is interdisciplinary and global in scope.

Futurology

The first use of the term 'futurology" in the early twentieth century was to refer to poets, to playwrights, or to painters. The first use of the term in published materials came in 1943 when Ossip K. Flechtheim coined the term while visiting this country. It comes from the Latin *futurum* and the Greek *logos,* or science. Flechtheim indicates that futurology embraces:

1. All types of prognoses, projections, linear programming, and so on.

2. All planning procedures in economics, education, traffic.

3. An assessment of goals, norms, and values pertaining to the future (Jungk and Galtung, 1969, p. 264).

Some scientists argue against such a definition since it implies that there is a science of the future. Flechtheim indeed suggests that futurology suggests a pure science, that it approaches an applied science, and that it comes close to philosophy. Those who debate his definition argue that there can be no science of the future in the sense that there is a science of living things (biology) or the earth (geology), because one cannot study what does not exist. The debate goes on, but the study of the future gains intensity daily.

"The Wild Birds Find a Corporate Roost," an article published in a 1964 *Fortune* magazine, describes how large corporations like General Electric and the Department of Defense utilize futurists. For lack of a better term, the author referred to the futurist as a seer and a wild bird. One year later, *Time* magazine published an article called, "The Futurists: Looking Toward A.D. 2000." In that same year (1966), the World Future Society with its widely acclaimed journal *The Futurist,* was formed. Today, this organization, with a global membership of over sixteen thousand members in over eighty countries, has held two international conferences on the study of the future and has sponsored many other conferences on the future.

The surge of interest in the study of the future has fostered many other organizations. Programs for preparing the professional futurist have been implemented in a number of universities in the world. New methodologies have been designed to assist the futurists so they can offer possibilities or probabilities with technological, scientific, and social trends as their data base. Since 1970, more than a dozen studies have been implemented at the state level. In 1971, Hawaii formed a State Commission on the Year 2000 to explore the future of the islands though the year 2000. The book *Hawaii 2000* resulted. In 1974, a group called Alternatives for Washington was formed to study alternative futures for that state. Other programs for studying the future have been implemented in other states (Iowa 2000; Commission on Minnesota's Future; Massachusetts' Legislative Commission on the Effects of Growth Patterns on the Quality of Life in the Commonwealth; Commission on Maine's Future; Goals for Georgia Program; the Delaware Tomorrow Commission; and California Tomorrow). In 1973, the city of Atlanta addressed itself to the future via the *Atlanta 2000* magazine. These and many other projects are still in their formative years, but as goal-setting and long-range planning become necessities, the impact of these groups will be most significant.

DISCUSSION QUESTIONS

1. What concerns do you have about our technological society that might be solved by technology assessment?

2. Who should be involved in the assessment process? Should it be left to the persons trained in this field?

3. Identify assessments that need to be done on a global scale.

4. Will the technology assessment movement become an important part of our lifestyle, or will your children experience a decision-

making process that is cavalier, slipshod, and profit-centered?

5. What changes must be made in our educational system in order to cope with the future?

6. Can you envision your lifestyle in the year 2000? What about that of your children in the year 2050?

7. Can we search for alternatives when the future is always an unknown?

8. Even if we can predict the future, can our institutions make the necessary adjustments?

BIBLIOGRAPHY

Ayres, R. U. *Technological Forecasting and Long-range Planning.* New York: McGraw-Hill Book Co., 1969.

Baier, K., and Rescher, N. *Values and the Future.* New York: The Free Press, 1969.

Bright, J. R. *Technological Forecasting for Industry and Government.* Englewood Cliffs, N.J.: Prentice-Hall, 1968.

Bright, J. R., and Schoeman, M. E. F. *A Guide to Practical Technological Forecasting.* Englewood Cliffs, N.J.: Prentice-Hall, 1973.

Cetron, M. J. *Technological Forecasting.* New York: Gordon & Breach, Science Publishers, 1969.

Chacko, G. J. *Technological Forecontrol: Prospects, Problems, and Policy.* New York: North Holland/American Elsevier, 1975.

Chaplin, G., and Paige, G. D. *Hawaii 2000.* Honolulu: The University Press of Hawaii, 1973.

Coates, J. F. "Technology Assessment—a Tool Kit." *Chemtech,* June 1976.

Congress of the United States. Office of Technology Assessment. *News Release,* February 12, 1974.

Cross, N. et al. *Man-Made Futures.* London: Hutchinson & Co., 1974.

Ehrenfeld, D. *Biological Conservation.* New York: Holt, Rinehart, Winston, 1970.

Ferkiss, V. *The Future of Technological Civilization.* New York: George Braziller, 1974.

Florida Defenders of the Environment. *Environmental Impact of the Cross-Florida Barge Canal.* Gainesville, Fla.: January 1971.

Humanist Manifesto I and II. Buffalo, New York: Prometheus Books, 1973.

International Society for Technology Assessment. *Memorandum to Membership from Walter A. Hahn, President.* July 1973.

Jones, M. V. "The Methodology of Technology Assessment." *The Futurist,* February 1972.

————. *A Technology Assessment Methodology.* Vol. I. Springfield, Va.: NTIS, June 1971.

Jungk, R., and Galtung, J. *Mankind 2000.* Oslo, Norway: Universitetsforlaget, 1969.

Kahn, H., and Wiener, A. J. *The Year 2000.* New York: The Macmillan Co., 1967.

Kasper, R. G. *Technology Assessment.* New York: Praeger Publishers, 1972.

Kennedy, E. M. "Toward the Year 2000." *Technological Forecasting and Social Change* 8 (1976).

Kleinberg, B. S. *American Society in the Post-industrial Age.* Columbus: Charles E. Merrill Publishing Co., 1973.

Kranzberg, M. *Historical Aspects of Technology Assessment.* Occasional Paper No. 4 of the Program of Policy Studies in Science and Technology, The George Washington University, August 1969.

Lanford, H. W. *Technological Forecasting Methodologies*. New York: American Management Association, Inc., 1972.

Lauda, D. P. "Technology Assessment: Implications for Industrial Arts." *Industrial Arts and a Humane Technology for the Future*. Proceedings of the American Industrial Arts Association 36th Annual Conference, Seattle, 1974.

Martino, J. P. "How the Soviets Forecast Technology." *The Futurist*, February 1973.

————. "The Role of Forecasting in Technology Assessment." *The Futurist*, October 1972.

————. *Technological Forecasting for Decisionmaking*. New York: American Elsevier Publishing Co., 1972.

McHale, J. *The Future of the Future*. New York: George Braziller, 1969.

Mishan, E. J. *Technology and Growth: The Price We Pay*. New York: Praeger Publishers, 1970.

Newman, J. *1994: The World of Tomorrow*. Washington, D.C.: U.S. News & World Report, 1973.

Polak, F. L. *Prognostics*. New York: Elsevier Publishing Co., 1971.

Science Policy Research Division. Congressional Research Division. *Office of Technology Assessment: Background and Status*. U.S. Government Printing Office Publication 99–672 0, August 1973.

Senate Hearings Before the Committee on Appropriations. 93rd Congress, First Session. *Legislative Branch Appropriations, Fiscal Years 1973 and 1974*, H.R. 7447 and H.R. 6691. U.S. Government Printing Office Publication 99–767 0, 1973.

Spekke, A. A. *The Next 25 Years*. Washington, D.C.: World Future Society, 1975.

Subcommittee on Computer Services. Committee on Rules and Administration, United States Senate. *Technology Assessment for the Congress*. U.S. Government Printing Office Publication 85–598. November 1, 1972.

Teich, A. H., ed. *Technology and Man's Future*. New York: St. Martin's Press, 1972.

Toffler, A. *Future Shock*. New York: Random House, 1970.

————. *The Futurists*. New York: Random House, 1972.

Tugwell, F. *Search for Alternatives, Public Policy and the Study of the Future*. Cambridge, Mass.: Winthrop Publishers, Inc., 1973.

U.S. Department of Commerce. Office of Technology Assessment and Forecast. *Initial Publication*. Washington, D.C.: May 1973.

U.S. Department of Commerce. Office of Technology Assessment and Forecast. *Fourth Report*. Washington, D.C.: January, 1975.

United States 92nd Congress. *Public Law 92–484, H.R. 10243*, October 13, 1972.

Wallia, C. S. *Toward Century 21*. New York: Basic Books, 1970.

Wells, H. G. *Anticipations*. New York: Harper & Bros., 1902.

In Conclusion

Homo sapiens is the dominant form of life on planet Earth. With cognitive and psychomotor components far superior to those of all other forms of life, humans have been able to develop their culture much faster than the rate of biological evolution. When the contingencies for survival of a society change, culture, like a species, must also change. Therefore, no culture is in permanent equilibrium, especially in our lifetime. Henry Adams stated in 1909 that the growth of technology increased one thousand times between 1800 to 1900. While this estimate is remarkable, it cannot compare to the changes that have taken place in just the past twenty-five years. Even more thought-provoking is to consider the changes that will take place before the end of this century. No evidence supports the contention that the pace is reducing its speed. Indeed, as the process of innovation and invention carries us into the inevitable future, quite the opposite is true.

This avalanche of progress precludes the possibility of our returning to a static society isolated from scientific theory and technological application. Evidence of decaying traditional values and social systems is a sure sign that we will not turn back. Science and technology, no longer subservient to our basic institutions as they were in medieval times, are the epitome of verified knowledge. As long as the growth pattern continues, and there is no reason to think it will not, we have no choice but to face up to the potential contingencies.

We realize that every technical innovation or invention presents a corresponding social consequence. In many cases, technological growth has outdistanced social theory, leaving society to face catastrophic consequences with no moratorium on growth in sight. As a result, we must restore social theory to cope with rapid change and the emerging technologies. Direction, or planned change, is needed as new cultural syntheses evolve. Since rapid change affects the total fabric of culture, all disciplines must interpret potential consequences in advance of their adoption. Someone must assume responsibility for these consequences: We cannot blame technology for social ills; we must blame the human, decision-making process.

Our future will depend to a great extent on the degree to which we predict the changes we deem viable. Just as nature functions within a set of regulating patterns and interrelationships, so must *homo sapiens*. The design and control of our future must work in harmony, while striving for symbiosis within the total ecosystem. Our future discoveries will not evolve solely around scientific and technological exploits, but around institutions as well. Our institutions are not immutable, but like technology, they can be adjusted. The decisions we make today will reverberate for centuries to come.

In the midst of rapid technological growth, one of the most crucial issues facing humankind is the need for a global perspective. Technology transcends national boundaries, thereby making all people irrevocably linked in a complex web of global interdependence. Just as we share the same atmosphere, so must we learn to share all global resources, material and human. The new technologies are proving to be viable links with other countries and other political systems; the pooling of human and natural resources holds a greater promise for humankind than any other endeavor undertaken in human history. Our communication, transportation, and production systems make this promise more than a possibility. Just imagine what could be done if all resources were directed towards the elimination of pollution, disease, and hunger. These problems are not technological; rather, they are "people" problems caused by a lack of commitment.

To control technology means to make sure that it is amenable to fostering human life. A new development does not mandate that it must be utilized. We have learned our lesson too well and know that negative results occur too often. At the same time, excessive regulations and inadequate incentives have stifled innovations. What is needed is direction: Humane priorities must direct our research and development efforts.

Whether we view technology negatively, positively, or passively, we find ourselves making value judgments about it. Individuals must understand their relationship in this environment. The technological man must learn that technology is a process and a determinant of culture. The result of such an understanding is his ability to select technology that will serve social ends and to select social controls that will control technology. Our only constraints are self-imposed. What we need is a philosophy, a psychology, an ethic of understanding to help us utilize relational units of analysis and transfer them into cross-cultural applications.

We are optimistic about the future. We see changes that can aid human survival. The 1960s created an awareness of problems and the beginning of this new ethic. Issues are now in the open and discussed by all levels of society. Referents for determining the good life are surfacing as questions to our value system. We need only contrast today's lifestyle with that of the 1960s. We see more innovation and invention in the form of tangible products and in social innovation. Technology assessment, technological forecasting, and futurism are just a few examples of recent innovations recognized as viable disciplines in which to determine technological change.

Any study of human endeavor, such as the study of technology, can only end with more questions than answers. The questions have been presented throughout this book. The answers will not come easily, but they *must* come. We are living in a provocative era in which the answers to many questions will literally ensure survival of the human race. Who is to provide these answers? What are the guidelines? We believe that an understanding of technology as a process is the beginning. It is this process that is reserved for the human and that perpetuates human life. You have just begun your reading about and contemplation of technology. Even as you read these words, many changes are altering your culture, changes that must be directed to serve humane goals. To ignore these changes is to deny you and your offspring a future of promise. Who can deny any human a sense of purpose? Only through conscious effort as we move through the process we call technology can we plan THE future, rather than plan FOR the future.

Index